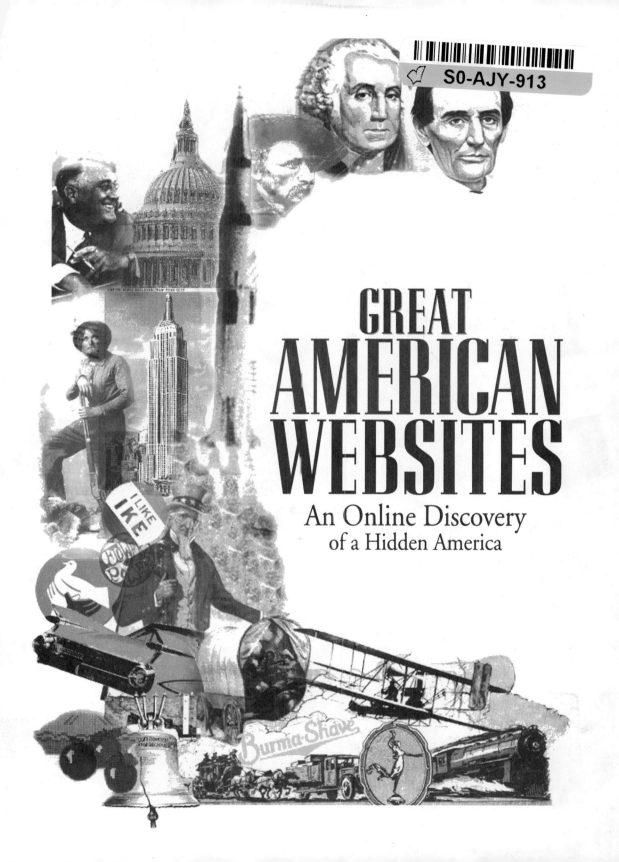

GREAT AMERICAN WEBSITES

An Online Discovery
of a Hidden America

GREAT AMERICAN WEBSITES:

AN ONLINE DISCOVERY OF A HIDDEN AMERICA

Edward J. Renehan, Jr.

Osborne **McGraw-Hill**
Berkeley New York St. Louis San Francisco
Auckland Bogotá Hamburg London Madrid
Mexico City Milan Montreal New Delhi Panama City
Paris São Paulo Singapore Sydney
Tokyo Toronto

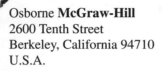

Osborne **McGraw-Hill**
2600 Tenth Street
Berkeley, California 94710
U.S.A.

For information on translations or book distribu-
tors outside the U.S.A., or to arrange bulk purchase discounts for sales promotions, premiums,
or fundraisers, please contact Osborne/
McGraw-Hill at the above address.

Great American Websites:
An Online Discovery of a Hidden America

1234567890 DOC 9987

ISBN 0-07-882304-8

Publisher
Brandon A. Nordin

Editor-in-Chief
Scott Rogers

Acquisitions Editor
Megg Bonar

Project Editor
Claire Splan

Associate Project Editor
Cynthia Douglas

Editorial Assistant
Gordon Hurd

Copy Editor
Danny Carnahan

Proofreader
Stefany Otis

Indexer
Valerie Robbins

Computer Designer
Sylvia Brown

Illustrator & Series Designer
Leslee Bassin

Cover Designer
Alan Dolgins

This book is dedicated to my friends
Pete and Toshi Seeger
(http://ourworld.compuserve.com/homepages/JimCapaldi)

About the Author...

Edward J. Renehan, Jr. has written many best-selling books on Internet and American History topics, including *1,001 Really Cool Web Sites* and *Net Worth: Creating & Maximizing Wealth with the Internet.* His histories include *The Secret Six: The True Tale of the Men Who Conspired with John Brown.* He is currently at work on a study of Theodore Roosevelt and his family during the First World War. In the 1970s, Renehan worked as a professional musician and made recordings with Pete Seeger. He was formerly the manager of the largest computer book club in the United States.

CONTENTS AT A GLANCE

★★★★★★★★★★

1   American Sports   1

2   Architecture   23

3   Crime & Criminals, American Style   45

4   Food & Drink   63

5   The Great Outdoors   81

6   Great Patriots   105

7   The History Highway   123

8   Individualis Americanus   145

9   Kingdom of Kitsch   165

10 Law   181

11 Literature American Style   195

12 Local History   225

13 Made in the U.S.A.   245

14 Maps and Other Things Geographical 271

15 Music, American Style 287

16 Extavaganzas, Parades & Festivals 315

17 Politics: Oh What a Tangled Web 333

18 Pop Till You Drop 359

19 Religion 377

20 Science Made in the USA 395

21 Visual Arts in America 419

A Searching the Web 439

CONTENTS

★★★★★★★★★

Acknowledgments xxix

Introduction xxxi

1

American Sports 1

Finding Common Ground 2
Brahmins Play More than Just
    Football 4
    All-Time, All-Star Baseball
        Team 6
    American Amateur Baseball
        Congress 7
    American Basketball
        Association (R.I.P.) 7
    America's Sports
        Headquarters on the Web 7
    The Atlanta Braves 7
    The Atlanta Hawks 8
    Baseball Online 8
    Basketball Highway 8
    The Boston Celtics Official
        Home Page 8
    Boston Marathon Home Page 8
    Boston Patriots Home Page 9
    The Boston Red Sox 9
    Casey at the Bat 9
    CBS Sports 9
    The Chicago Bulls 9

Roger Clemens Home Page 10
Ty Cobb Home Page 10
ESPN Sportszone 10
Fastball 11
Lou Gehrig Home Page 11
Green Bay Packers Home
    Page 11
The Harlem Globetrotters 12
The Internet Simulated
    Baseball League 12
"Shoeless" Joe Jackson Home
    Page 13
Kentucky Derby Official
    Home Page 13
The Los Angeles Dodgers 14
Louisville Slugger Online 14
Major League Baseball Official
    Home Page 14
Major League Baseball Players
    Alumni Association 14
Minor League Baseball 14
National Baseball Hall of
    Fame 15
National Basketball
    Association 15
National Football League 16
National Hockey League 16
NBC Sports 17
Negro Leagues Home Page 17
The New York Yankees 17

Professional Bowling
   Association 17
Professional Golfers
   Association (PGA) 18
Babe Ruth Home Page 18
Society for Baseball Research
   (SABR) 18
Jim Thorpe: All American 19
USA Basketball Official Home
   Page 19
Honus Wagner Home Page 19
Ted Williams Home Page 20
Yacht Racing Rules Online 20
Cy Young Award Winners
   Since 1956 20

2

Architecture 23

The View from My Window 24
A Bit More on Conspicuous
   Construction 27
History Repeats (Just Like Bad
   Hamburger) 29
American Architecture in
   Cyberspace 32
   Ansel Adams: Fiat Lux 32
   American Institute of
      Architects 33
   Architecture in America: State
      Houses to Skyscrapers 33
   Brief Biographies of American
      Architects 33
   Carnegie Mellon Architecture
      Archives 34
   The Charleston Multimedia
      Project 34
   Chicago Architecture
      Foundation 35
   Chicago Architecture Image
      Base 35

Covered Bridges of
   Southeastern Pennsylvania
   and Nearby Areas 35
Digital Archive of American
   Architecture 36
Doctoral Dissertations
   Relating to American
   Architectural History,
   1897-1995 36
Buckminster Fuller: The
   Dymaxion House and
   Geodesic Domes 37
Gargoyles and Architectural
   Details of New York City 37
Hildene: Home of the
   Descendants of Abraham
   Lincoln 37
Thomas Jefferson's
   Monticello 38
Philip Johnson, Architect 39
Kansas City Architecture 39
Louisiana Architecture 39
National Building Museum 40
National Trust for Historic
   Preservation 40
New York Images, 1883 40
Newport Mansions 41
Frederick Law Olmstead 41
Philadelphia Historic District:
   Virtual Walking Tour 41
Betsy Ross Home: Virtual
   Tour 42
San Francisco Architecture:
   The Victorians 42
Temple of Liberty: Building
   the Capitol for a New
   Nation 42
University of Pennsylvania
   Architectural Archives 43
Women in Architecture 43

Frank Lloyd Wright: Designs
for an American Landscape,
1922-32 43

3

Crime & Criminals, American Style 45

Americans Are Crime Voyeurs 46
Crime as Theater 47
Crime on the Web 49
  Alcatraz 50
  Billy the Kid 50
  The Bonnie and Clyde
    Archive 51
  John Wilkes Booth 51
  Al Capone 52
  Cattle Rustling 52
  Courtroom Sketches 52
  Criminals.com 52
  The Dalton Gang 53
  Death Penalty Pages from the
    ACLU 53
  John Dillinger 53
  Wyatt Earp 54
  The Electric Chair 54
  The FBI's Famous Cases
    Archive 55
  The FBI's Top Ten Most
    Wanted Fugitives 55
  Gang Land: Jerry Capeci's
    New York Mob Column 55
  John Gotti Tribute Page 56
  Doc Holliday 56
  The James-Younger Gang 57
  The Kennedy Assassination 57
  The Lincoln Assassination 58
  Charlie Manson: Cult
    Murderer and Songwriter
    for the Beach Boys 59
  Bat Masterson 59
  My Lai Massacre 60
  Oklahombres 60

  Lee Harvey Oswald 60
  Simpson Murder Trial
    Resources 61
  Richard Speck: One Bad, Bad
    Boy 61
  Henry Starr 61
  The Unabomber's Manifesto:
    Industrial Society and Its
    Future 62
  United States Department of
    Justice Crime Statistics 62

4

Food & Drink 63

Out of Africa 64
My Affinity for Pumpkins 66
The Most Famous American Meal
  Ever Eaten 68
Food and Cooking in the Melting
  Pot Called the Web 69
  American Apple Pie 70
  American Wine on the Web
    Archives 70
  Annie's Pumpkin Walnut
    Cheesecake: A Recipe 70
  The Bay Area Restaurant
    Guide 70
  Black-Eyed Peas: A Spicy
    Recipe 71
  Boston (and Boston Region)
    Restaurant Guides 71
  Buffalo Meat Is Good for You 71
  Buffalo Wings Recipe Archive 72
  Chicago Restaurant Guide 72
  The Culinary Institute of
    America 72
  Dallas Restaurant Guide 73
  Gumbo 73
  Hartford, Connecticut
    Restaurants 73

Los Angeles Restaurants, a.k.a. "Eating L.A." 73
Microbreweries of America: A Guide 74
Native American Recipes 74
New England Clam Chowder: A Recipe 74
New England Culinary Institute 74
New Orleans Restaurants and Recipes 75
New York Restaurant Super Guide 75
Phoenix Metro Restaurant Guide 76
Popcorn: Why Does It Pop? 76
Pumpkin Bread: A Recipe 76
Pumpkin Crunch: A Recipe 77
Pumpkin Custard Pie: A Recipe 77
Pumpkin Nut Bread: A Recipe 77
Rhode Island Restaurants 77
Scottsdale Culinary Institute 77
Seattle Restaurant Information 78
Tasty Maine Lobster Recipes 78
Tex-Mex Hash: A Recipe 78
Tex-Mex Home Fries: A Recipe 78
Turkey Trivia Game 79

5

The Great Outdoors 81

The Roots of Conservation 82
John Burroughs and the Literature of Conservation 84
A Word on Hunting 87
A Word on Rachel 89

Park Information and Other Environmental Resources on the Web 90
All Outdoors 90
The American Park Network 90
Appalachian Mountain Club 91
Appalachian Trail Home Page 91
Rachel Carson Links 92
Catskill Fly-Fishing Center and Museum 92
Chesapeake Bay Trust 92
Conservation Land Trust Network (Maine) 92
Defenders of Wildlife 93
EnviroLink 93
Everglades National Park 93
Fish and Wildlife Service 93
Friends of the Earth—U.S. 95
Glacier National Park 95
The Grand Canyon 95
Grand Teton National Park: A History 96
Hudson River Sloop Clearwater 96
Information Center for the Environment at U.C. Davis 96
LandTrust.com 96
The League of Conservation Voters 97
Aldo Leopold Links 97
Mohonk Mountain House, New Paltz, NY 97
John Muir Links 97
National Audubon Society 98
National Park Service: ParkNet 98
National Parks & Conservation Association 98
National Wildlife Federation 99

Natural Resources
   Conservation Service 99
Natural Resources Defense
   Council 99
The Nature Conservancy 99
Olympic National Park 100
Online Exhibit from the
   Library of Congress: The
   Evolution of the
   Conservation Movement,
   1850-1920 100
Outward Bound USA 100
Perspective on Deer Hunting 101
Petroglyph National
   Monument 101
Theodore Roosevelt National
   Park, Medora, North
   Dakota 101
Save the Bay 102
Sierra Club 102
Sportsman's Hunting and
   Fishing Guide 102
Utah National Parks 102
Washington State Parks Home
   Page 103
Westchester County (NY)
   Land Trust 103
Wild and Scenic Rivers 103
Yosemite National Park 104

George Washington Carver 114
William Ellery Channing 114
Clarence Darrow 114
Frederick Douglass 115
W.E.B. DuBois 115
Dwight David Eisenhower 116
Grace Hopper: Mother of
   Computing 116
Thomas Jefferson 117
Barbara Jordan 117
Martin Luther King, Jr. 118
Abraham Lincoln 118
Thurgood Marshall 118
Rosa Parks 118
A. Philip Randolph 119
Hyman Rickover 119
Sally Ride 119
Franklin Delano Roosevelt 119
Theodore Roosevelt 120
Theodore Roosevelt, Jr. 121
Sitting Bull 121
Harriet Tubman 121
Booker T. Washington 122
George Washington 122

Boston National Historical
  Park 132
Bulloch Hall, Roswell, GA:
  Home of Theodore
  Roosevelt's Maternal
  Ancestors 133
Bunker Hill Monument 133
Civil War Center: Louisiana
  State University, Baton
  Rouge 133
Custer and the Little Bighorn
  Home Page 134
Dead Presidents Tour 134
Ford's Theatre Virtual Tour 134
Gettysburg Battlefield 134
The Ulysses S. Grant Network
  Home Page (and Grant's
  Tomb) 134
Harpers Ferry, West Virginia 135
Herbert Hoover Presidential
  Library 135
Stonewall Jackson Home 135
John F. Kennedy Birthplace 136
Lincoln Home, Springfield 136
Lincoln Log Cabin 136
The Lincoln Tomb 137
Jack London Historic State
  Park 138
Longfellow National Historic
  Site 139
Lowell, Massachusetts,
  National Historic Park 139
Minute Man National
  Historical Park 139
Mount Vernon: Home of
  George Washington 139
National Register of Historic
  Places 140
Naval War College Museum,
  Newport, RI 140
Old American Prints 141
Peabody Essex Museum 141

Zadock Pratt Museum,
  Prattsville, NY 142
Sagamore Hill 142
Carl Sandburg Birthplace 142
Savannah & America's Black
  History 142
Slabsides: The Cabin of John
  Burroughs 143
Smithsonian Online 143
South Street Seaport Museum,
  NYC 143
Springwood: Home of
  Franklin Roosevelt 143
U.S. Army Center for Military
  History 144
Valley Forge 144

8

Individualis Americanus 145

The First Henry Villard 146
Oswald Garrison Villard 148
The Second Henry Villard 149
In Love and War 150
Henry and Mary and Me 153
Individualis Americanus 154
  Johnny Appleseed 154
  John Perry Barlow 155
  John Barrymore 155
  Alexander Graham Bell 155
  Bishop Berkeley 156
  William F. Buckley, Jr. 156
  Buffalo Bill Cody 156
  Esther Dyson 158
  Thomas Alva Edison 158
  Walker Evans 158
  Richard Feynman 158
  W.C. Fields 159
  Henry Ford 159
  Robert Green Ingersoll 159

Patricia Ireland, President of
  the National Organization
  for Women 160
Charles Lindbergh 160
Cotton Mather 160
S. Christa McAuliffe 161
H.L. Mencken 161
Lucretia Mott 162
Ralph Nader 162
Annie Oakley 162
J. Robert Oppenheimer 162
Robert Peary 163
Jacob Riis: Muckraking
  Journalist 163
Will Rogers 163
Elizabeth Cady Stanton 163
Henry Stimson 164
The Wright Brothers 164

9

Kingdom of Kitsch 165

Kitsch Is Fundamentally Useless 167
Grotesques in Cyberspace 168
A Celebration of Everything
  Lowbrow 169
    Baked Frito-Lay's Potato
      Chips Page 169
    Beavis Refrigerator Magnet 170
    Camera Van 170
    The Carpenters 170
    Bill Clinton Doll 170
    Cowboy Boot Cookie Jars 171
    Dan's Link O'Kitsch 171
    Debbie's Barbie Collection 171
    Dr Pepper: The Unofficial
      Home Page 171
    Edsels 172
    Famous Dogs, Cats, &
      Critters 172
    Figurines 173
    George's Matchbox Page 173

Hearses in the Movies 173
Hippo Hat 173
Howdy Doody 173
Illustrated Guide to Crackers 174
Innocent Inanimate Objects 174
Ken's Collection of A&W Root
  Beer Mugs 174
Kewpie Dolls 174
The Kitsch Corner: Kitsch of
  the Month 175
Kitty Kitsch 175
Lawn Ornament Gallery 175
Los Angeles Cacophony
  Society 175
Lunch Boxes 176
Archie McPhee Catalog 176
Marie Osmond Porcelain Doll
  Collection 176
Outhouses of America Tour 176
Patriotic Party Supplies 177
Pecking Chicken 177
Pez Dispensers: An Online
  Exhibit 177
Planet Kitsch: An
  Audio-Visual Tour of Four
  Sci-Fi Camp Classics 177
Roadside America 178
Route 66 178
Rubber Band Ball 178
Spoon Dolls 179
Twinkies 179
Lawrence Welk 179
What's In My Desk Drawer? 180
Wonder Bread 180
Yogurt Top Collection 180

10

Law 181

Law and Cyberspace 182
Where Law Is Just and Necessary:
  Protecting the Commonwealth 185

Law Resources on the Web 186
   Advertising Law Information 186
   American Civil Liberties
     Union (ACLU) 187
   The Association of American
     Law Schools 187
   Brooklyn Law School 187
   Center for Law and Social
     Policy 188
   Columbia Law School 188
   Earthlaw 188
   Ecology Law Quarterly 188
   Emory University School of
     Law 189
   Entertainment Law
     Resources 189
   The Environmental Lawyer 189
   Federal Judiciary of the United
     States 189
   Federal Judicial Center 190
   Fletcher School of Law &
     Diplomacy, Tufts
     University 190
   Georgetown University Law
     School 190
   Harvard Law School 190
   Information Law Web 191
   Illinois Bar Association 191
   Intellectual Property Law
     Center 191
   Lawyer Jokes 191
   Legal dot Net 191
   Milbank, Tweed, Hadley &
     McCloy 192
   National Association of Patent
     Practitioners 192
   National Consumer Law
     Center 192
   New York State Bar
     Association 192
   New York University School of
     Law 193

   Queer Legal Resources 193
   St. John's University School of
     Law 193
   U.S. House of Representatives
     Internet Law Library 193
   U.S. Sentencing Commission 193
   U.S. Supreme Court
     Decisions 194
   USSC+: U.S. Supreme Court
     Database 194
   Wyoming State Supreme
     Court 194
   Yale Law School 194

11

Literature American Style 195

Over the Hill and Behind the Trees ... 196
A Bit About Walt Whitman 197
Such Were the Stories 201
Enter Mr. Ginsberg 202
American Literature on the Web 203
   George Ade 204
   Louisa May Alcott 204
   Authors Guild 204
   Bartleby 205
   Madison Smartt Bell 205
   Ambrose Bierce 206
   Ray Bradbury 206
   Richard Brautigan 206
   William Cullen Bryant 207
   Pearl Buck 207
   Edgar Rice Burroughs 208
   Truman Capote 208
   Raymond Chandler 208
   Stephen Crane 209
   Philip K. Dick 209
   Emily Dickinson 209
   John Dos Passos 209
   Theodore Dreiser 210
   T.S. (Thomas Stearns) Eliot 210
   Ralph Waldo Emerson 210

William Faulkner 211
F. Scott Fitzgerald 211
Erle Stanley Gardner 211
Allen Ginsberg Interview 211
Bret Harte 212
Nathaniel Hawthorne 212
Ernest Hemingway 212
William Dean Howells 212
Washington Irving 213
Henry James 213
Jack Kerouac 213
Stephen King 213
Ring Lardner 214
Literary Kicks 214
Jack London 214
H.P. Lovecraft 215
Norman Mailer 215
Herman Melville 215
Edna St. Vincent Millay 215
National Book Award Winners
  in Fiction 216
Flannery O'Connor 216
Eugene O'Neill 216
Dorothy Parker 216
George Plimpton 217
Edgar Allen Poe 217
Ezra Pound 217
Ayn Rand 218
John Crowe Ransom 218
"The Ransom of Red Chief"
  by O. Henry 218
Gertrude Stein 219
John Steinbeck 219
Harriet Beecher Stowe 219
Henry David Thoreau 220
James Thurber 220
Mark Twain 220
Gore Vidal: Monotheism and
  Its Discontents 221
Kurt Vonnegut, Jr. 221
Alice Walker 221
Edith Wharton 222

Walt Whitman 222
John Greenleaf Whittier 222
William Carlos Williams 223

12

Local History 225
Saving the New-York Historical
  Society 226
My Local History 228
Local History on the Web 229
  Albany County (Wyoming)
    Historical Society 230
  Albemarle County (Virginia)
    Historical Society 230
  Amana Colonies 230
  Arizona Historical Society 230
  Aspen (Colorado) Historical
    Society 231
  Berks County (Pennsylvania)
    Historical Society 231
  Besancon (Indiana) Historical
    Society 231
  Burlingame (California)
    Historical Society 231
  Chicago Historical Society 232
  Columbia: The Magazine of
    Northwest History 232
  Cranford (New Jersey)
    Historical Society 232
  Dallas Jewish Historical
    Society 232
  Evanston (Illinois) Historical
    Society 233
  Grand Trunk Western
    Historical Society 233
  Hart County (Kentucky)
    Historical Society 233
  Hudson River Maritime
    Museum 233
  Issaquah (Washington)
    Historical Society 234

Itawamba Historical Society
(Mississippi) 234
The Jewish Historical Society
of Maryland 234
The La Jolla (California)
Historical Society 234
Lake Erie Islands
Historical Society 235
Lancaster County
(Pennsylvania) Historical
Society 235
The Lenni Lenape Historical
Society, Allentown,
Pennsylvania 235
Lexington (Massachusetts)
Historical Society 236
The Louisville & Nashville
Railroad Historical Society 236
Minnesota Historical Society 236
Missouri Historical Society 236
Monroe (New Jersey)
Historical Society 236
Nevada County (California)
Historical Society 237
New Bedford (Massachusetts)
Whaling Museum of the Old
Dartmouth Historical
Society 237
New Hampshire Historical
Society 237
Ohio Historical Society 237
Otter Tail County (Minnesota)
Historical Society 238
Oyster Bay (New York)
Historical Society 238
Palisades Amusement Park
(New Jersey) Historical
Society 238
Pejepscot (Maine) Historical
Society 238
Plymouth (Pennsylvania)
History 239

The Historical Society of
Princeton (New Jersey) 239
Puget Sound Maritime
Historical Society
(Washington) 239
Rhode Island History
Bookstore 240
Santa Clarita Valley Historical
Society Home Page 240
Shasta (California) Historical
Society 240
Smoky Mountain Historical
Society (Tennessee) 240
Southern Oregon Historical
Society 241
Suffolk County (New York)
Historical Society 241
Texas Panhandle Railroad
Historical Society 241
Utah History Home Page 242
Valley Forge Historical
Society 242
Vigo County (Indiana)
Historical Society 242
Western Reserve Historical
Society (Ohio) 243

13

Made in the U.S.A. 245

What's in a Name? George
Eastman and Kodak 246
A Level Playing Field 247
Miles to Go 249
   Amana 249
   American Express 249
   Amish Handmade Quilts 249
   Apple Computer 250
   AT&T 250
   Barnwood Originals 250
   L.L. Bean 250
   Ben & Jerry's Ice Cream 251

Bethlehem Steel 251
Bird Houses Handmade in
    North Carolina 251
H.H. Brown 251
Canes and Walking Sticks
    Handmade in Wilderville,
    Oregon 252
Caterpillar 252
The Chubb Group 252
Coca Cola 252
Country Brooms Handcrafted
    in the U.S.A. 253
Crosby Saddles 253
Damn Fine Clocks 253
John Deere 254
Digital Equipment 254
Disney 254
Dow Chemical 254
Duck Decoys 254
DuPont 255
Electric Boat Corporation 255
Ellsworth Handcrafted
    Bicycles from California 255
Ford Motor Company 256
General Motors 256
Goodyear Tire and Rubber
    Company 256
Harley-Davidson
    Motorcycles 257
HarperCollins Publishers 257
Ted Hood Yachts, Rhode
    Island 257
IBM: International Business
    Machines 257
Intel 258
Jack Daniel's Distillery 259
Johnson & Johnson 259
Kayaks Handmade in the
    U.S.A. 259
Kelloggs 259
Lands' End Direct Merchants 260
Levi Strauss Jeans 260

Eli Lilly 260
Lionel Trains 260
Lockheed Martin 261
Lotus 261
Martin Guitars 261
Mauna Loa Macadamia Nuts 261
Merrill Lynch 261
Microsoft Company 262
Minnesota Mining and
    Manufacturing (3M) 262
Mobil 262
Morgan Stanley 263
Northrop Grumman 263
Northstar Hand-Carved
    Wooden Pens from Texas 263
Ogilvy & Mather Advertising 263
Owens Corning 264
Pepsi 265
Piper Aircraft 265
Pixar 265
Porcelain Dolls Handcrafted in
    Pennsylvania 266
Procter & Gamble 266
Random House Publishing
    Group 266
Raytheon 266
Samuel Adams Brewery 267
Schlage Locks 267
Sears 267
Singer Sewing Machine
    Company 267
Sun Microsystems 267
Tabasco Sauce 268
United Parcel Service 268
U.S.A. Made 268
Vermont Maple Syrup 268
Wells Fargo 269
Westinghouse 269
Whirlpool 269
Zippo Lighters 269

14

Maps and Other Things Geographical

Maps and Other Things Geographical 271

The United States Geological
    Survey (USGS) 272
Maps of All Kinds 273
Maps and Geography on the Web 275
    Boston Online Map 275
    California Geographical
        Survey 275
    Cape Cod Map 276
    The Census Bureau 276
    Chalk Butte Digital Maps 276
    Charleston, South Carolina
        Map: 1869 276
    Chicago Map: Free 277
    Classification of Wetlands and
        Deep Water Habitats of the
        United States 277
    Clearview U.S. Relief Maps 277
    Dallas Map 277
    Detroit Map 277
    Fredericksburg and
        Spotsylvania (Virginia)
        National Military
        Park Map 278
    Geography Departments in
        the United States 278
    Geologic Mapping and
        Regional Geologic Studies in
        the Eastern United States 278
    Hammond Maps 278
    Historical Las Vegas Strip
        Casino Map 279
    Kickapoo Maps 279
    La Jolla (California) Surf Map 279
    Las Vegas Map 279
    Long Island Sound Map 280
    Los Angeles Map 280
    Los Angeles Rock and Roll
        Road Map 280

    Manhattan Subway Map
        (Interactive) 280
    Massachusetts Map from the
        18th Century 281
    Mississippi River Basin
        Headwaters Map 281
    National Cooperative
        Geologic Mapping
        Program 281
    New Orleans Maps 281
    New York City Vertical
        Subterranean Map 282
    New York State Map 282
    Philadelphia Map 282
    Potomac Watershed Network 282
    Providence (Rhode Island)
        Map 282
    Railroad, Subway and Tram
        Maps 283
    San Francisco Bay Area Relief
        Map 283
    Seattle Map 283
    South County, Rhode Island 283
    Southern California
        Earthquake Maps 283
    Thomas Bros. Maps 284
    T.I. Maps, Moab, Utah 284
    Trails Illustrated Topographic
        Maps 284
    Virginia in the 18th Century 284
    Washington, D.C. Metro Map 285
    Washington State Map 285
    Washington State Parks Maps ... 285
    Wetlands Division of the EPA 285
    Wolf Recovery Map 285

15

Music, American Style 287

Me and Gary 288
Me and Moe 290
American Music in Cyberspace 293

Louis Armstrong	....	293
P.D.Q. Bach	....	293
Joan Baez	....	294
The Band	....	294
Irving Berlin	....	294
Leonard Bernstein	....	294
The Blue Highway	....	294
Boston Symphony Orchestra	.....	295
The Byrds	....	295
John Cage	....	295
Carnegie Hall	....	296
John Coltrane	....	296
Aaron Copland	....	296
Dallas Symphony Orchestra	......	297
Miles Davis	....	297
Dirty Linen Magazine	....	297
Bob Dylan	....	298
The Everly Brothers	....	298
Folk Book	....	298
Folk-Legacy Records	....	298
Aretha Franklin	....	298
George and Ira Gershwin		
Archive	....	299
The Grateful Dead	....	299
Nanci Griffith	....	299
Arlo Guthrie: Arlonet	....	299
Woody Guthrie	....	300
Merle Haggard	....	301
John Hammond, Jr.	....	301
Yip Harburg	....	302
Billie Holiday: Lady Day	....	302
Jazz Central Station	....	302
Blind Lemon Jefferson	....	302
Jefferson Airplane	....	303
Spike Jones	....	303
Kronos Quartet	....	303
Leadbelly	....	304
Miss Peggy Lee	....	304
Tom Lehrer	....	304
Jerry Lee Lewis	....	305
Lincoln Center	....	305
Little Richard	....	305
Los Angeles Philharmonic	....	305
Bobby McFerrin	....	305
The Mills Brothers	....	306
Joni Mitchell	....	306
Bill Monroe & the Bluegrass		
Boys	....	306
Phil Ochs	....	306
Peter, Paul & Mary	....	307
U. Utah Phillips	....	307
Buddy Rich	....	307
Paul Robeson	....	307
Rock & Roll Hall of Fame &		
Museum	....	307
Run D.M.C.	....	308
Gil Scott-Heron	....	308
John Sebastian	....	308
Pete Seeger Appreciation		
Page	....	309
Frank Sinatra	....	309
Sing Out! Magazine	....	309
Bessie Smith	....	310
Smithsonian/Folkways		
Records	....	310
John Philip Sousa	....	310
Bruce Springsteen	....	310
Sweet Honey in the Rock	....	310
Livingston Taylor	....	311
Sonny Terry and Brownie		
McGhee	....	311
Jay Ungar and Molly Mason	......	311
Susanne Vega	....	311
Loudon Wainwright III	....	311
Fats Waller	....	312
Orson Welk	....	312
Robin & Linda Williams	....	312
Windham Hill Records	....	313
Wolf Trap Foundation for the		
Performing Arts	....	313
Neil Young	....	313

16

Extavaganzas, Parades & Festivals .. 315

The Spectacle of Oscar 316
The Spectacle of the Macy's
    Thanksgiving Parade 317
The Spectacle of the Circus 319
Spectacles and Ceremonies
    on the Web 321
    All American Music Festival 321
    Bluegrass Festivals
        Nationwide 321
    Boston Marathon 322
    Britt Festivals, Jacksonville,
        Oregon 322
    Cable Ace Awards 322
    Chicago Blues Festival 322
    Chicago Fringe & Buskers
        Festival 323
    Chicago Underground Film
        Festival 323
    Chinese New Year as
        Celebrated in the United
        States 323
    Christmas Tree Lighting
        Festivals 323
    Circus Art at the John and
        Mable Ringling Museum 324
    Circus World Museum 324
    Civil War Reenactments 324
    Clowns of America
        International 324
    Coney Island 325
    DucKon 325
    Florida Folk Festival 325
    The Flying High Circus 325
    Fourth of July in Washington,
        D.C. 326
    The Grammy Awards 326
    The Great Circus Parade 326
    The Great Hudson River
        Revival 326

The Iditarod: The Last Great
    Race on Earth 327
The Kennedy Center Honors 327
Kentucky Derby 327
The Kerrville Folk Festival 327
Maine Arts Festival 328
Mardi Gras 328
Mystery Dinner Theatre 329
New Orleans Jazz and
    Heritage 329
New York Jazz Festival 329
New York Lesbian and Gay
    Film Festival 330
New York Underground Film
    Festival 330
Newport Folk Festival 330
Northwest Folklife Festival,
    Seattle 330
Oregon Shakespeare Festival,
    Ashland 330
Renaissance Faires 331
San Francisco Carnaval
    Parade 331
San Francisco Mime Troupe 331
Society For Creative
    Anachronism: Pennsic War 331
Sundance Film Festival 332
The Superbowl 332
Telluride Wine Festival 332
Tournament of Roses 332

17

Politics: Oh What a Tangled Web 333

Profile in Pragmatism 336
Evening the Score 340
Politics on the Web 344
    All Politics 344
    All Things Political 344
    American Conservative
        Union 344

American Legislative
  Exchange Council 345
The American Prospect 345
California Public Interest
  Research Group
  (CALPIRG) 345
Capital Research Center 346
The Cato Institute 346
Center for Individual Rights 346
Central Intelligence Agency 346
The Claremont Institute for
  the
  Study of Statesmanship and
  Political Philosophy 347
Congressional Quarterly 347
Conservative Site of the Day 347
Democratic Party 347
The Discovery Institute 348
Electronic Frontier
  Foundation 348
Environmental Protection
  Agency 348
FECInfo: The Non-Partisan
  Federal Candidate
  Campaign Money Page 348
Federal Communications
  Commission 349
The Federal Reserve 349
The Federalist Society 349
Green Party 349
The Heartland Institute 350
The Heritage Foundation 350
Lyndon B. Johnson
  Presidential Library and
  Museum 350
League of Women Voters 351
Libertarian.org 351
The Nation—Digital Edition 351
National Conference of
  State Legislatures 351
National Review Magazine 352
The Netizen 352

Richard Nixon Library and
  Birthplace 352
P.J. O'Rourke Unofficial Home
  Page 352
Panama Canal Commission 353
Progress and Freedom
  Foundation 353
Republican National
  Committee 354
The Right Side of the Web 354
Savers and Investors League 354
Socialist Party USA
  Cybercenter 354
Thomas: Legislative
  Information on the Internet 355
Town Hall 355
U.S. Department of
  Education 355
The U.S. House of
  Representatives 356
U.S. Office of Government
  Ethics 356
The United States Senate 356
Vera Institute of Justice 356
The White House 357

18

Pop Till You Drop 359

Immortal James Dean 360
Immortal Marilyn 361
And Of Course We Can't Forget
  Bogie... 362
...Or Those Who Are Not Quite
  Dead Yet 364
...Or Those Who Never Lived 365
  Muhammad Ali 366
  Lucille Ball 366
  John Barrymore 367
  The Beaver: Jerry Mathers 367
  Bewitched 368
  Humphrey Bogart 368

Steve Buscemi 368
Johnny Carson 368
Charlie Chaplin 369
Dick Clark 369
Joan Collins 369
Bill Cosby 369
Bing Crosby 370
Betty Ford 370
Zsa Zsa Gabor 370
Judy Garland 370
Andy Griffith and The
    Andy Griffith Show 371
Michael Jackson 371
Michael Jordan 371
Kids' TV of the Fifties 371
Spike Lee 372
Liberace 372
The Marx Brothers 372
Marilyn Monroe 372
Mary Tyler Moore 373
Jacqueline Bouvier Kennedy
    Onassis 373
Dolly Parton 373
Peanuts: Charlie Brown,
    Snoopy,
    and Friends 373
Pee-Wee Herman 373
Vincent Price 374
Roy Rogers and Dale Evans 374
Superman 374
Elizabeth Taylor 374
Shirley Temple 374
Star Trek 375
TV Guide Classic Cover
    Gallery 375
Abigail Van Buren (Dear
    Abby) 376
John Wayne: AMC's Ultimate
    Duke Directory 376

19

Religion 377
More on the Carrolls 378
I Still Consider Myself a Catholic,
    Albeit an Eccentric One 380
Heaven's Gate 382
American Religion on the Web 387
    The African Methodist
        Episcopal (AME) Church 387
    American Buddhist Congress 387
    The American Jewish World
        Service 388
    Daniel Berrigan, S.J. 388
    The Byzantine Catholic
        Church in America 388
    Christus Rex 389
    ChurchSurf 389
    Conservative Baptist
        Church of America 389
    Council of Jewish
        Federations 389
    Evangelical Lutheran Church
        in America 390
    Free Methodist Church of
        North America 390
    Holy Cross Monastery 390
    Jewish Genealogical Society 391
    Maryknoll 391
    Thomas Merton 391
    The Mormon Church 391
    The Quakers 392
    Touro Synagogue, Newport,
        RI 392
    U.S. Catholic Magazine 393
    Washington National
        Cathedral 393

20

Science Made in the USA 395

Scientists and the Birth of the Web 396
A Brief History of American
    Science 397
Science Present and Past Meet on
    the Web 400
    American Association of
        Anatomists (AAA) 401
    American Association for
        Artificial Intelligence 401
    American Astronomical
        Society 402
    American Geological
        Institute 402
    American Institute of Physics 402
    American Physical Society 402
    Anthropology at the California
        Academy of Sciences 403
    Applied Chaos Laboratory at
        Georgia Tech 403
    Astronomy Image Library at
        UMass 403
    Baylor Biological Databases 403
    The Beekeeping Home Page 404
    Boyce Thompson Institute at
        Cornell 404
    Carnegie-Mellon University
        (CMU) Artificial Intelligence
        Repository 404
    Center for Coastal Physical
        Oceanography 404
    Center for Marine Science
        Research, University of
        North Carolina,
        Wilmington 405
    Chaos: The Course 405
    Chaos at The University of
        Maryland 405
    Chemistry Hypermedia
        Project at Virginia Tech 406

Coastal and Marine Geology
    Projects of the U.S.
    Geological Survey 406
Ecology Resources Home Page
    of the Kennedy Space
    Center 406
The Edison Project for
    Communicating Chemistry
    (Columbia University) 406
Electric/Hybrid Vehicles
    Homepage 407
Field Museum of Natural
    History 407
Fermi National Accellerator
    Laboratory 407
Benjamin Franklin's
    Autobiography 408
Geological Society of
    America 408
Geologic Time: A Hypertext
    Reference from Berkeley 408
The Geometry Center at The
    University of Minnesota 408
Goddard Space Flight Center:
    Systems Engineering
    Homepage 409
Great Lakes Program of the
    State University of New
    York, Buffalo 409
Harvard Biological
    Laboratories 409
Harvard Robotics Lab 409
Hot Air: The Annals of
    Improbable Research 409
Imaging System Laboratory,
    University of Illinois 410
Indiana University
    Biogeochemical
    Laboratories 410
Iowa State University
    Artificial Intelligence
    Group 410

Jet Propulsion Lab at NASA 410
Journal of Artificial
    Intelligence Research 411
Lamont-Doherty Earth
    Observatory at Columbia
    University 411
Mad Science 411
The Maine Cooperative
    Distributed Problem-Solving
    Research Group 412
The Massachusetts Institute of
    Technology (MIT) 412
Michigan Technological
    University Volcanoes Page 412
Monterey Bay Aquarium
    Research Institute 412
Mount Wilson Observatory 413
NASA 413
The National Estuary Program
    of the Environmental
    Protection Agency (EPA) 413
National Marine Fisheries
    Service 413
National Museum of Natural
    History: Ocean Planet
    Exhibit 414
National Oceanic and
    Atmospheric
    Administration (U.S.
    Department of Commerce) 414
National Public Radio: Science
    Friday Hot Spots 414
National Science Foundation 414
National Weather Service 415
Oak Ridge National
    Laboratory 415
The Oceanography Society 416
Periodic Table at Illinois
    Institute of Technology 416
Physics/Consciousness
    Research Group 416

Clifford A. Pickover Home
    Page 416
Rob's Granite Page 417
San Diego Zoo 417
Scientific American Magazine
    of the 19th Century 417
Scripps Institution of
    Oceanography Library 417
Virtual Hospital 418
Woods Hole Oceanographic
    Institution 418
Yale Geology and Geophysics:
    The Kline Geology
    Laboratory 418

21

Visual Arts in America 419

A Tale of Two Cultures 420
Towards the Modern 423
Art in the White House 424
American Art on the Web 425
    Washington Allston 426
    Thomas Hart Benton 426
    Albert Bierstadt 426
    Gutzon Borglum 426
    Boston Museum of Fine Arts 427
    Alexander Calder 427
    Mary Cassatt 427
    William Merritt Chase 428
    Frederick Church 428
    John Singleton Copley 428
    Currier & Ives 428
    Willem de Kooning 428
    M.H. De Young Memorial
        Museum, San Francisco 429
    Thomas Eakins 429
    J. Paul Getty Museum, Malibu,
        California 429
    Sanford Robinson Gifford 430
    Edward Hicks 430
    Winslow Homer 430

Edward Hopper 430
Hudson River School of
    Landscape Painting 431
Emanuel Leutze's
    "Washington Crossing the
    Delaware" 431
Samuel F.B. Morse 431
Grandma Moses 432
National Museum of
    American Art 432
National Portrait Gallery 432
Native American Art Exhibit 432
Isamu Noguchi Garden
    Museum 433
Georgia O'Keeffe 433
150 Years of American
    Painting 433
Peabody Essex Museum:
    American Paintings 434
Philadelphia Print Shop 434
Jackson Pollock 434
Man Ray 434
Frederic Remington 435
The Rhode Island School of
    Design 435
Norman Rockwell 435

Mark Rothko 435
Augustus Saint-Gaudens 435
John Singer Sargent 436
Joseph Stella 436
Gilbert Stuart 436
John Trumbull 436
John Vanderlyn 437
Andy Warhol Museum 437
James Abbot McNeill
    Whistler 437
Whitney Museum of American
    Art 438
Grant Wood 438

A

Searching the Web 439

Directories and Search Engines 440
A Directory—Yahoo! 443
A Search Engine—AltaVista
    Search 449
Undertaking Your Own Journey 458

Index 465

Acknowledgments

I would like to thank my editor, Megg Bonar, for coming up with the idea for this book. I would also like to thank Megg's assistant, Gordon Hurd, for first-rate follow-up and good-natured support throughout, and Danny Carnahan for providing invaluable help in pulling the final strings of the project together. Thanks also to Eric Ray for his work on the appendix. My publisher, Brandon Nordin, has been likewise supportive. I would further like to thank my wife and family for putting up with me while I labored on this tome.

Lastly, I must thank the Rain Forest Action Network (**http://www.ran.org**) for providing the vehicle—the Protect-An-Acre Program—via which I will protect two trees for every one felled to produce this book. The imperative for such action becomes clear when we realize that somewhere in the world a section of rain forest the size of ten city blocks is burned off *every minute*. Ninety-six thousand acres of rain forest disappear every day. Please join me in helping to stop this wanton destruction of the environment.

—Edward J. Renehan, Jr.
http://members.aol.com/EJRen/EJRen.html
ejren@ids.net

Introduction

In a sense, seeking out America and Americans via the information superhighway is nothing new. People have always taken to highways in order to discover the personalities, geography, and culture of this remarkable land. It is just the texture and convenience of the road that has changed.

Two surveyors of the mid-18th century, George Washington (**http://www.mountvernon.org**) and Thomas Jefferson (**http://www.monticello.org**), used ancient Native American trails to explore and map the Virginia backcountry. Similar trails were used by Jefferson's friend and Albemarle County neighbor Merriwether Lewis (**http://www.cp.duluth.mn.us/~tmcs/lewis.htm**) when, along with William Clark, he went on his 1803-06 expedition to explore the continent all the way to the Pacific.

A Few Words on de Tocqueville, Meatspace, and Comdex

Alexis de Tocqueville—the French liberal politician who visited the United States during 1831-32 and wrote up his experiences in the classic *Democracy in America*—did most of his traveling by horse and stagecoach over rough roads that traced the edge of the wilderness. De Tocqueville (Figure 1) found the people and manners of the young country as unpredictable and unfinished as the thoroughfares. However, he assessed the prospects for the new nation generously. In the rich ground of the New World, said de Tocqueville, the seeds of the Enlightenment would produce the fairest of fruits. More than 160 years later, we Americans find ourselves still struggling to make de Tocqueville's optimistic forecast come true.

Alexis de Tocqueville did not do much traveling by train. The system of rails that would come to dominate the landscape of America during the late 19th century was still in its infancy in the 1830s. By the 1860s, however, the railroads were prevalent enough for a few Luddites to start complaining about them. "We are removed from nature and life by the whole distance of our wealth and refinement," wrote the naturalist John Burroughs (**http://www1.mhv.net/~omi/jb.htm**) in 1866. "The earth is overlaid with inventions and improvements....A man may live now and travel without hardly coming in contact with the earth or air. He can go around the world in a parlor. Life is intensely artificial."

FIGURE 1

Read the complete text of de Toqueville's Democracy in America on the Web (http://xroads.virginia.edu/ ~HYPER/DETOC/ home.html)

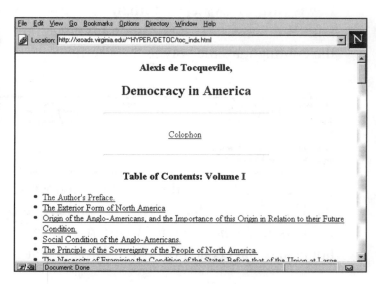

Interestingly, the complaint Burroughs voiced about trains and other 19th century conveniences is essentially the same complaint we hear voiced today by critics of cybertechnology and cyberspace. There is great and vocal concern about how artificial virtual environments threaten our humanity by removing us from that truer reality to be found offline, out-of-the box in what cyberphilosopher (and former Grateful Dead lyricist) John Perry Barlow (**http://www.eff.org/~barlow**) calls "meatspace."

If Burroughs was concerned about technology in 1866, he was frantic with fear ten years later after visiting the Centennial Exhibition in Philadelphia (Figure 2). The Exhibition—a technology show if there ever was one—promised to provide Americans with a window into the future as they embarked upon the second hundred years of democratic nationhood. The event was a vast tribute to the era Thomas Carlyle was already calling "the age of machinery in every inward and outward sense."

This was the Comdex (**http://www.comdex.com**) of its day, only bigger. All 450 acres of Philadelphia's Fairmont Park were given

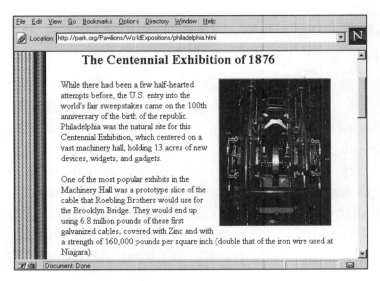

FIGURE 2

Learn more aobut the Centennial Exhibition (http://park.org/Pavilions/ WorldExpositions/ philadelphia.html)

over to dozens of enormous glass and iron halls, one of them said to be the largest in the world, all of them housing the latest examples of modern invention. The park was serviced by a new state-of-the-art railroad depot designed to handle two trains every minute. In the course of six months (10 May to 10 November) eight million visitors (one out of every five Americans) wandered the grounds of the Exhibition and marveled at the product of the country's science and industry.

The heart of the Exhibition was a linked pair of four-story steam engines supplying electrical current to some eight thousand presses, pumps, gins, and lathes in a building called "Machinery Hall." The steam engines fed a hellish cacophony of pounding hammers, hissing steam, blowing whistles, and whirling turbines.

In addition to remarkable machines, the Exhibition also boasted people—remarkable people. The Belgian Zenobe Gramme demonstrated a dynamo that lit a tiny arc of light in a glass globe. Not far away, young Thomas Edison (**http://edison-ford-estate.com/ed_bio.htm**) showed off his quadruplex telegraph system while Alexander Graham Bell (**http://jefferson.village.virginia.edu/albell/homepage.html**) dazzled audiences with his "speaking telephone."

They were all in attendance: all the entrepreneurial innovators of the day, all the Gateses and Wozniaks and Bricklins of the 19th century.

And so were their boosters and publicists, *their Dvoraks*. "It is in these things of iron and steel," wrote William Dean Howells (**http://www.tiac.net/users/eldred/wdh/howells.html**), "that the national genius most freely speaks." A German reporter wrote that in Machinery Hall "the diligence, energy, and inventive gift of the North Americans celebrates its triumph over all that has ever been achieved by other nations in the invention and construction of machines." The British philosopher Herbert Spencer (**http://userwww.sfsu.edu/~rsauzier/Spencer.html**) used the Exhibition as an example when he suggested the old military and feudal orders, founded upon theology, were inevitably bound to give way to a new industrial order inimical to militarism, founded upon the increased productivity made possible by the advance of modern science.

Amid all the hosannas and hallelujahs, however, there were a few voices (along with John Burroughs') raised in protest and warning. Herman Melville's book-length poem *Clarel*, published that centennial year, cast science and technology as menaces to God, nature, and social order. "Always," wrote Melville, "machinery strikes strange dread into the human heart, as some living, panting Behemoth might." In his short story "The Bell Tower," Melville (Figure 3) made a mechanical clock-figure strike its maker dead. "So the blind slave obeyed its blinder lord; but, in obedience, slew him." Henry Adams (**http://www.chesco.com/~artman/hbadams.html**)—historian, social philosopher, and grandson and great-grandson of presidents—was equally disaffected. "Man has mounted science," he wrote, "and is now run away with. I firmly believe that before many centuries more, science will be the master of man. The engines he will have invented will be beyond his control."

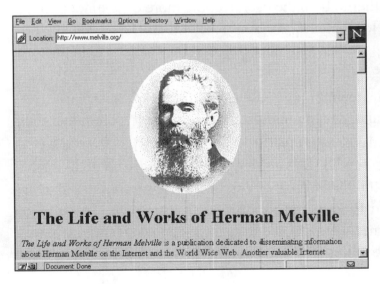

FIGURE 3
Herman Melville;
novelist, poet,
and Luddite
(***http://www.melville.org/***)

It was Ralph Waldo Emerson (**http://www.calpoly.edu/ ~jhardest/emerson.html**) who provided the most balanced and lucid appraisal of late-19th century technology. Emerson recognized and warned against the dehumanizing risk inherent in all machines. Yet he likewise understood how, if used wisely, technology could help make the land more fruitful, the people more productive, and life in general more healthy and wholesome.

Emerson embraced what he called the "technological sublime." He wrote that machines were "new and necessary facts" that, when employed toward positive ends, were in "essential" harmony with nature. All that was needed, said Emerson, was the proper moral and spiritual vision to guide the results of industrial science.

The discussion of technology really hasn't changed much at all, has it? Today, commentators such as John Perry Barlow and Cliff Stoll urge the computer revolution onward while at the same time suggesting caution. They insist—and properly so—that no man-made reality (no "virtual reality" in cyberspace) will ever replace the natural, God-made reality found in the broad light of day. They ask for an inspired use of cybertechnology as a tool not to dehumanize the user, but rather to help the user become more efficient, comfortable, and knowledgeable. Cyberspace is not really a place at all, they remind us, but a *method* for enhancing and improving life in the only real space there is.

Emerson said technology could and should help Americans come into a closer and deeper understanding of their continent, their institutions, and their compatriots. His allusion, of course, was to improved rail and telegraph infrastructures designed to help people travel and communicate with ease.

What would Emerson think of today's information superhighway—the Internet—on which one can, in seconds, wend one's way across both the miles *and the decades* that comprise the United

States, easily accessing images and sounds and other resources touching on every aspect of American history and culture? I think he would be delighted. And he would be busily at it, as should we, in the spirit of de Tocqueville and other curious travelers.

Great American Websites is meant to be your guide to all things uniquely American on the Internet and the World Wide Web. In this book I cover the range of individuals and interests—from Bonnie and Clyde to Margaret Bourke-White, from the Sierra Club to jazz, and from Dick Tracy to Edith Wharton. It is all here from the sublime (the Grand Canyon, the Declaration of Independence, the 1963 March on Washington) to the ridiculous (a.k.a., the Partridge Family).

About This Book and Its Author, a.k.a. Me

The good people at Osborne/McGraw-Hill (**http://www.osborne. com**) have asked me (**http://members.aol.com/EJRen/EJRen. html**) to be your tour guide on this adventure because of my strange mix of credentials. You see, I have two main (and, up until this moment, divergent) fields of expertise. I am the author of several critically praised works of American history, including studies of John Burroughs, John Brown (the renegade abolitionist), and Theodore Roosevelt (**http://www.abcland.com/~jwiedman/tr**). But I am also versed in the mystical secrets of the Internet, about which I've authored several popular volumes.

Another of my qualifications for writing *Great American Websites* is, of course, that I am thoroughly American. To the bone. The most recent émigré of my name is Matthew Renehan, who came from a distinguished Irish family of scholars, clerics, and physicians and traveled to the United States via England around 1840. But other bloodlines in my system go back much further.

A great, great, great, great, great-grandfather of mine, Charles Carroll of Carrollton (1737-1832), was the only Catholic signer of the Declaration of Independence. (He wound up also being the last surviving signer after the deaths of Thomas Jefferson and John Adams, within hours of each other, on July 4, 1826.) He was from Maryland (Figure 4) and he was the son of Charles Carroll of Doughoregan.

Carroll was one of the wealthiest men in colonial and post-colonial America and President of the Maryland State Senate (1782-83). Carroll's cousins were equally distinguished. Daniel Carroll (1730-96) was a member of the Maryland State Senate, a delegate to the Continental Congress from Maryland, and U.S. Representative (1789-91). John Carroll (1735-1815) became the first Roman Catholic Bishop of the United States. The appointment occurred after John's good friend Benjamin Franklin urged it in a letter to the Holy See. (By the way, the grandfather of all three of the Carroll boys, another Charles, was in his time attorney general of the Maryland Colony.)

FIGURE 4
*Charles Carroll's Annapolis home is now a museum open to the public (**http://www.capitalonline. com/capital/tour/passport/ carroll.html**)*

My last qualification for writing this tome is that I know quite a bit about the music of the United States, most especially its folk music. In the 1970s I was a professional player of traditional American music, and I recorded with Pete Seeger (Figure 5) for Folkways Records (now called Smithsonian/Folkways).

Pete, of course, is an American institution. "When I hear America singing," wrote Carl Sandburg, "Pete Seeger is there." In 1938 Pete dropped out of Harvard (where he was in the same class as John F. Kennedy, the class of 1940) and eventually wound up hopping freight trains and hitching rides down highways with Woody Guthrie (**http://www.artsci.wustl.edu/~davida/woody.html**) in order, as Pete put it to me once, to "learn the things about America college could not teach."

He went on to compose a number of classic songs including "Where Have All the Flowers Gone," "Turn, Turn, Turn," and "If I Had a Hammer." He formed and recorded with the Weavers. He survived the blacklist of the late '50s and early '60s. And he continues to this day—at age 78—to be a dedicated and vocal activist

FIGURE 5
Meet Pete Seeger
(http://ourworld.
compuserve.com/
homepages/JimCapaldi/)

working for human rights, environmental sanity, and economic justice. Not long ago he was awarded the Presidential Medal for the Arts at the Kennedy Center Honors. In 1996, he was inducted into the Rock 'n' Roll Hall of Fame (**http://www.rockhall.com/induct/seegpete.html**). As I write, in early 1997, Pete has just won a Grammy in the Traditional Folk Category for his 1996 CD entitled simply *Pete* (**http://www.gaia.org/livingmusic/pete/index.html**).

When I was in my teens and early twenties, Pete and Toshi Seeger's house overlooking the Hudson River outside Beacon, New York, was something of a second home to me. During those, my years of struggling and uncertainty, Pete and Toshi taught me a number of things about America—and myself—that college could not teach. I am a better person and a better American for knowing them, and in that spirit this book is dedicated to them.

We can find so many fascinating people on the Internet—Pete, Woody, and countless other original American heroes, among them Crazy Horse, Julia Ward Howe, Vince Lombardi, Eleanor Roosevelt, Frank Lloyd Wright, and Martin Luther King, Jr., to name just a few. The cyberroad leads us to places with names that are synonymous with central defining moments in the American saga: names like *Lexington, Concord, Harpers Ferry, Gettysburg, Little Big Horn, Wounded Knee, Woodstock*, and *Kent State*.

The new information superhighway, just like old Route 66 (the Lincoln Highway), is there to bring us face to face with all the brave and fascinating individuals, all the vibrant yesterdays and todays, all the haunted places, which, in sum, define our country. They are out there beckoning us, inviting us to come, contemplate, and understand. Like de Tocqueville, Guthrie, Dos Passos, Kerouac, and countless others before us, all we need do is get on the road—the best and fastest road we can find—and ride.

Are you with me?

—EJR
Wickford, North Kingstown, RI
ejren@ids.net

Web Search Engines: What They Are & How to Use Them

The book you are holding in your hands should be your first stop when searching for World Wide Web resources related to the United States of America. But it should not be your only stop.

There are thousands upon thousands of excellent, useful Web resources related to the United States and Americana generally—far too many to include in this book.

Should you be looking for information on some esoteric piece of Americana not incorporated in the book (say, American-made antique cookie jars, for example), there are a number of excellent search engines you can use to ferret out the data you need on the Web.

They are all quite efficient. They are all available 24 hours a day. And they all come for the mere price of oxygen. In other words, they are free. My three favorites are AltaVista, Lycos, and Yahoo!.

AltaVista (**http://www.altavista.digital.com**) and Lycos (**http://www.lycos.com**) take parameters you provide (keywords such as "antique," "American," "cookie," "jar") and use them to create indexes of documents they find on the Web containing those keywords.

AltaVista and Lycos each present the results of their searches in prioritized order. The first Web page listed among a group of AltaVista or Lycos search results is the one with the highest number of "hits" within the text of the page for the keywords you have specified. Thus, obviously, Web pages noted at the bottom of a group of AltaVista or Lycos results are less likely to meet your needs than those near the top.

The Yahoo! search engine (**http://www.yahoo.com**) works somewhat differently. Yahoo! is an extensive database of Websites. (There are, in fact, more than 40,000 of them in the database with 100 to 200 links added each day.) Yahoo!'s various pages are organized in subject categories, and you have the option of searching within a given category or scanning the entire database with a keyword search. As with AltaVista and Lycos, a prioritized list of clickable links is the result.

Because of subtle differences in the way they hold archives and the way they search the Web for data, these various search engines can, at times, produce remarkably dissimilar results while using the same set of keywords. A Website that one engine misses, however, another is likely to catch. That is why I recommend using all three to be sure to find the Web resources you need.

For more detailed information on using search engines, take a look at Appendix A.

Happy hunting.

1

American
Sports

A great-uncle on my father's side, a fellow by the name of Jimmy Torrens (1874-1952), was a Democratic member of Congress from New York back in the days of FDR. In fact, it was FDR who asked him to run for office. Today you can find Uncle Jimmy where he's been since 1952: Gate of Heaven Cemetery in Hawthorne, New York (Westchester County). There Uncle Jimmy rests not far from his old partner in crime James Aloysius Farley, Chairman of the Democratic National Committee from 1932-40. Strangely enough, Uncle Jimmy is also just a row or two away from James Cagney (**http://www.tdl.com/ ~madigan/cagney.html**). More importantly, however, he is within speaking distance of the most legendary figure ever to stalk across the landscape of American baseball: Babe Ruth. And do you know who else is here? Billy Martin, the indomitable Yankees manager, sober at last (**http://www.cmgww.com/baseball/martin/martin.html**).

As I write, I can see my Uncle Jimmy's walking stick hung up on the wall above my desk. It is a walking stick he used when he visited FDR in the White House and at Hyde Park. Like FDR, Uncle Jimmy was a great Yankees fan.

Finding Common Ground

According to what my father told me, sports made for peace within my family, for the Yankees were one of the few things Uncle Jimmy and my grandfather (an FDR-hating Republican banker) could agree upon. Making the most of that common ground, Uncle Jimmy and my grand-father (the venerable Edward Jefferson Renehan of Manhattan's Corn Exchange Bank) attended many games together up at "the house that Ruth built" in the Bronx.

Baseball and other great American sports have always been related to common ground of one kind or another. The first early, anxious fields of play were quite literally common grounds: such as Boston Common (**http://www.ci.boston.ma.us/bostoncommon.html**) and Central Park (**http://centralpark.org**). And it was on the anxious—and highly democratic—fields of play that people from all walks of life met, either as spectators or players, equal in their love of sport and their willingness to give it their all.

On the playing field, a man's or woman's background and pedigree do not count for much compared to the stamina, drive, wit, and talent they are prepared to show in pursuit of victory. It is no accident that in the tribal lore of our nation one of the most famous football games ever played was that between Harvard (**http://www.harvard.edu**) and Carlisle (the Pennsylvania school for Native Americans) for the National College Championship in 1908. It lives in memory not only because it was great football, but also because it was a study in contrasts.

Jim Thorpe was the lead player for Carlisle, under the legendary "Pop" Warner (**http://www.trycom.com/popwarner.htm**) as coach. The Harvard team featured a young, 6' 4", 200-pound tackle by the name of Hamilton Fish, a descendant of the Stuyvesant and Fish families whose grandfather—of the same name—had been Secretary of State under U.S. Grant. Harvard won the game, but not by much.

As I allude to later in this chapter, Jim Thorpe, who came from the most humble of beginnings, went on to have a semidistinguished career. He was both a great man and a great athlete, but he was unfairly treated in many ways throughout his life and wound up with little (except a profoundly insightful and motivated daughter, about whom more in due course). Ham Fish, who came from anything but humble beginnings, went on to have a remarkable life as well. As a young man he was a close friend of Theodore Roosevelt (whose family hailed from the same New York Brahmin society as Ham Fish's). He was elected to New York's State

Assembly (**http://assembly.state.ny.us**) on TR's Bull Moose ticket in 1914. As a white officer he commanded an otherwise black regiment in combat in the First World War. And he later served as a member of Congress for 25 years from New York's Dutchess County.

I met him in 1990 when he was 101. This was at a reception on Long Island where Fish had come to be honored by the Theodore Roosevelt Association. Despite his age, Fish stood erect and delivered a lengthy, cogent speech without notes and without a microphone. No one had trouble hearing him. And no one had trouble comprehending every point he considered important to make. He had many of them. His long and passionate speech was focused and clear and loaded with patriotic images. And it was followed by a standing ovation.

It was such a striking speech, in fact, that Paul Nitze (**http://www.sais-jhu.edu**), the other man to be honored that night, simply folded his notes, thanked the Theodore Roosevelt Association for inviting him, and allowed that he could not compete with what Mr. Fish had said. (Ham Fish was just my grandfather Renehan's type of guy, by the way. He thundered his disapproval of FDR and the New Deal as vehemently in 1990 as he had in 1935.)

It is hard to think of two more different people than the ultimately disenfranchised Jim Thorpe and the confident scion of the establishment Ham Fish, but they shared two fundamental things in common: a passion for football as a game, and four quarters played on a vanished field—quarters that today remain the stuff of legend.

Brahmins Play More than Just Football

There have been, are, and always will be many more democratizing moments emanating from America's national fascination with sports.

I remember a picture, which I've found reproduced on the Web, of two striking figures standing side-by-side (Figure 1-1). The older man is George Herman Ruth—the Babe. He is dressed in a business suit. He looks frail and sickly and old. The younger man is also named George. His last name is Bush. It is 1948 and George Bush—recently returned from meritorious service in the Army Air Corps—is the captain of the Yale baseball team. On behalf of the team, he is accepting an inscribed copy of Babe Ruth's recently published autobiography.

What do these two have in common besides the game? Here you have Ruth, the child of the slums. And there you have George Bush, son of a United States Senator, scion of generations of great wealth. Baseball is their common ground. Baseball and the United States, that is. A few years earlier Bush had served among men with whom he had little in common other than duty in the face of a strong enemy. It was then that the battle of warfare—just like the battle of sport—became a profound, democratizing experience.

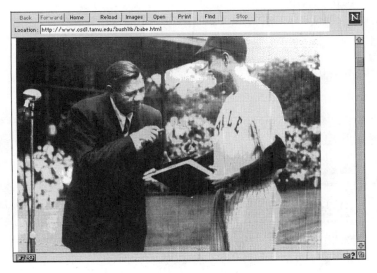

FIGURE 1-1

Yale baseball team captian George Bush receives an autographed autobiography from the dying Babe Ruth in 1948 (***http://www.csdl.tamu.edu/ bushlib/babe.html***)

Just like baseball and football, so is basketball a thoroughly democratizing, uniquely American game. Hockey, for its part, is very nearly an American game, since it got its start just north of the border in Canada. Of course, it has been adopted with great enthusiasm by fans in New York, Chicago, and Seattle. It is not my cup of tea, however. Not violent enough. (Kidding!) Then we have our own uniquely American blend of thoroughbred racing as represented by the Kentucky Derby and the other races of the Triple Crown, not to mention the yacht racing and marathon running with which all regions of the country seem fascinated.

And the largest piece of common ground for sports we have today is the World Wide Web. The resources on the Web relating to American sports are absolutely staggering in their depth and breadth. All the major professional teams have their own Web pages, as do the major umbrella organizations such as the National Hockey League, the National Basketball Association, and major league baseball's National and American Leagues. Most college Websites chronicle the various college teams and leagues. And then the networks weigh in with extensive Web pages providing stats and opinions from famous sports commentators. Thus the computerized sports nut can spend weeks surfing the various sports information on the Web and never once hit the same page twice.

Let's browse through a few.

⭐⭐⭐⭐⭐⭐⭐⭐⭐

All-Time, All-Star Baseball Team

☞ http://terrapin.umd.edu/~lori/team.html

Check out the world's all-time best team, assuming we could wipe out the laws of physics, stop time in its tracks, and bring the dead back to life. On first base we have Lou Gehrig. Second base: Rogers Hornsby. Short stop: Honus Wagner. Third base: Mike Schmidt. Catcher: Josh Gibson. Outfield: Ty Cobb, Hank Aaron, Roger Maris, Ted Williams, and Joe DiMaggio. Pitching staff: Walter Johnson, Christy Matthewson, Nolan Ryan, Satchel Paige, and Bob Feller. Designated hitter: Babe Ruth. Manager: Casey Stengel. Pitching coach: Cy Young. Hitting coach: Mickey Mantle.

American Amateur Baseball Congress

 http://www.voyager.net/aabc/

Can't get enough of America's favorite pastime? Read up on the American Amateur Baseball Congress (AABC)—the largest amateur baseball organization in the world. With seven age divisions (including an unlimited age division) the AABC has produced pros the likes of Cal Ripken, Jr., Barry Larkin, Ken Griffey, Jr., and Ozzie Smith. Even ex-pros can join in the fun (provided there are no more than five of them on a team). State champions ascend to national world series, some of which are attended by as many as 80,000 fans.

American Basketball Association (R.I.P.)

 http://www.geocities.com/ Colosseum/5290/

The purpose of this unofficial page is to provide an online reference guide to the defunct American Basketball Association (ABA). Each ABA team from 1967 through 1976 is profiled, complete with stats, player and coach profiles, and more.

America's Sports Headquarters on the Web

 http://www.sport-hq.com/sport/

It is all here: amateur, professional, and college sports. Baseball, football, basketball, soccer, and more. Here you have editorials, commentaries, stats, schedules, and links all pulled together with a keyword search engine.

The Atlanta Braves

 http://www.atlantabraves.com/

They were the 1996 National League champions. They are also the team which gave us Hank Aaron. Need I say more? Hank is my all-time favorite baseball player: both an excellent athlete and an excellent human being.

Welcome to 1996 National League Champion Braves Headquarters

The Atlanta Hawks

 http://www.nba.com/hawks/

We are talking about one fine basketball team: the Hawks. They are one of the leading teams in the Central Division of the NBA, and promise to be for some time to come. This is the page for Hawk lovers everywhere.

Baseball Online

 http://www.baseball-online.com/

This site provides a great online publication documenting minor league baseball through detailed feature articles and commentaries. All the up-and-coming stars are profiled here. Get a peek into baseball's next decade.

Basketball Highway

 http://www.bbhighway.com/

A great resource for teachers and coaches of basketball. But be warned: the first page takes *forever* to load. Once you manage to get past the first page, however, you have no limit of practical tips, hints, and strategies for achieving excellence in coaching.

The Boston Celtics Official Home Page

 http://www.nba.com/celtics/

We are celebrating 50 years of the Celtics this year. Come to this page for schedules, news, stats, and more. The one thing missing, of course, is the gorgeous old Boston Garden, evacuated last year after many seasons of pleasure.

Boston Marathon Home Page

 http://www.baa.org/

The Boston Marathon is surely one of the oldest in the world. The first running was held in 1897 and won by an American named J.J. McDermott. Since then, winners of the Boston Marathon have hailed from every corner of the Americas, Europe, Asia, and Africa. This Website is replete with history and factoids about the Boston Marathon, and running in general. View the re-

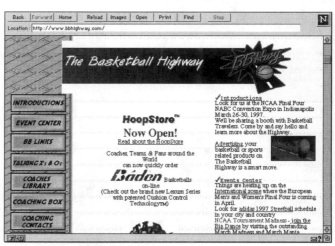

sults of every Boston Marathon ever run (including the women's, wheelchair, and elite divisions), or hook into the searchable database to find the results of a contestant you know.

Boston Patriots Home Page

 http://www.patriots.com/

They may have lost the Super Bowl, but they will be back next year. Just wait and see. Get the latest news and gossip of personnel changes right here at the official home page of New England's favorite football team, the Boston Patriots.

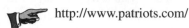

The Boston Red Sox

 http://www.redsox.com/

Come to this Web location for the latest news of the Red Sox as well as detailed histories of the team and the park in which they play: grand old Fenway. It is a ballpark that carries more nostalgia with it than just about any other I can think of.

Casey at the Bat

 http://www.csh.rit.edu/~kenny/poetry/casey.html

Here is the classic poem of American baseball written by Ernest Lawrence Thayer circa 1888. Thayer built a career as a stage performer reciting this much-loved poem. In fact, he toured the world with the performance and once even gave a recitation at the White House.

CBS Sports

 http://www.cbs.com/sports/

This Web resource provides all the details on CBS coverage of auto racing, college basketball, golf, tennis, and much more. Here you not only get CBS air-time schedules for games, you also get insightful commentary from CBS announcers and analysts.

The Chicago Bulls

 http://www.nba.com/bulls/

The Bulls, currently in first place of the Central Division, are looking mean and undefeatable. This is my second hometown, Chicago. It is where my mother's family resides. A part of me will always be a Bulls fan.

Roger Clemens Home Page

 http://www.majorleaguebaseball.com/bios/015074.sml

Roger Clemens. He is one of the most dominating pitchers baseball has ever known. The talented right-hander has been a three-time Cy Young Award winner and has the record for most strikeouts in a game (20). He was named an all-star player while pitching for Spring Wood High School in Houston, Texas and later led the University of Texas to a championship in the College World Series. After being drafted 19th overall by the Red Sox in the amateur draft of June 1983, the multitalented Clemens turned down lucrative offers to play basketball with the Seattle Supersonics and the Boston Celtics so that he could instead play baseball for the Sox. Get much more information on Roger at this informative home page.

Ty Cobb Home Page

 http://wso.williams.edu/~jkossuth/cobb/

A 1942 survey of former major league managers pointed the finger towards Ty Cobb as the greatest baseball player of all time. Many excellent players have surfaced on the diamond, but none out-hit, out-played, or out-hustled the man they called "the Georgia Peach." Over 24 seasons, most with the Detroit Tigers and a couple with the Philadelphia Athletics, Cobb compiled a .366 career batting average, the highest in the history of the game. He is the leader in runs scored with 2,245, and was the all-time hit leader until the mid-1980s when Pete Rose eclipsed him. In 1936, Ty Cobb became the first inductee of baseball's Hall of Fame, earning 222 out of a possible 226 votes in the process.

ESPN Sportszone

 http://espnet.sportszone.com/

This site, courtesy of ESPN, is packed with the latest news, views, and images related to football, basketball, hockey, baseball, and every other sport you can think of, whether professional, college, or amateur.

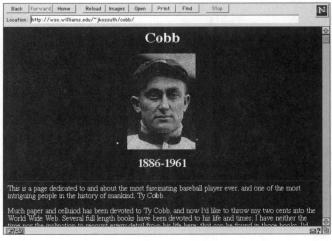

Fastball

 http://www.fastball.com/

Fastball is your complete off-season source for major league baseball information on the Web. Fastball features up-to-the-minute news about every team, hundreds of statistics, numerous discussion and chat areas and, during the season, the latest scores updated every three minutes. You also get audio game updates, box scores, and in-depth coverage of all teams.

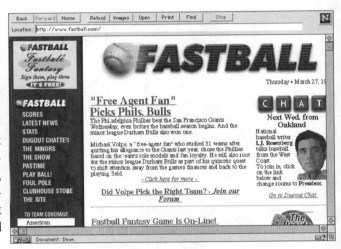

Lou Gehrig Home Page

 http://www.cmgww.com/baseball/gehrig/gehrig.html

Here you'll find complete details on the life and career of Lou Gehrig. The site also contains information on how to license the name and likeness of Lou Gehrig for

commercial purposes. Note that the heirs of Lou Gehrig donate all license fees to Columbia Presbyterian Hospital and the Caldwell Esselstryn Foundation. Unlike the heirs of Babe Ruth, they do not license Gehrig's name or likeness for the sake of tobacco products.

Green Bay Packers Home Page

 http://www.packers.com/

Visit the home page of three-time Super Bowl winners, the Green Bay Packers. Here you'll find team portraits, bios, and stats along with scouting reports, coaching information, and "front office" gossip about the organization. Here you also will find RealAudio interviews with Andre Rison, Reggie White, and others, along with real-time on-screen video clips. Go for it!

The Harlem Globetrotters

 http://www.harlemglobetrotters.com/

The official home page of the Harlem Globetrotters offers a wealth of interesting facts and trivia, as well as the history of this unique and hilarious basketball team. Did you know that the Harlem Globetrotters played to the largest crowd ever assembled to see a basketball game? That the Globetrotters pioneered the fast break offense, the forward and guard positions, and the slam dunk? Read detailed bios on each of the Globetrotter team members, learn about the Globetrotter's annual "Summer Camp for Kids," and order Globetrotter memorabilia online. The team also posts their game schedule online.

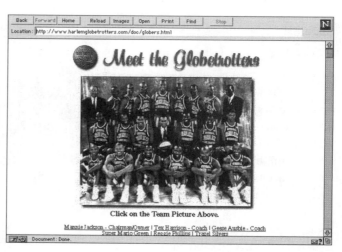

The Internet Simulated Baseball League

 http://www.isbl.com/

The Internet Simulated Baseball League was created to give people a chance to prove themselves as managers of virtual baseball teams. This online virtual league uses Diamond Mind Baseball software in order to play all games.

Diamond Mind Baseball is the single most accurate baseball simulator available for the computer. What it lacks in graphics, it more than makes up for with easy, excellent game play, allowing you the chance to be the general manager and manager of your own team without having to worry about coordination or great computer knowledge to help you win.

In the Internet Simulated Baseball League you are the general manager and owner of a fantasy baseball team which consists of real major league players. As the season commences, the 24 owners engage in a 62-game long marathon of decisions all in the hopes of being the team that takes the championship when all is said and done. Somewhere between where the season begins and ends, they will have dealt with better teams, juries, sneaky trades, and all the other ulcer-inducing events that take place in the course of a "normal" season.

Good luck!

"Shoeless" Joe Jackson Home Page

 http://www.polaris.net/
~shoeless/shoeless.htm

W as there ever a more tragic figure in baseball than "Shoeless" Joe Jackson?

Say it ain't so, Joe.

We all remember the phrase. But do we remember the context?

Jackson was one of the greatest players the game has ever known. His glove was described as "the place where triples go to die." His quick instincts and precise skill at measuring the angle of the ball as it traveled off the bat made Jackson perhaps the greatest fielder the game has ever seen.

Over thirteen glorious seasons with the Athletics, Indians, and White Sox, Jackson led the league in triples eight times, batted over the .340 mark eight times, and even hit .408 in the 1911 season.

Unfortunately for Joe, his .356 lifetime batting average and unmatched outfield prowess will forever be overshadowed by the "Black Sox" scandal of 1919. Joe received a lifetime ban from baseball for allegedly helping to throw the 1919 World Series: a charge he denied vehemently for the rest of his life. In the 1919 Series that he supposedly helped "fix" so that his team would lose, he had the most hits (12) and the highest batting average (.375) of any player on either side, and not a single error. When accused in a court of law, he was found innocent by a jury. But the baseball commissioner left the ban in place.

Another good Shoeless Joe site is to be found at **http://www.dennismc.com/baseball/sjj/sjohmpg1.html**. You should also check out the *Shoeless Joe Jackson Times* at **http://userwww.service.emory.edu/~tkram01/**.

Kentucky Derby Official Home Page

 http://www.kentuckyderby.com/

F or well over a century, the Kentucky Derby has been the flagship of horse races in the U.S. and the gem of the Triple Crown. Located at Churchill Downs near Louisville Kentucky, the Derby is the oldest consecutively held thoroughbred race in the Americas.

Read here about the history and pageantry of this great annual race and the track it's run on. This site also offers information about race schedules, entries, betting, live and simulcast racing, and lists of winners, milestones, and Kentucky Derby traditions.

The Los Angeles Dodgers

 http://www.dodgers.com/

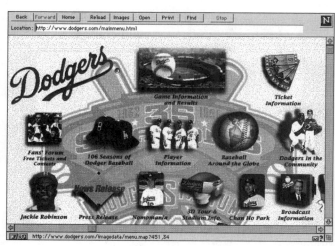

The official home page of the Dodgers provides information on team history, play schedules, ticket information, and much more, including a detailed set of pages concerning one of my great heroes: Jackie Robinson.

Robinson, who starred with the Dodgers from 1947 through 1956, will always be remembered as the man who served as the instrument for the destruction of segregation in American baseball.

dates, stats, and trivia. This is the official site, so all the information is absolutely authoritative and up-to-the-minute.

Louisville Slugger Online

 http://www.slugger.com

There is only one baseball bat that matters. And these guys make it. Take a cyber-tour of the factory, learn the history of the Louisville Slugger Company, view the on-line catalog of bats, and, if you'd care to, order one for yourself.

Major League Baseball Official Home Page

 http://www.majorleaguebaseball.com/

Get the scoop on everything that is happening in major league ball. This includes team and league information, player up-

Major League Baseball Players Alumni Association

 http://www.mlbpaa.org

Former major league players have come together to support the game, conduct free youth clinics, and in general give back to the game which has given so much to them. Members include Bob Feller, Brooks Robinson, and Bert Campaneris.

Minor League Baseball

 http://www.minorleaguebaseball.com/

There's nothing I like better than big league fun at minor league prices. What is more, I think minor league baseball is

more exciting and interesting to watch than big league play. When I go to see the Pawtucket Red Sox (farm team for the Boston Red Sox) here in Rhode Island, I see a level of passion and drama that you don't often get in the "fat" majors. The men playing for Pawtucket have a lot on the line. They are motivated. They are hungry. The young men, stuggling to get promoted up to the majors, give everything they've got in order to show their stuff. The older players, recently "sent down" from the majors for under-performance, are also fighting back—trying to show they've still got what it takes.

This, the official home page of American minor league baseball, includes complete information on teams, leagues, and standings. It also provides well-written baseball commentary and news features.

treasures and artifacts of American baseball history. The Hall of Fame Website offers a list of Hall of Fame inductees with detailed information on each, and interesting links to historical tidbits, press releases, the Hall of Fame Library and Museum, educational programs, and information about visiting the real library and museum in Cooperstown.

National Baseball Hall of Fame

 http://www.enews.com/bas_hall_fame/overview.html

Tucked away on a street called Main, in a town called Cooperstown, is the National Baseball Hall of Fame. The Hall of Fame also has a small presence in cyberspace where, among other things, you can learn such interesting sidelights as the fascinating (and often neglected) history of women in baseball.

The Hall of Fame was established in 1939 to enshrine the greatest of baseball players and to collect and display the many

National Basketball Association

 http://www.nba.com

Here you have the official Website of the National Basketball Association (NBA) featuring news and features, player info, team info, scores, and statistics. There are also NBA goodies for sale including jerseys, balls, and other official equipment. And you get expert commentary by the likes of Jack Ramsay, Phil Jackson, and Jerry West.

National Football League

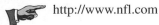 http://www.nfl.com

Get the latest scoop on the Patriots and the Packers and the game of the century both at this site and at **http://superbowl.com**. Along with all the latest NFL news, these Web pages provide stats, images, schedules, and more. The site also offers real-time on-line chats with the likes of Colts quarterback Bert Jones, Chargers punter Darren Bennett, Dolphins quarterback Bernie Kosar, and Broncos running back Terrell Davis. This is the official Website of the National Football League, by the way. So there is no better place in cyberspace for professional football die-hards.

National Hockey League

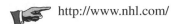 http://www.nhl.com/

The National Hockey League's Web pages provide complete stats, scores, and schedules for the League plus excellent photographs, an online edition of the official League rules, and some very nice official NHL memorabilia and books for sale via their online store. Get all the details on all your favorite players. When did they start playing hockey? Who were their childhood heroes? What team do they fear the most? It is all here, along with

in-depth analysis and comments by the likes of Greg Millen, John Davidson, and Don Cherry.

All the teams are covered. In the Northeast Division (Eastern Conference) you have the Boston Bruins, the Buffalo Sabres, the Hartford Whalers, the Pittsburgh Penguins, the Montreal Canadians, and the Ottawa Senators. In the Atlantic Division (Eastern Conference) you have the Florida Panthers, the New York Islanders, the New York Rangers, the New Jersey Devils, the Philadelphia Flyers, the Tampa Bay Lightning, and the Washington Capitols. In the Central Division (Western Conference) there's the Chicago Blackhawks, the Dallas Stars, the Detroit Red Wings, the St. Louis Blues, the Phoenix Coyotes, and the Toronto Maple Leafs. Then in the Pacific Division (Western Conference) there's the Mighty Ducks of Anaheim, the Calgary Flames, the Colorado Avalanche, the Edmonton Oilers, the Los Angeles Kings, the San Jose Sharks, and the Vancouver Canucks.

The NHL Website provides detailed player bios, schedules, stats, and standings for each team, division, and conference.

NBC Sports

 http://www.nbc.com/sports/

Get the latest on all the sports action planned for the NBC network, including highlights, stats, expert commentary, and more. In addition to game schedules, the site also includes game forecasts, player evaluations, and league standings.

Negro Leagues Home Page

 http://www.negro-league.columbus. oh.us/

Some of the greatest players the game has ever known never made it to the house that Ruth built. Find out about them at this Web page dedicated to the history of the Negro leagues which thrived in the first half of the twentieth century.

The New York Yankees

 http://www.yankees.com/

They were the 1996 World Series champions. Will they do it again in '97? Well, this former New York boy sure hopes so. It is the team of Babe Ruth and Lou Gehrig—the team with the most old baseball nostalgia attached to it. 1997 will be bittersweet in a way. It'll be the Yankees first season in thirteen without Don Mattingly, who is retiring after spending his entire major league career in Yankee pinstripes. He is also only the tenth player in the entire history of the team to have been named captain. Come to the Yankees' Web pages for complete schedules and stats, interesting interviews, and links to such cool places as Don Mattingly's personal home page.

Professional Bowling Association

 http://www.pba.org/

Although officially an international association, the PBA is actually predominantly American, as is the sport of bowling. The PBA started out with 33 charter members in 1958. Today, it has

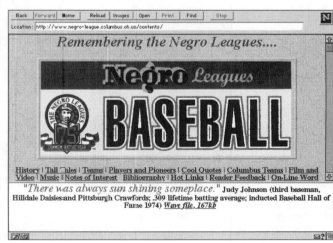

over 3,300 members competing for more than $5 million in prize money on the national tour.

Professional Golfers Association (PGA)

 http://www.pga.com/

G olf, of course, is international. And so is professional golf. However, professional golfing got its start in the United States, as did the PGA itself.

The organization was founded in 1916 with just 82 charter members. Today, of course, it is enormous. And the sum of its large entirety is described here, at the PGA's official Website, in detail.

Babe Ruth Home Page

 http://www.baberuth.com/

T his is the official site administered by the heirs of Babe Ruth. It is loaded with statistics, images, and a useful biography. It is also loaded with details on how you can license the name and likeness of the Babe to promote virtually anything under the sun including tobacco. Yup, the list of outfits that have licensed the name and likeness of the Babe includes Brown & Williamson. The Babe, of course, was a lifetime smoker and died of lung cancer. And I must say I think it is very classy for Babe's heirs to make money by allowing the Babe to be used to encourage young people to smoke. Bravo!

Society for Baseball Research (SABR)

 http://www.sabr.org/

F ormed in the early 1970s, the Society for Baseball Research (SABR) is an organization of more than 6,500 members dedicated to promoting baseball as an institution and keeping accurate historical accounts of baseball events and issues. SABR sponsors a national convention each summer featuring guest speakers, a player's panel, a local ball game, trivia contests, and other fun and games. In short, SABR is a club for baseball enthusiasts. Here on SABR's Web pages, you can read more about the organization and its events, and find out how to join.

Jim Thorpe: All American

 http://www.alphacdc.com/necona/
jimthorp.html

James Francis Thorpe may well have been the greatest athlete ever to don a pair of gym socks. But what makes Jim Thorpe's story truly compelling is Jim Thorpe himself. Born a Sac and Fox Indian in Oklahoma in 1888, Thorpe overcame tremendous odds to conquer amateur and professional sports on the world stage. Thorpe won two gold medals in the 1912 Olympic Games that were later stripped by the International Olympic Committee because Thorpe had played semiprofessional baseball while a student at Carlisle Indian Industrial School.

Sweden's King Gustav V called Thorpe "the greatest athlete in the world." And in 1950, Thorpe was identified by the Associated Press as the greatest football player and greatest all-around athlete of the previous 50 years. Right now his daughter, Grace Thorpe (who in her spare time is a dedicated activist for Native American rights) is lobbying to get Jim named the greatest athlete of the century. This Web page is her platform.

Stop by, sign the online petition, e-mail chat with Grace, and learn more about a great man and his dedicated daughter.

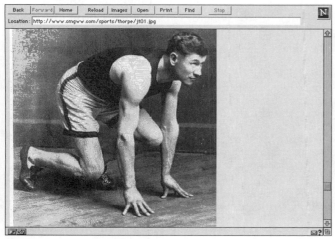

USA Basketball Official Home Page

 http://www.usabasketball.com/

USA Basketball is the organization responsible for assembling the U.S. men's and women's Dream Teams every two years at the Olympic Games and World Championships. During 1996 in the global spotlight of the Atlanta Olympics, the USA Basketball men's and women's Olympic teams once again proved the USA to be the world's hoops leader with their gold medal-winning performances.

Honus Wagner Home Page

 http://www.cmgww.com/
baseball/honus/honus.html

The most valuable baseball card in the world is the 1909 card featuring young Honus Wagner of the Pittsburgh Pirates. The card is worth more than $450,000. Why is this card so valuable? Obviously, it's rare. But why, besides being old, is it so rare? It's rare because Wagner had the card recalled right after it was issued.

In those days, baseball cards were packaged with tobacco, and Wagner didn't want to be included in such a promotion because he wanted to set a good example for children.

Some also consider Wagner to have been one of the greatest baseball players in history. Come to this Website for much more information on the inimitable Honus Wagner including his amazing batting statistics.

Ted Williams Home Page

 http://hitter.com

Here, at the official Ted Williams Website, you will find great images and a detailed biography of the man who set out at age 20 to become the greatest hitter who ever lived. Here you can also buy Ted Wil-

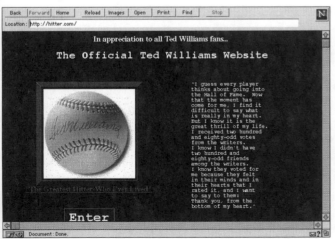

liams memorabilia, including his autograph, right online. The site is run by Ted Williams Family Enterprises.

Yacht Racing Rules Online

 http://www.lainet.com/~engel/rules.htm

This is an online edition of the international rules for yacht racing which apply as much in the United States as anywhere. These rules are promulgated by the International Sailing Federation (ISAF).

Cy Young Award Winners Since 1956

 http://www.majorleaguebaseball.
com/library/cyyoung.sml

Established in 1956, the Cy Young Award is a sort of "most valuable player" award for pitchers in major league baseball. Originally, one award was given each year for both leagues, but since 1967, two have been given annually: one for the American League and one for the National League. On this Web page, you'll find a complete listing of every Cy Young Award winner, together with a detailed history of the award.

2

Architecture

————⟨⟨⟨∞⟩⟩⟩————

During my later teenage years, when I wasn't squatting at the home of Pete and Toshi Seeger (where I most often wound up in a bedroll perched high in the cupola at the top of their barn), I lived on an old estate on the western shore of the Hudson River (**http://www. envirolonk.org/orgs/hrwa/guide.htm**).

The estate was 90 miles north of Manhattan and just a bit to the south of Kingston, New York. The town where I lived was called West Park—so named because it lay directly across the river from Hyde Park.

The View from My Window

Looking south out my bedroom window I could see the bend in the river called Krum Elbow beyond which, on the opposite shore, was the home of Franklin Delano Roosevelt (**http://www.academic.marist.edu/ fdr.htm**). Looking directly across the river, the view was of the stately mansion built by Frederick W. Vanderbilt (grandson of Cornelius Vanderbilt) in 1898. The home is one of the best examples of a Beaux Arts country house in the entire United States.

The Vanderbilt house was designed by Charles Follen McKim and his partners William Rutherford Mead and Stanford White. The firm McKim, Mead & White dominated the architecture of the northeast during the last quarter of the 19th century, when great fortunes were made and spent and social ambitions soared without limits. McKim and his partners made a business of turning the robber barons' desire for aristocratic grandeur into a reality.

In New York and Boston they built neoclassical banks, libraries, and monuments (including the Boston Public Library and Manhattan's Washington Square Arch). They also erected a host of Renaissance mansions such as the Vanderbilt place in Hyde Park. In Newport, Rhode Island, they contrived exquisite summer "cottages"—as the super-rich called their seaside mansions—along with the famous Newport Casino and other landmarks.

Borrowing from the monuments of ancient Rome and the *palazzi* of Florence and Venice, McKim and his cohorts gave physical form to the aspirations and achievements of their generation's great princes of commerce. Emphasizing decorative beauty—from the design of spectacularly marbled, paneled, and painted walls to the employment of sculptors and craftsmen like Augustus Saint-Gaudens and Louis Tiffany—McKim, Mead & White created both public and private palaces of pleasure.

The period in which McKim, Mead & White did their work was called the Gilded Age (**http://morton.wm.edu/~srnels/gilded.html**). The epoch took its name from an 1873 novel written by Mark Twain and Charles Dudley Warner. In their book, Twain and Warner suggested that, like the heroes of another civilization, America's new multimillionaires were being made into pharaohs. Their pyramids were their mansions. Twain and Warner further suggested that the Gilded Age was characterized by money-lust, hardness, and cynicism. It was a time, in Twain's words, "of incredible rottenness." The agnostic Twain went so far as to suggest that cold cash was the closest thing to a God that modern man possessed—the one great common denominator. "Who is God, the one, only, and true?" he asked readers of the *New York Tribune* in the fall of 1871. "Money is God. Gold and Greenbacks and Stock—father, son and the ghost of same—three persons in one; these are the true and only God, mighty and supreme."

The object of Twain's and Warner's special loathing was another man with a fine house on the Hudson River—the great-grandfather of my friend Kingdon Gould, Jr.: Jay Gould. Born in 1836, Jay Gould rose from a childhood of near-poverty in the rural Catskill Mountains to a position where he was worth nearly $90 million. In the process, he became, in the public's eye, the quintessential robber baron—a person the man-on-the-street (and many men above the street) loved to hate.

Henry and Charles Francis Adams—the grandsons and great-grand-sons of presidents—vilified Gould in their 1870 book, *Chapters of Erie*, where they dissected his financial dealings in taking over the Erie Railroad and also his role in the infamous "Gold Corner" affair. The financier Daniel Drew was quoted in newspapers saying Gould's touch was "death." James R. Keene, another Wall Street operator, denounced Gould as "the worst man on earth since the beginning of the Christian era. He is treacherous, false, cowardly, and a despicable worm incapable of a generous nature." Joseph Pulitzer called him "one of the most sinister figures that have ever flitted bat-like across the vision of the American people."

In reality, Gould was no better and no worse than any other mogul of the Gilded Age. But he encouraged his image as a furtive, heartless financial genius, a vampire against whom resistance was futile. The image was convenient for business. Thus, when Jay went shopping for a home in 1880, he sought out the Gothic (Figure 2-1).

Jay Gould's old home sits sixty miles south of the Vanderbilt's Hyde Park place, overlooking the Hudson at Tarrytown. The home, called Lynd-hurst, is one of America's finest Gothic revival mansions. Designed by

FIGURE 2-1
Jay Gould's Lyndhurst
(http://cmg.hitachi.com/
european_art/castle/
castlepic.html)

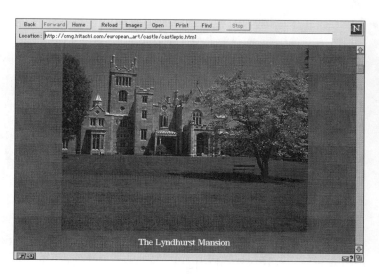

Alexander Jackson Davis, the house was originally built in 1838. Gould acquired Lyndhurst in 1880 and lived there until his death in 1892. Gould's daughter Helen inherited it. After Helen's death in 1938, her sister Anna, Duchess of Telleyrand-Periford, returned from France and lived at Lyndhurst until her death in 1961. Today the estate is owned and operated by the National Trust for Historic Preservation (**http://www.nthp.org**).

A Bit More on Conspicuous Construction

There are several similarities between today's cyberbarons and their robber baron forebears. Both groups of millionaires made their enormous fortunes from dramatic technological shifts which changed society in fundamental ways. And both groups have demonstrated a knack for what we might call, with a tip of the hat to John Kenneth Galbraith, "conspicuous construction."

Bill Gates' $30 million, 45,000-square-foot adventure in architecture is a case in point. It certainly rivals anything ever built by the Vanderbilts, Whitneys, Rockefellers, or Morgans. Ensconced in its hillside outside Seattle like the funerary temple of Hatshepsut (**http://www.memphis.edu/egypt/img0025.htm**), this study in extremes has already become the pyramid most commonly associated with pharaoh Bill.

But Gates isn't the only billionaire nerd building his ostentatious nest. Consider Paul Allen's Scandinavian inspired compound on Mercer Island (**http://www.celestial.com/mi.html**). The place comprises 74,000 square feet and includes a basketball court, a recording studio, an office tower, and a made-to-order meditation grotto.

Or consider what is happening in Woodside—a Silicon Valley mink and manure enclave where "Equestrian Crossing" signs dot the roadsides. Here Oracle (**http://www.oracle.com**) founder Lawrence J. Ellison is building a $40 million, 23-acre "Japanese" retreat. The project involves airlifting a mansion by Julia Morgan, the architect of William Randolph Hearst's San Simeon (**http://www.sansimeon-online.com**), to Stanford University (**http://www.stanford.edu**) from the spot where Mr. Ellison wants to put one of two meditative ponds.

In addition to the meditative ponds, the retreat will feature a 7,000-square-foot main house with boat docks, a "moon pavilion" for *sake* and contemplation, a stroll garden, three guest houses (including a "Katsura house" modeled after the summer palace near Kyoto), and a hot tub in a cast-bronze boulder. The compound's timber-framed buildings, with their earthen walls and hand-adzed beams, will be enclosed within a wall of Okabe clay, to absorb the house's "physical and spiritual energy."

Mr. Ellison, whose sense of competition would prove a match for that of Jay Gould, has often spoken of his love for samurai culture, which balances a blistering desire to skewer the competition—perhaps symbolized by the archery range he is building—with a love of poetry and flower-arranging.

At Medina, Washington—on Lake Washington—Microsoft's chief programming wizard Charles Simonyi enjoys a 20,500-square-foot lakeside home with a cantilevered terrace. The house is hermetically sealed. It has been devised with mathematical precision and includes a glass-enclosed 60-foot-long swimming pool and networks of stainless steel trusses. The glinting, sprawling structure, designed by Seattle architect Wendell Lovett for about $10 million, tilts at a seven-degree angle and looks like it has been hit by a slight earthquake. The tilt was inspired by the eye-bending paintings of Victor Vasarely (**http://www.sunnetwork. com/art/vv.html**), which Mr. Simonyi collects. Simonyi says the angle of the house reflects a "digital premonition." The trusses, in fact, make the building quite stable, despite its lopsided appearance. The building is vast, and includes within it Mr. Simonyi's private atelier—a computer lab with magnetized walls where he and colleagues can brainstorm.

And in Atherton, Tom Proulx, co-founder of Intuit (**http://www.intuit. com**), is melding the traditional look and feel of the English country house with cutting-edge technology. Even though Proulx's house looks like something out of a Thackeray novel, it is more a Jetson's-style "smart house" in which light switches and household appliances conspire to tend to all wants while remaining invisible—just like the maids and butlers of the Gilded Age. For example, a tiny camera at the door takes a snapshot of a guest and then, like the doddering butler announcing a visitor, generates a picture that is routed to the home's owners wherever they might be in the household (the house knows where to find them).

The new Techno-Pile Style of architecture ranges from CyberBaronial to Techno-Nouveau. But the homes of the new cyberbarons all share certain fundamental traits, such as an emphasis on privacy and state-of-the-art gadgetry. CEOs who as teenage nerds locked themselves in their bedrooms with their computers now lock themselves in their customized compounds, such as the one owned by Microsoft V.P. Joe Vetter, who has a miniature version of the fabled outdoor amphitheater at Epidaurus in his backyard.

History Repeats (Just Like Bad Hamburger)

According to Patterson Sims, a former associate director of the Seattle Art Museum (**http://www.vra.oberlin.edu/mus.html**) who is now a deputy director at the Museum of Modern Art in New York (**http://www.moma.org**), the villas of the cyberbarons share certain fundamental qualities with the villas of the cyberbarons' forebears, including "a passion for size and the American fantasy of unabashed, unself-conscious expenditure." Architectural historian Mark Alan Hewitt reminds us that "American culture does repeat itself." For the cyberbarons, just as for the robber barons, "houses are perhaps the most important status symbols."

But then there has always been a socioeconomic aspect to architecture.

During the early years of settlement in America, colonization was dominated by four great European nations: Spain, England, France, and Holland. Some of the first homes built in Virginia in 1611 and 1612 were small, two-storied, half-timbered townhouses to match the Tudor homes which still predominated in London. These were shortly followed by all-brick Tudor-Gothic homes with which increasingly affluent Virginia colonists sought to match their contemporaries back in England with regard to comfort and decoration. Meanwhile, to the south and west, the Spanish brought the mission-style architecture which quickly merged with various aspects of adobe construction as practiced by the Pueblo Indians. In New York, Dutch row houses defined the landscape. And to the north, Montreal started off looking like another Paris.

Early on, the only truly original American architecture was crude and driven by poverty. It was a purely utilitarian architecture of the cheap and the near-at-hand. I refer to the log cabin: easy-to-build, and without the luxury of ornament. As the decades progressed, however, the country grew more affluent. And amid that affluence, those few architects who, unlike McKim and his Renaissance-inspired cohorts, chose to be innovators rather than imitators, came up with new approaches and forms as unique to the world's architecture as were blues and jazz to the world's music.

Frank Lloyd Wright (Figure 2-2) was the epitome of this. Wright (1867-1959) is often described as the greatest American architect—an opinion he himself was quick to agree with, objecting only to what he considered the unwelcome lessening of his place in history implied by the adjective "American." Indeed, he believed himself to be one of the greatest architects who ever lived—a genius beside whom contemporaries such as Le Corbusier and Mies van der Rohe (not to mention predecessors like Christopher Wren and Michelangelo) were mere bungling amateurs.

Frank Lloyd Wright: The Architect

About Frank Lloyd Wright

Frank Lloyd Wright (1867-1959) Wright was born in Wisconsin and educated at the University of Wisconsin. He was a famous architect who created buildings all over the world. Many of his treasures still stand today. Upon visiting the Madison area, you could visit Taliesin, the Unitarian Meeting House, or stay at the Seth Peterson Cottage.

The New Convention Center

Exciting things are happening in Madison in 1995. Construction has begun on a convention center that was designed by Frank Lloyd Wright. It is being built on Lake Monona.

Document: Done.

FIGURE 2-2
Everything you always wanted to know about Frank Lloyd Wright but were afraid to ask (http://198.150.8.9/ flw.html)

Wright's flamboyant, egomaniacal rantings aside, he *was* darn good and darn important—as is demonstrated by the famous "Fallingwater" house and other works of genius, not the least of which is the Guggenheim Museum (**http://www.guggenheim.org**) in Manhattan.

Wright was a child of the Luddite revolt against the Industrial Revolution as embodied in the famous "Arts and Crafts" movement of the late 19th century. In his famous 1901 lecture, "The Art and Craft of the Machine," he argued that art must be made to dominate the machine, or else industrial society would prove "soul-killing" and thus, ultimately, be the end of man.   •

In this spirit, Wright became the leading exponent of "organic" architecture. He saw a close relationship between a building, the landscape in which it reposed, and the materials used for construction which he insisted be not only natural but also "native to place." Buildings he designed for the Southwest were adobe-based while buildings he designed for northern forest areas were all wood and rock.

Wright's "prairie-style" houses—with their long, low horizontal lines and visual merging of an unbroken interior with the surrounding landscape—revolutionized American domestic architecture immediately after the turn of the century.

While Wright labored throughout the early 20th century to create new architectural forms that were aesthetically one with nature, he at the same time spent a good deal of time criticizing the great "imitations of mediocrity" which he saw so many other architects offering their clients. Wright issued blistering attacks on "bumbling replicas" of "archaic ideas" such as the many mansions and public buildings which borrowed from traditional Greek, Italian, and British styles. Throughout his long life, Wright made plain his belief that American architecture should be something new under the sun—just like America itself.

American Architecture in Cyberspace

As we browse the Internet, we find a rich cornucopia of resources relating to all facets of American architecture, past and present. From the first Tudor homes in Virginia to the latest high-rises of Manhattan and Los Angeles, here we have details on all the major buildings—and styles of buildings—along with their makers. The depth and richness of architectural information on the Internet is staggering. It'll take some time to get through even a small, representative sample of the resources we have available to us—so let's start browsing.

✯ ✯ ✯ ✯ ✯ ✯ ✯ ✯ ✯

Ansel Adams: Fiat Lux

☞ http://www.book.uci.edu/AAA.html

In 1966 world-renowned photographer Ansel Adams took on the assignment of documenting the campuses of the University of California in honor of that institution's 1968 centennial. Here you'll find all the photographs published online along with a great Ansel Adams interview plus critical essays on the photographs and the buildings they depict.

American Institute of Architects

 http://www.aia.org

Since 1857 the AIA has been the collective voice of America's architects. Representing 58,000 members, the Institute advances the value of architects and architecture and their shared roles in shaping the quality of life in America. Here you'll find the AIA's mission statement, along with a brief history of the Institute, an overview of member services, and directories for AIA chapter offices. Here you'll also find thoughts on what's involved in choosing architecture as a career, and details on the American Architectural Foundation (AAF), which strives to create a society that participates in shaping its environment through an understanding of the power of architecture to elevate and enrich the human experience.

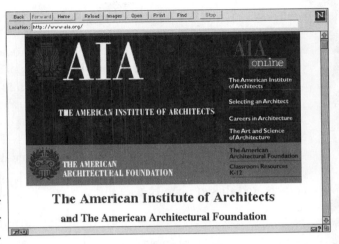

The American Institute of Architects

and The American Architectural Foundation

Architecture in America: State Houses to Skyscrapers

 http://lcweb2.loc.gov/detroit/archamer. html

Visit these Web pages and enjoy a fantastic collection of photographs (most of them old and classic) of state houses, skyscrapers, and other important buildings across the country, complete with details on their architects and other historical information. Among the images are the Massachusetts, Virginia, and Alabama state houses, the Flatiron Building and Woolworth Tower in New York City, and the White House.

The list of featured architects includes Gridley J. F. Bryant, Charles Bullfinch, Ernest Flagg, Cass Gilbert, Arthur Delavan Gilman, James Hoban, Richard Morris Hunt, William Le Baron Jenney, Benjamin Henry Latrobe, John McArthur, Jr., John McComb, Jr., Montgomery Meigs, Alfred Mullett, Frederick Law Olmstead, George Browne Post, Louis H. Sullivan, William Thornton, and Thomas Ustick Walter. The online database includes extensive biographies for each of these men. (Most historical resources relating to American architecture emphasize male architects, simply because it is only recently that women have been permitted to come into their own within the profession.)

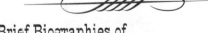

Brief Biographies of American Architects

 http://www.upenn.edu/sah/aame/ bioint.html

Come to this extensive alphabetical database providing brief biographies of more than 1,200 important American architects who died between 1897 and 1947. The bios are actually obituaries which appeared originally in the *American Art Annual* and, later, in *Who's Who in American Art*. Recognizing the value of these collected obituaries as a biographical resource, Earle G. Shettleworth, Jr., who in his spare time is Director of the Maine Historic Preservation Commission, has painstakingly transcribed and created this eminently useful database on the Web.

Carnegie Mellon Architecture Archives

 http://www.library.cmu.edu/Guide/Architecture/

Established in 1984, the Carnegie Mellon Architecture Archives collects, conserves, and promotes the use of architectural records that document the work of architects and architecture of Pittsburgh and the surrounding areas including western Pennsylvania, eastern Ohio, and northern West

Virginia. During the Archives' short history, its collection has grown rapidly. Today, the Archives' exhibits include thousands of architectural blueprints and drawings, manuscripts, photographs, and architectural models—preserving the work of hundreds of architects and designers.

The Archives' Web pages feature a complete inventory database documenting most of the Archives' holdings. The database is searchable by architect, client, location, date, or project type (i.e., church versus railway station).

The Charleston Multimedia Project

 http://www.awod.com/ccl/cmh_title_page.html

The Charleston Multimedia Project is a pictorial guidebook to the seven historic districts of 18th and 19th century Charleston. Charleston is renown for its importance in American history with events such as the first major naval battle of the Revolutionary War, and the site of the opening shots of the Civil War. But Charleston has also been an architectural showcase from its earliest days. Recognizing this, Charleston has been proactive in preserving and restoring entire neighborhoods of 18th and 19th century buildings to pristine condition.

The Charleston Multimedia Project includes a street-by-street, building-by-building guide to the historic district of Charleston, complete with links to hundreds of great images.

Back | Forward | Home | Reload | Images | Open | Print | Find | Stop

Location: http://www.library.cmu.edu/Guide/Architecture/

Carnegie Mellon University
ARCHITECTURE ARCHIVES

- Architectural Records
- Collections Information
- Collections Database
- Services
- A Campus Renewed: A Decade of Building at Carnegie Mellon, 1986-1996 (exhibit) NEW
- Architectural Archives Internet Sites

The Carnegie Mellon University Architecture Archives was created in 1984 to collect, conserve and promote the use of architectural records that document the architects and architecture of Pittsburgh and the tri-state region of western Pennsylvania, eastern Ohio and northern West Virginia.

Chicago Architecture Foundation

 http://www.architecture.org

The Chicago Architecture Foundation (or CAF) promotes public awareness, interest and education in Chicago's tremendous architectural legacy by offering tours, exhibitions, lectures, and other special events. On their Web pages, the CAF offers virtual tours through the city, information on upcoming presentations, and an archive of information about accomplished Chicago architects—their stories and their buildings.

Chicago Architecture Image Base

 http://www.uic.edu/~pbhales/imagebas.html

Those interested in the Chicago architecture should also check out the Chicago Architecture Image Base. This Website offers many images and documents relating to the architecture of Chicago and its history. The pages here are packed with historical photographs, various views of significant buildings, and views of whole blocks and neighborhoods, as well as historical maps. Another place worth visiting on the Web, by the way, is the Chicago Athenaeum Museum of Architecture & Design (**http://www. chi-athenaeum. org/**).

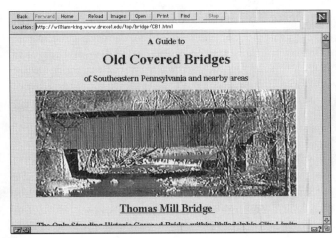

Covered Bridges of Southeastern Pennsylvania and Nearby Areas

 http://william-king.www. drexel.edu/top/bridge/ CB1.html

Americans nurture a love affair with the old covered wooden bridges of the East and Northeast. Coffee-table books and even movies have been written around the old "kissing bridges." Read here about the history of these 19th century marvels—about why they were built, why they were covered, why they were made of wood, and why so many of them are still around today to be enjoyed by us long after their designers and builders are gone. The documents and images on these Web pages provide an exhaustive, illustrated guide to the old covered bridges of southeastern Pennsylvania and the surrounding areas.

Digital Archive of American Architecture

 http://www.bc.edu/bc_org/avp/cas/fnart/fa267/

Created by Professor Jeff Howe of the Department of Architecture, Boston College, this archive consists of more than 600

images documenting four centuries of American architecture, from saltbox to skyscraper. Users are invited to search the image database by building date, style, purpose, and location. The images are supplemented with very useful commentary composed by Professor Howe.

Doctoral Dissertations Relating to American Architectural History, 1897-1995

 http://www.upenn.edu/sah/daah/daah1.html

Compiled by James M. Goode, this database allows you to search through thousands of doctoral dissertations on various aspects of American architecture composed between 1897 and 1995. The dissertations cover every aspect of the built environment, not just buildings *per se* but also cemeteries, roads, and other man-made structures. The database may be searched by author, degree-granting institution, subject, or dissertation year. Along with authors and titles, a search will yield an indication of exactly where the full text of the dissertation may be obtained (i.e., from the degree-granting institution or from a microfilm publisher such as University Microfilms). This resource comes to you courtesy of the Chicago-based Society of Architectural Historians.

Buckminster Fuller: The Dymaxion House and Geodesic Domes

 http://www.wnet.org/bucky/dare.html

The scion of an old New England family which included transcendentalist Margaret Fuller, Buckminster Fuller was born in 1895. Throughout his professional career, his goal was to "find ways of doing things with less to the end that all people—everywhere—can have more and more." Seeking to fulfill this ambition, Fuller designed a number of new and unique types of structures. His most famous design was the pole-suspended dwelling called a *Dymaxion House*. Fuller derived the word *Dymaxion* from the words "dynamic," "maximum," and "ion."

Fuller later went on to create the geodesic dome: a hemispherical structure constructed of flat, triangular panels. Geodesic domes were easy to produce and lightweight, yet strong and space-efficient. Fuller died in 1983.

Gargoyles and Architectural Details of New York City

 http://www.users.interport.net/
~ameliaw/gargoyle.html

Check out the monsters of Wall Street, the demons of Gramercy Park, or the ghouls of Madison Avenue. Or visit monster central: Central Park West, which the ghouls of the Ghostbusters films made

famous. Then of course you have the Cathedral of St. John the Divine—often neglected prime creature territory. The photographs and commentary which make up these cyberwalking tours are the work of gargoyle lovers Edgar Holski and Amelia Wilson.

Hildene: Home of the Descendants of Abraham Lincoln

 http://matrix.neinfo.net/~Hildene

Until 1975, the descendants of Abraham Lincoln lived in the 24-room Georgian Revival mansion called *Hildene*, located in Manchester, Vermont. After the death of Robert Todd Lincoln Beckwith—great-grandson of Abraham Lincoln—the property came into the hands of the nonprofit foundation which now owns and operates it as a museum. These Web pages offer a cybertour of the house and grounds, the house containing many Lincoln family artifacts.

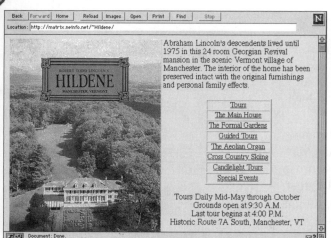

Back | Forward | Home | Reload | Images | Open | Print | Find | Stop

Location: http://matrix.neinfo.net/~Hildene/

ROBERT TODD LINCOLN'S
HILDENE
MANCHESTER, VERMONT

Abraham Lincoln's descendents lived until 1975 in this 24 room Georgian Revival mansion in the scenic Vermont village of Manchester. The interior of the home has been preserved intact with the original furnishings and personal family effects.

Tours
The Main House
The Formal Gardens
Guided Tours
The Aeolian Organ
Cross Country Skiing
Candlelight Tours
Special Events

Tours Daily Mid-May through October
Grounds open at 9:30 A.M.
Last tour begins at 4:00 P.M.
Historic Route 7A South, Manchester, VT

Document: Done.

Hildene was built at the turn of the century as the summer home of Robert Todd Lincoln, the eldest and only surviving child of Abraham and Mary Todd Lincoln. Robert, who died in 1926, had a varied career which included stints as Secretary of War, president of the Pullman Company, and ambassador to England. At 21 he graduated from Harvard (class of 1864) and went on to serve with distinction as a captain in the Union Army. As assistant adjutant general to General Grant, Robert Lincoln witnessed the fall of Petersburg and the pursuit and capture of Lee's army. He was later present at Appomattox and witnessed Lee's surrender.

Here is an interesting anecdote about Robert Lincoln. By the early 1920s—when nearly 80 and probably a bit senile along with it—the son of the "Great Liberator" had taken on a decided and vocal dislike of black people. This dislike was so extreme that he did not want the black doormen at his country club to touch his Rolls Royce.

But this was the early 1920s, remember, and there were no white doormen. However, the manager of the country club found a young light-skinned boy—the son of a prominent Harlem minister—who was working at the club for the summer as a busboy. He told the boy to keep a sharp eye out for Mr. Lincoln, who pulled up every day at about noon for lunch and a round of golf, and to be sure to be the one to help the son of the late president out of his car and into the club.

Mistaking the busboy for a white, Robert Lincoln took a liking to him and tipped him a silver dollar every day. At the end of the summer, when the boy went back to Harlem, he was the richest child in his neighborhood. Now, here comes the kicker. Do you know who the little boy was? Adam Clayton Powell, Jr.

Thomas Jefferson's Monticello

 http://www.monticello.org

In 1782, the Marquis de Chastellux wrote that in the wilds of Virginia he had found "an American, who without ever having quitted his own country, is musician, draftsman, surveyor, astronomer, natural philosopher, jurist, and statesman." Thomas Jefferson was also an architect, the creator of his own unique space which he built and rebuilt in the Albemarle County wilderness, and where he died in 1826. Visit these beautiful Web pages for images and a detailed history of graceful, domed Monticello.

Philip Johnson, Architect

 http://www.architecture.org/
PJohnson.html

Regarded by many as the most important architect of the 20th century, Philip Johnson has been credited with bringing the International Style to America through his show at the Museum of Modern Art in New York in 1932. Johnson's unique geometric style and his association with other International Style designers won him prominence early on in his architectural design career. Johnson is often considered an important trendsetter because of this and his work with the Post-Modern style.

in Chicago

Famed for such works as the Glass House in New Canaan, Connecticut, AT&T Corporate Headquarters in New York, and 190 South LaSalle in Chicago, Philip Johnson participated in a one-evening-only dialogue investigating the nature of his work and contemporary issues in design. Two preparatory sessions preceded Johnson's visit and were led by Ujjval Vyas, whose doctoral work at the University of Chicago focuses on Johnson's architecture. Franz Schulze, author of the recent biography, **Philip Johnson: Life and Work**, and Chicago architectural historian's Kevin Harrington and Sidney Robinson also facilitated the three-part colloquium.

Philip Johnson has been called the most important architect of the 20th century by numerous architects and architectural critics. He is credited with bringing the International Style to America through his

as well as Wright's Community Christian Church building. The tour also includes residences designed by Louis Curtiss, Burnham & Root, and Bruce Goff along with offices designed by Seligson Associates and Kivett & Meyers.

Kansas City Architecture

 http://cctr.umkc.edu/user/pmichell/
kcarch.htm

This cybertour of Kansas City architecture includes many Frank Lloyd Wright homes

Louisiana Architecture

 http://www.prysm.net/~samassoc/
la/la.htm

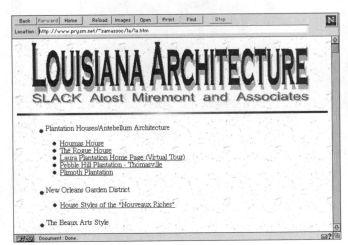

Take several great cybertours of Louisiana's plantation houses and antebellum architecture, the New Orleans Garden District, and much more. Explore the Beaux Arts style and learn what's being done to preserve New Orlean's historic architecture. There is a real mood to Louisiana: a texture and feel you don't find anywhere else. And it is represented in the mock-French architecture you find everywhere, as well as the Southern Gothic.

National Building Museum

 http://www.nbm.org/

Created by an act of Congress, the National Building Museum (or NBM) is dedicated to chronicling American achievements in architecture, construction, design, and engineering. The Museum collects design and construction artifacts, publishes books and a journal, and offers a variety of exhibits and programs including tours of landmark buildings, conferences, and lectures. Access this Web page for more information.

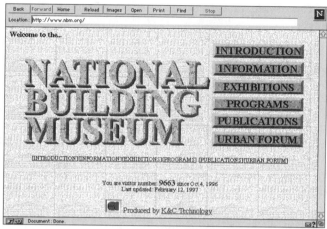

National Trust for Historic Preservation

 http://www.nthp.org

The National Trust for Historic Preservation promotes citizen involvement in saving America's historic communities and sites. Some of the sites owned and operated by the Trust include the Frank Lloyd Wright home and studio at Oak Park, Illinois, Jay Gould's Lyndhurst, and the Woodrow Wilson home in Washington, D.C. The Web pages for the National Trust include images and information relating to all their properties.

New York Images, 1883

 http://www.preserve.org/nyalbum/
nyalbum.htm

Access these Web pages to view a large collection of photographs from the *New York Album* published by Wittemann Brothers in 1883. Here you have classic images of City Hall, New York harbor, the Hudson River, various hospitals, the Metropolitan

Images from *New York Album*

published 1883 by Wittemann Bros.

Opera, the New York Academy of Design, and the New York Casino, as well as pictures of churches, monuments, and the Stock Exchange.

Newport Mansions

 http://198.49.179.4/mansions.html

The Newport Mansions' Web pages of the Preservation Society of Newport County provide an excellent window into the great summer "cottages" of Newport, Rhode Island, including the two great Vanderbilt homes designed by Richard Morris Hunt in the 1890s. It was Mrs. William K. Vanderbilt who commissioned Hunt to design and build Marble House, a palace in the French Baroque style that incorporated nearly a half-million cubic feet of marble. Vanderbilt intended for the palace to be an Ameri-

can "temple to the arts." Shortly thereafter, in 1893, Hunt was engaged by Cornelius Vanderbilt II, President and Chairman of the New York Central Railroad to design The Breakers—a house modeled after the 16th century palaces of Genoa.

Frederick Law Olmstead

 http://www.views.com/prudential/ newton/infop/olm.html

The career and works of Frederick Law Olmstead (1822-1903), designer of Central Park and other great turn-of-the-century landscapes, are detailed here in words and images.

Philadelphia Historic District: Virtual Walking Tour

 http://www.libertynet. org:80/iha/virtual.html

This annotated cyberwalk will take you to the American Philosophical Society Library, the Arch Street Friends Meeting House, the Bishop White House, Christ Church and its burial ground, Congress Hall, Independence Hall, the U.S. Mint, and dozens of Philadelphia's other architectural and historical treasures.

Betsy Ross Home: Virtual Tour

 http://www.libertynet.org:80/iha/betsy/
index.html

Take a virtual tour of the Philadelphia home of Betsy Ross, who designed and sewed the first American flag. While you are at it, learn the history of the flag and a bit more about Betsy herself, and access a wide range of flag-related Web links.

San Francisco Architecture: The Victorians

 http://www.kqed.org/Cell/Calhist/
victorians.html

These profusely illustrated Web pages provide a great introduction to the three predominant styles of San Francisco Victorian homes, namely: the Italianate, Stick-Eastlake, and Queen Anne style houses. The Italianate first appeared in San Francisco in the 1850s as an outgrowth of the "English Roman" style used in London row houses. More common was the Stick-Eastlake style (sometimes called "San Francisco Gothic") which was popular between 1875 and 1885. The Stick-Eastlake houses were the first inexpensive, mass-produced Victorians and were characterized by their sharp, angular, often square appearance. Finally, the Queen Anne (or "Royal Victorian") was the style of home which reigned in San Francisco from 1885 to 1898. As an architectural style it had nothing whatsoever to do with the period of the reign of Queen Anne, but was rather a combination of Elizabethan and Tudor styles, mixed with 19th century fashions, most notably Romanesque. In short, it was a hodgepodge—and therefore the most thoroughly American of all San Francisco Victorian styles.

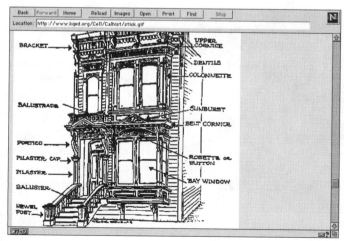

Temple of Liberty: Building the Capitol for a New Nation

 http://lcweb.loc.gov/exhibits/
us.capitol/s0.html

Ratified in 1788, the Constitution gave the new United States its governing framework. Three years later, George Washington and Thomas Jefferson wanted the new country's capitol to be a strong expression of America's fundamental ethics and new political might. Politicians and designers had difficulty agreeing on how to achieve a practical and efficient building that would incorporate the symbolism of the new country in the Neoclassical framework. It took more than three decades to complete the first Capitol which was not yet finished when Congress first met there in 1800. Even before the first building was completed, proposals were being floated for expansion in the form of the north and south wings. This extensive, profusely-illustrated online exhibit documents the entire process of the designing and building of our nation's Capitol.

Wilson Eyre, Frank Furness, Edmund Gilchrist, Lawrence Halprin, Warren Powers Laird, and John Nolan. Come to these Web pages for details on the holdings of the Archive along with many outstanding images.

Women in Architecture

http://ic.www.media.mit.edu/ Woarch/womaninarch.html

These extensive Web pages document the lives and works of three major contemporary female architects: Ellen Dunham-Jones, Jane Weinzapfel, and Andrea Leers. The site includes interviews with all three.

Frank Lloyd Wright: Designs for an American Landscape, 1922-32

http://lcweb.loc.gov/ exhibits/flw/flw.html

Organized by the Library of Congress, the Canadian Centre for Architecture and the Frank Lloyd Wright Foundation, this online exhibition includes over 150 original drawings and newly commissioned digital "models" reconstructing five unbuilt Frank Lloyd Wright projects that, in the words of curator David DeLong, "imagined nothing less than a new American landscape, integrating terrain, architecture, and the automobile on a vast scale."

University of Pennsylvania Architectural Archives

 http://www.upenn.edu/gsfa/archives/ archives.html

This Archive is home to the papers of such great American architects as Louis I. Cahn, Alfred Bendiner, Frank Miles Day,

3

Crime & Criminals, American Style

America's criminals have a way of entering into our folklore. Very often, they become urban and/or rural legends, with something of a Robin Hood mystique hovering about them. Even the deadly Al Capone, John Dillinger, and John Gotti are somehow attractive to our imaginations. Americans are inclined to respect—if not actually *like*—just about anyone who rebels against authority, assuming they have some semblance of a reason. There is a certain libertarian panache in this. *Don't tread on me*.

On the other hand, Americans react against those aspects of criminality which are profoundly more evil than they are practical or romantic. I speak of the realms of the serial killer, the sexual predator, and other such depraved individuals. I also speak of the thoroughly unromantic street crime and criminals we see chronicled on *Cops* and other real-life television programs.

Americans Are Crime Voyeurs

What is it about crime that fascinates us? Why is the real-life drama of *Cops* so popular? Why, as a people, have Americans always followed criminal trials with such scrutiny? Today we focus on the trial of O.J. Simpson (Figure 3-1) with the same rapt attention our great-grandparents gave to the trial of the conspirators in the Lincoln assassination.

One thing I've observed, however, is that we American crime voyeurs like different types of criminals doled out to us in profoundly different ways. Sometimes—through the safe medium of the documentarian's lens—we want to experience criminals *raw*, as they manifest naturally on the street. Yet in other instances we want criminals sanitized and refined to reinforce certain biases and stereotypes that are dear to us, in order that we may like them.

FIGURE 3-1

*For more on O.J. Simpson and the trial than you'll ever need to know, check out Dmitri's O.J. Simpson Trial Center (**http://www.cs. indiana.edu/hyplan/ dmiguse/oj.html**)*

When we detest an offender completely and cannot in any way find reason to justify his or her crime, then we usually want both crime and criminal presented to us in all their tawdry horribleness, without pretense or cosmetics. Those we demonize and detest we want to see in the flesh, squirming and receiving real justice either in a courtroom or on a street. We don't want them filtered or dressed up or humanized. We'd prefer they simply remain icons for the evil they have chosen to represent through their actions. We'd prefer they remain—in our perception of them—as unlike *us* as possible. Such cases as this explain the success of the straight-shooting documentary reports on *Court TV* and *Cops*.

Crime as Theater

For those felons whom we idealize, however, we demand a different style of presentation. We still want to see and experience them. (We are and will always remain crime voyeurs, after all.) Yet we do *not* want to see our idealized felons squirm and receive real justice. Nor do we want to confront the reality of their crimes. We delight in having them cleaned up and sanitized for us. We want to be protected from the base facts of their unsentimentalized, bloody and often stupid reality.

The criminals we have some sympathy with and to whom we relate as human beings are those we like to think operate with a measure of shrewdness, pragmatism, and independence. We like felons who do not appear to be fundamentally evil. We like felons who appear to be smart, albeit sometimes maliciously so. We admire them. They don't sit there and take it, like all the rest of us. They stand up for their turf. They make their world. They control their destiny (or at least they appear to). And we just might be like them, if we could be.

I am speaking of the likes of Jesse James, Meyer Lansky, Al Capone, and Bugsy Siegal. I am also speaking of the outlaw class which rose out of the dirty thirties, when times were hard, banks were the people's enemy, and outlaws seemed to be revolutionaries rather than mere stick-up artists. Such was the case with John Dillinger, Bonnie and Clyde, Pretty Boy Floyd and others of their generation.

How many films have been made about Jesse James? Tons. How many films do we have which glamorize Al Capone's Depression era bootlegging? Plenty. *The Untouchables* comes immediately to mind. How many films romanticize life in the Mafia (Figure 3-2)? Plenty. The success of the *Godfather* trilogy is a case in point. How many films do we have which glamorize gangsterdom in the wild west? Lots. Consider *Butch Cassidy and the Sundance Kid*, in which Paul Newman (**http://www.pair.com/marilynn/newman.htm**) and Robert Redford (**http://moviehq.com/index/actors/redfordr.htm**) portray the notorious thugs as being attractive and witty. And how many films give us brave tales of the midwestern and southwestern bandits of the 1930s? Dozens. Just look at *Bonnie and Clyde*, with the highly attractive Faye Dunaway (**http://www.mrshowbiz.com/starbios/fayedunaway/a.html**) and Warren Beatty (**http://www.moviesunlimited.com/star_bio.htm**) representing a couple who were anything but handsome in real life.

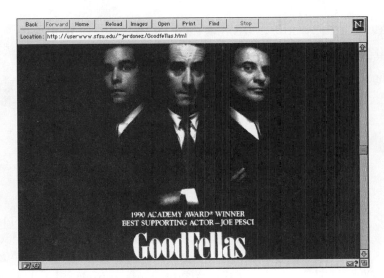

FIGURE 3-2
The film Goodfellas *chronicled three decades of life in the Mafia. It starred Ray Liotta, Robert DeNiro, and Joe Pesci (**http:// userwww.sfsu.edu/ ~jordonez/Goodfellas. html**)*

It's funny how crime so often migrates to film. It's funny, also, how our trials have a strong sense of drama to them and are followed by large audiences. It's also remarkable how popular shows such as *Cops* make entertainment out of the reality of hunting down felons. Jean Genet (**http://phoebe.cair.du.edu/~jdaniell/genet.html**), the French thief turned playwright, once wrote that the only thing more exciting than committing a crime was getting caught. He loved being on trial. "The world—the criminal's audience—is amazed and appalled by what you have done," he wrote. "It's almost theater."

Crime on the Web

As in all things, the American information superhighway mirrors the country when it comes to crime and criminals. The ways we view American outlawdom on the Web are just as divided as the ways we view the same phenomena in meatspace. Those criminals who we assume to be demons continue to be demonized in cyberspace. Those criminals we assume to be "goodfellas" continue to be romanticized in cyberspace.

Nothing changes save for the point-and-click ease of getting quite close, in a virtual sense, to your favorite crime guy or gal.

There is lots to see regarding American crime and criminals on the Web, so let's start browsing.

Alcatraz

 http://www.nps.gov/alcatraz/

Welcome to Alcatraz—a.k.a. "The Rock," "Hellcatraz," and "Uncle Sam's Devil's Island." Alcatraz was first visited in 1775 by the Spanish explorer Manuel de Ayala who named it "La Isla de los Alcatraces" after the many pelicans he found flocking there. It has been an army base and a site occupied by Native American activists (1969-71). And it remains the sisite of the West Coast's first (and oldest operating) lighthouse. But it is best known for its 29 years (1934-1963) as a maximum-security prison where some of America's most notorious criminals were incarcerated.

Where were the cells of famous prisoners such as Al Capone and "the Birdman" Robert Stroud, and what do those cells look like today? How many people lived, worked, and died here—and who were they? Get all the facts about Alcatraz from this great set of Web pages maintained by the National Park Service. All the answers are here.

PALS

TOM O'FOLLIARD DIED DEC 1880

WILLIAM H BONNEY ALIAS BILLY THE KID DIED JULY 1881

CHARLIE BOWDRE DIED DEC 1880

Experience The Legend

There's many a man with face fine and fair
Who starts out in life with a chance to be square

Billy the Kid

 http://www.nfcs.tbci.org/~kevinh/billy.html

In the 1870s and 1880s the Territory of New Mexico experienced a wave of rampant lawlessness unparalleled in American history. The most famous of the New Mexican outlaws was indisputably Henry McCarty, alias Kid Antrim, alias William H. Bonney, alias Billy the Kid. Born in the east, he came to New Mexico in the 1870s where he embarked upon a life of crime. He was killed by Detective Pat Garrett at Old Fort Sumner on July 14, 1881. Today, in the cemetery there, a vagrant wind whisks across the plain and "the Kid" lies where he has slept for more than a hundred years.

Visit this detailed collection of Web pages for more information on the Kid. Another excellent source of information on his life and career (including details on his boyhood and photographs of the houses where he was born, lived, and died) is to be found at the URL **http://www.enmu.edu/~schroeda/learn/billy.html**.

The Bonnie and Clyde Archive

 http://gatesville.htcomp.net/wolvie/

Bonnie and Clyde (Bonnie Parker and Clyde Barrow) are two of the most famous gangsters in American history. Read here about the life of Clyde Barrow,

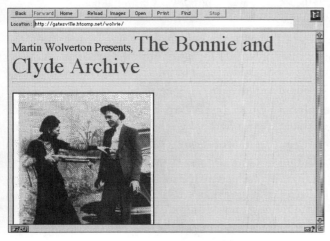

Martin Wolverton Presents, The Bonnie and Clyde Archive

interesting facts about Bonnie Parker, how Bonnie and Clyde met, and information about movies, museums, and reenactments. Martin Wolverton's great archive of Bonnie and Clyde-related links and information provides a rich collection of resources putting the Barrow Gang in their true historical context.

John Wilkes Booth

 http://www.nps.gov/foth/booth.htm

Just hearing the name of John Wilkes Booth brings to mind the dastardly assassination of Abraham Lincoln—probably the greatest president this country has known. But Booth wasn't completely unknown prior to playing his most famous role. In fact, the Booth family name in the 19th century was strongly identified with the American theater.

John's father—Junius Brutus Booth, Sr.—was an Englishman who came to the United States in 1821 and quickly established himself as one of the most prominent Shakespearean actors in the Americas. His sons, Edwin, John Wilkes, and Junius Brutus, Jr., all followed in his footsteps with Edwin rising to become one of the great Shakespearean actors of his generation. Edwin was also the founder of the Players Club in Manhattan. Come to this Website for much more information on the assassin and his family.

Al Capone

 http://www.well.com/user/mod79/
gangsters/capone.html

We all know the story of Al Capone, bloodthirsty mobland boss of 1920s Chicago. My mother was raised in Chicago (well, Oak Park, actually) in the period when Al ran the town. The father of a boy in her grammar school class, one Jake Lingle, was one of Al's cohorts and was "rubbed out" by some of Al's enemies. He had a very fine funeral. Lots of flowers.

The Al Capone who is less well known to us is the Al Capone who was released from Alcatraz in 1939 for health reasons: an advanced case of syphilis which left him semidemented. Capone lived out the remainder of his days in Florida where he died in 1947.

Cattle Rustling

 http://vd1.magibox.net/lonesome_turkey/
support/html/outlaws_rustlers.html

The wild west drew all sorts of people looking to make lives for themselves on the frontier—explorers, settlers, and folks looking to make their personal fortunes. Conditions on the western frontier made law and order somewhat difficult to maintain. The law was hard to find, and the prospect of getting rich quick—whether by legal means or not—was a driving force. Large herds of cattle grazing the open range proved too much of a temptation for some.

Even outlaws like Butch Cassidy tried their hands at cattle rustling. But for the most part, cattle rustling was too much work and didn't pay nearly as well as robbing trains or banks. Find out more about rustling as a crime and a way of life through these informative Web pages.

Courtroom Sketches

 http://www.thegremlin.com/
courtart.html

Check out Marcia Clark, Johnnie Cochran, Robert Shapiro, and O.J. Simpson at the criminal pretrial hearing in 1994 (before the TV cameras were allowed in!). The site also includes sketches from the trials of John Gotti, Charles Manson, and others.

Criminals.com

 http://www.criminal.net

Criminals.com is the Net-age version of the post office bulletin board. This Website was created to give bonding companies and law enforcement agencies a nationwide forum for posting wanted posters. There are photographs, descriptions, and supplemental information (such as rewards) for dozens of fugitives. Come to this virtual rogues' gallery to see many more thieves and murderers than you will at your local post office.

The Dalton Gang

http://www.gunslinger.com/
dalton.html

The Dalton Boys. They started out as lawmen and ended up as criminals: dead criminals after the famous Coffeyville Raid of October 1892. At this Website you'll find their story—and that of the gang which followed them, the famous "Wild Bunch," otherwise known as the Doolin-Dalton Gang—along with images and other resources.

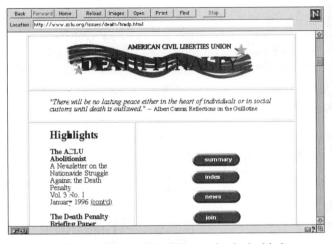

Death Penalty Pages from the ACLU

http://www.aclu.org/issues/death/
hmdp.html

The ACLU's Web pages present information in support of abolition of the death penalty.

A few thoughts:

I live in Rhode Island, which is one of a minority of states that has not as yet legalized the killing of its citizens by lethal injection or any other means. Not coincidentally, Rhode Island has one of the lowest murder rates among the fifty states. Also not coincidentally, the United States has by far the highest murder rate among industrialized nations, yet is the only one among them to employ the death penalty.

What can we infer from these facts?

John Dillinger

http://www.hotcong.com/
dillinger.htm

John Dillinger has come to personify the image of the classic 1930s Depression era "Public Enemy Number 1."

Dillinger's career included all the cliché highlights—bank robberies, escapes, wild chases, and dramatic machine gun battles. Police pursuing Dillinger attempted to incite jealousy and discord among the members of Dillinger's gang by encouraging Dillinger's publicity. Instead, they contributed to Dillinger's celebrity status.

His daring escapes—single-handed with a revolver made out of soap at Crown Point Jail, for instance, or through the deathly fire of dozens of FBI agents at Little Bohemia Lodge—increased his legend until he was finally subdued and killed at the Biograph Theater in Chicago on July 22, 1934.

Wyatt Earp

 http://www.techline.com/~nicks/earp.htm

Wyatt Earp was one of several western lawmen whose exploits have been transformed by television and movies into heroic and legendary episodes. The reality, however, is considerably less than noble.

Wyatt Berry Stapp Earp was born in Monmouth, Illinois, on March 19, 1848. By 1864 his family was living in California. He held a variety of jobs—buffalo hunter, stagecoach driver, miner, peace officer—before settling temporarily in Dodge City, Kansas, as Assistant Marshall in 1876. There he became friends with Bat Masterson and Doc Holliday and moonlighted as a card-dealer for the game of faro at the famous Long Branch Saloon.

In the late 1870s Earp and some of his associates moved to Tombstone, Arizona, where his brother Virgil became the town Marshal. It was here that the three Earp brothers, Wyatt, Virgil, and Morgan, and Doc Holliday fought the Ike Clanton gang in what has become known as the gunfight at the O.K. Corral. The event occurred on October 26, 1881. The Clanton gang lost, ending what was really just a bitter feud, not a triumph of justice.

Wyatt spent his last years in California, living off real estate and mining income. He died in Los Angeles on January 13, 1929. Find out more about Wyatt at the URL itemized earlier. The Website includes many facts about Wyatt as well as a large gallery of images including, unaccountably, a semi-nude photo of Mrs. Wyatt Earp taken in Tombstone in 1881.

The Electric Chair

 http://www.theelectricchair.com/index.htm

Take a virtual video tour of New York State's Death House. Hear an interview with the designer of the electric chair used at Sing Sing. See a rare original photo of an actual electrocution as well as photos of Ted Bundy immediately after he died in Florida's electric chair. Read about the history of the electric chair, the biology of electrocution, women who have died in the electric chair, and the tangled histories of the many botched electrocutions in which the electric chair has been involved.

The site also includes a listing of anti-death penalty organizations and resources, lists of people currently on death rows nationwide, and a state-by-state update regarding death penalty legislation.

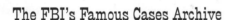

The FBI's Famous Cases Archive

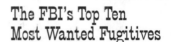 http://www.fbi.gov/famcases/
famcases.htm

Here you'll find detailed, profusely illustrated histories of all the FBI's most famous cases, including the Brinks Robbery and the investigations of such nasties as John Dillinger, Al Capone, Baby Face Nel-

sor, and Bruno Richard Hauptmann (the Lindbergh kidnapper).

The FBI's Top Ten Most Wanted Fugitives

 http://www.ajc.com/staff/duffy/
toplist.htm

The FBI uses its "Ten Most Wanted Fugitives" program to publicize the names, photos, and details of the Bureau's most sought-after criminals. Contrary to popular belief, the fugitives listed in the Top Ten list are not ranked in any order. All of the individuals on the list have a lengthy record of violent crime. Their pictures and details of their criminal past are recorded here, along with their last-known whereabouts. It must be emphasized that you are not to take any action yourself to apprehend anyone on the list, should you chance upon them. They are all armed and dangerous. (That's how they got on the list!) Call the FBI and let them do what you pay them to do: bust the bad guys.

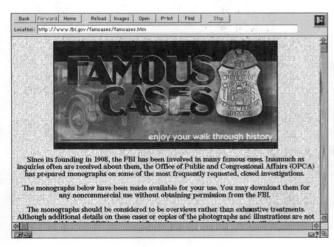

Gang Land: Jerry Capeci's New York Mob Column

http://www-leland.stanford.
edu/~jercap/index.html

Jerry Capeci is a reporter for the New York *Daily News*. During the last ten years he has written articles about organized crime for the *Daily News* and many other magazines and newspapers across the United States, Canada, Europe, and Asia. He has also coauthored three books about the Mafia and has appeared as an organized crime expert on network and cable TV across the U.S.

From January 1989 through August 1995 he wrote a weekly column for the *Daily News* about organized crime called *GangLand*. Jerry's editors have discontinued his *Daily News* column, but he is still writing it and posting it here to this Website. Some come here to get all the latest scoops on the baddest of the bad boys in crime.

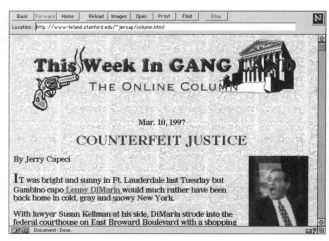

John Gotti Tribute Page

 http://www.gotti.com/

Even though he is stuck inside Marion Federal Penitentiary, John Gotti still has his PR engine working for him, including this unabashedly pro-Gotti (i.e., "Gotti is not a mobster") Website. Writing about this Website, *Playboy Magazine* suggested that we just think of it as a black Lincoln Town Car on the information superhighway.

You learn all about Gotti and his pals, how and why he was "unjustly" accused and convicted, where to write to protest his conviction, and so on. You even get sneak peeks at Gotti in his cell at Marion via exclusive photographs to be found only on these Web pages.

Doc Holliday

 http://www.americanwest.com/
pages/docholid.htm

Born in 1851, John Henry "Doc" Holliday was one of the fastest guns the West has ever known. He studied dentistry in Philadelphia and practiced in the east for a time until, still in his twenties, he was diagnosed with tuberculosis. The disease was then incurable, but his doctor told him he could prolong his life if he moved to a dry climate: the southwest. He tried practicing dentistry in Dallas. The tuberculosis, however, resulted in severe coughing spells at the most embarrassing times, such as in the midst of filling a tooth or making an extraction. His practice never really got off the ground and he had to look for another way to make a living.

Thus he became a professional gambler which, in those days, meant more than just being a good card player. One also had to be able to protect one's self and enforce one's claim of winnings. Doc bought a knife. Then he bought a gun. He learned how to use both. Arguments occurred. Men died. Murder warrants were issued. But Doc's lawmen friends—such as Bat Masterson and Wyatt Earp—to whom he often offered his considerable skills with a sixgun, protected him just as he protected them during such altercations as the shootout at the O.K. Corral.

It was the tuberculosis which killed him. It happened in the autumn of 1887. He'd been in bed for 57 days and had been delirious for 14 of them. On November 8, he awoke clear-eyed and asked for a glass of whiskey. This was given to him and he drank it down with enjoyment. Then he said: "Funny," and died.

The James-Younger Gang

☞ http://www.islandnet.com/~the-gang/index.html

The James-Younger Gang, originally organized in 1866 by Jesse James, his brother Frank, and Cole Younger, was reorganized by some of their descendants in 1993. The gang doesn't ride horses anymore. In fact, at least one of them, Frank Younger, is a biker (along with being a turbogeek Web author and noted astronomer). And the Gang has given up robbing banks. The Gang of the 1990s is a fully-registered, not-for-profit educational and historical corporation based in Missouri. In addition to maintaining this great set of Web resources packed with information about the original James-Younger Gang, today's Gang helps support the James Farm Museum in Kearny, Missouri, and several other related educational and historical endeavors.

The Kennedy Assassination

☞ http://mcadams.posc.mu.edu/home.htm

Well, was there a conspiracy or wasn't there? Was Oswald a lone gunman? Or was he just a "patsy" in a byzantine plot involving agencies of several governments. I'm sure you have an opinion. It seems everyone does. Me, I don't buy the conspiracy thing. I subscribe to the lone-wacko theory. But I'm willing to be proved wrong.

Hosted and edited by John McAdams, the Website listed here is largely anticonspiracy in approach. I believe it is the best collection of Kennedy assassination-related information on the Web. (Another Website that is worth visiting, even though it is generally proconspiracy, is called *Fair Play Magazine* and is located at the URL

http://rmii.com/~jkelin/fp.html.) Kennedy assassination buffs will also want to check out the National Archives and Record Administrations assassination records collection at **http://www.nara.gov/nara/jfk/jfk.html**. I would further recommend a visit to Robert Harris' JFK Assassination home page (**http://www. thuntek.net/~rharris/jfk.html#*.***). Harris has assembled a lot of witness testimony and plenty of graphic images to make the case for his particular scenario of the shooting in Dealey Plaza.

The Lincoln Assassination

 http://members.aol.com/RVSNorton/Lincoln.html

To my mind, one of the most remarkable aspects of the Lincoln assassination is the tale of one of the conspirators: John Surratt.

His mother, Mary Surratt, was also a part of the John Wilkes Booth cabal. She was

caught and put on trial with the rest of them, and was hanged on July 7, 1865. Son John, however, escaped.

First he fled to Canada. Then he went to England, from where he traveled to Rome. In Rome he joined the Papal Zouaves and became a guard at the Vatican. When his identity was found out, however, he absconded to Alexandria, Egypt. There he was arrested on November 27, 1866. Surratt was brought back to the United States and put on trial for murder and conspiracy to commit murder. The trial ended in the summer of 1867 with the jury deadlocked. Surratt went free.

He became a teacher in Rockville, Maryland. At the courthouse there on December 6, 1879 he delivered a lecture on the conspiracy. He admitted his role in a plot to abduct President Lincoln, but denied any part in the planning or execution of the assassination. A year or so later, Surratt left teaching and became an auditor for a steamship company. In 1872 he married Mary Victoria Hunter, a second cousin of Francis Scott Key, composer of "The Star Spangled Banner." The couple lived in Boston and had seven children.

John Surratt outlived everyone connected with the assassination. He died on April 21, 1916 at the age of 72. He is buried in the New Cathedral Cemetery in Baltimore.

But there are many more anecdotes and images associated with the Lincoln assassination, and you'll find them all right here at this excellent set of Web pages maintained by a former elementary school teacher who has long been fascinated by the events surrounding Lincoln's death.

Charlie Manson: Cult Murderer and Songwriter for the Beach Boys

 http://www.mayhem.net/Crime/ manson.html

To members of his notorious "family," Charlie Manson announced that he was both Christ and Satan. These days he is only a jailhouse psychotic. He will never be released, of course, but he nevertheless says that once he gets paroled he will go to Sri Lanka and New Delhi to shine "like the sun."

Perhaps he will also pick up the pieces of his career as a songwriter for the Beach Boys. That's right. Long before the murders, Charlie's song *Never Learn Not to Love* was released on the Beach Boys' album *20/20*. It was also the B-side to the single *Blue Birds Flew Over the Mountain*.

Delve into these and other unexpected facts about Charlie Manson by accessing this engaging set of Web pages.

Bat Masterson

 http://www.sni.net/patrol/History.html

Few people realize that western lawman and legendary gunfighter Bat Masterson

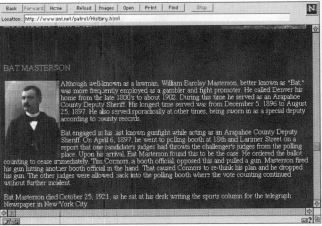

BAT MASTERSON

Although well-known as a lawman, William Barclay Masterson, better known as "Bat," was more frequently employed as a gambler and fight promoter. He called Denver his home from the late 1800's to about 1902. During this time he served as an Arapahoe County Deputy Sheriff. His longest time served was from December 5, 1896 to August 25, 1897. He also served sporadically at other times, being sworn in as a special deputy according to county records.

Bat engaged in his last known gunfight while acting as an Arapahoe County Deputy Sheriff. On April 6, 1897, he went to polling booth at 18th and Larimer Street on a report that one candidate's judges had thrown the challenger's judges from the polling place. Upon his arrival, Bat Masterson found this to be the case. He ordered the ballot counting to cease immediately. Tim Connors, a booth official, opposed this and pulled a gun. Masterson fired his gun hitting another booth official in the hand. That caused Connors to re-think his plan and he dropped his gun. The other judges were allowed back into the polling booth where the vote counting continued without further incident.

Bat Masterson died October 25, 1921, as he sat at his desk writing the sports column for the telegraph Newspaper in New York City.

spent his last decades in New York City as a sportswriter for the *Telegraph*. In fact, he died at his desk in Manhattan while typing out a column on October 25, 1921.

He made his reputation, however, in Dodge City where he worked with Wyatt Earp and others in the 1880s. He was also associated with Judge Roy Bean. Folks of my generation will remember Bat being played by Gene Barry in the long-running television program *Bat Masterson*.

My Lai Massacre

 http://www.you.net/~bent/my_lai.html

Not all American crimes happen in America. This one happened in Vietnam. All you have here is a picture—one that is worth a thousand words. Where is Lieutenant Calley these days, anyway?

Oklahombres

 http://www.qns.com/~dcordry/hombres.html

Oklahombres is dedicated to the careful research and preservation of the history of outlaws and lawmen in Oklahoma. Towards this end, the hombres have wonderful online resources including extensive image files and great hypertext documents discussing topics that include the stories of Pretty Boy Floyd, Ma Barker, Machine Gun Kelly, Alvin Karpis, Sam Starr, and others.

Back | Forward | Home | Reload | Images | Open | Print | Find | Stop
Location: http://www.qns.com/"doordry/hombres.html

OKLAHOMBRES Online!

Welcome to OKLAHOMBRES Online! Pictured is Deputy U.S. Marshal Henry Andrew 'Heck' Thomas of Oklahoma Territory.

OKLAHOMBRES is dedicated to the careful, correct research and preservation of lawman and outlaw history. The official purpose of OKLAHOMBRES is to support, encourage and promote education, research, writing and other journalistic efforts and endeavors in that portion of Oklahoma history involving lawmen and outlaws. OKLAHOMBRES publishes a quarterly journal featuring the efforts of our members, we present informative programs, and we host field trips to sites of interesting events in Oklahoma lawman and outlaw history. Our programs are open to the public.

'Oklahombres' is a term which gained wide use following the publication in 1929 of 'Oklahombres, Particularly the Wilder Ones' by Evett Dumas Nix. Nix, the former United States Marshal of Oklahoma Territory, told the story to author Gordon Hines. The book was filled with tales of the outlaws in Oklahoma and Indian Territories, and the lawmen who pursued them. Since that time, numerous other books and various publications have chronicled the exploits of the lawmen and outlaws of Oklahoma. Some of

Lee Harvey Oswald

 http://mcadams.posc.mu.edu/oswald.htm

Lee Harvey Oswald. At the end of the day, when we are done with all the crazy theories, he is guilty as charged. At this Website you'll find extensive information and graphics relating to loony little Lee. You'll get a complete timeline of his life, incisive commentary, and a large number of conspiracy-debunking facts. You'll even get a GIF copy of the bill for Oswald's funeral, which cost $710.00. The bill was paid by his long-suffering and eminently sane and honest brother Robert, an insurance salesman in Denton, Texas.

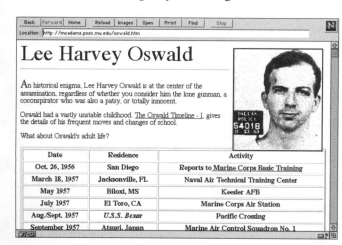

Back | Forward | Home | Reload | Images | Open | Print | Find | Stop
Location: http://mcadams.posc.mu.edu/oswald.htm

Lee Harvey Oswald

An historical enigma, Lee Harvey Oswald is at the center of the assassination, regardless of whether you consider him the lone gunman, a coconspirator who was also a patsy, or totally innocent.

Oswald had a vastly unstable childhood. The Oswald Timeline - I, gives the details of his frequent moves and changes of school.

What about Oswald's adult life?

Date	Residence	Activity
Oct. 26, 1956	San Diego	Reports to Marine Corps Basic Training
March 18, 1957	Jacksonville, FL	Naval Air Technical Training Center
May 1957	Biloxi, MS	Keesler AFB
July 1957	El Toro, CA	Marine Corps Air Station
Aug./Sept. 1957	U.S.S. Bexar	Pacific Crossing
September 1957	Atsugi, Japan	Marine Air Control Squadron No. 1

Simpson Murder Trial Resources

 http://www.lectlaw.com/oj.html

Here is a wonderful array of online resources relating to "the trial of the century." This includes texts of O.J.'s various public statements, Nicole Brown Simpson's autopsy report, Ron Goldman's autopsy report, Mark Fuhrman's complaint of libel against *The New Yorker*, prosecutor's witness lists and testimony dates, and much more.

Richard Speck: One Bad, Bad Boy

 http://www.you.net/~bent/speck.html

He had a tattoo which said "Born to raise Hell." And he took it literally. When asked why he strangled and slit the throats of seven nurses in Chicago one bloody evening in 1966, he replied laconically: "It just wasn't their night."

Henry Starr

http://www.gunslinger.com/henry.htm

Henry Starr is one of the most colorful of outlaws in American folklore. In his more than three decades of felonious activity he robbed more banks than both the James-Younger Gang and the Dalton Gang combined, and he probably stole over $6 million. Starr bridged the gap between the days of the horseback outlaw and the roadster-riding gangster. He was, in fact, the first person ever to use a car in a bank robbery.

Starr was born in 1873. He was a nephew to Sam Starr—the one married to Belle Starr, the famous "outlaw queen" of the old west. One quarter Cherokee, Starr served a term in prison in Oklahoma for bank robbery from 1909 to 1913, during which time he taught himself law and wrote a remarkable autobiography which became a bestseller: *Thrilling Events, Life of Henry Starr*. By 1914, however, he was back to robbing banks and was wanted dead or alive. He served another prison stretch in Oklahoma from 1915 to 1919.

Upon his release in 1919 he went into the movie business. He produced a silent film entitled *A Debtor to the Law*, which was based on events related to a bank robbery in Stroud, Oklahoma which Henry Starr had actually masterminded. The movie was an immediate success and Henry had an offer to come out to Hollywood and do another like it. Henry didn't go. He told a friend the movie business was for chumps. For all the success of *A Debtor to the Law*, he'd only made $15,000—this for several months of dedicated labor. Henry knew a line of work which required much less effort and paid much bigger returns.

On Friday, February 18, 1921, Henry and three companions hit the People's State Bank in Harrison, Arkansas. During the robbery, Henry was shot in the back by the former president of the bank. His partners fled, leaving him behind. He was carried to the local jail where doctors removed the bullet, but there was no saving him. He died on the morning of Tuesday, February 22. At his side were his wife, his mother, and his 17-year-old son. Just before he died he boasted to his doctors, "I've robbed more banks than any man in America."

The Unabomber's Manifesto: Industrial Society and Its Future

 http://www.stardot.com/~hhui/ unab-manifest.html

Read the mad rantings of the man who sent anonymous letter bombs to some of our best and brightest citizens.

United States Department of Justice Crime Statistics

 http://www.ojp.usdoj.gov/bjs/

The National Crime Victimization Survey (NCVS) is an ongoing survey of American households. The data collected by the NCVS gives an indication of the number of serious crimes (rape, sexual assault, robbery, burglaries, and vehicle thefts) experienced each year by U.S. residents over the age of 12.

4

Food & Drink

It was Yogi Berra (**http://www.msbl.com/colawd01/ im0712.htm**) who said that some foods are just about as American as apple pie. Leave it to Yogi. He's the same fellow who said, "If you see a fork in the road, take it" and "What would our country be without this great land of ours?"

What Yogi was trying to get at, I'm guessing, is that there are many foods that have become unique expressions of American culture in the same sense that ragtime piano or delta blues or the paintings of the Hudson River school have, at times, been expressions of that same culture. Thus Cajun and Creole foods say something about who we are as Americans, as does New England clam chowder, and Tex-Mex.

Out of Africa

Few people realize the enormous influence African cooking techniques and recipes have had on American cuisine. Consider the very word "yam." The word is derived from the West African verb "nyam," which means simply "to eat." Of course, what we commonly call a yam in the United States is nothing but a sweet potato, botanically speaking.

A genuine African yam is a large hairy tuber that is more woody and potentially fibrous. It is also definitely not sweet. The true yam, indigenous to Ghana and other countries of western Africa, is sacred there. New yams sprout out of old yams. By thus evoking life's cycle of birth and death, they have come to be venerated by West Africans, who also have loved to eat them for a thousand years or more.

African slaves found no true yams in the New World. But the sweet potatoes that grew here could be used the same way, and cooked the same way, as the yams from home. Thus the American yam.

There are, in fact, very few icons of American (particularly Southern) cooking which don't have an African origin, or weren't influenced by African cooking techniques. This can certainly be said for the basic techniques of making mashes and mushes, or pouring stews over starches. All these culinary traditions come right out of Africa.

Black-eyed peas, originally from Africa, are popular in a Nigerian fritter called "Akkra." They're also mixed with dried smoked shrimp and chile peppers in a Brazilian fritter. In New Orleans, where rice has always been plentiful, a fritter called a "Calas" was made with rice. Elsewhere in the South, fritters were made with corn.

The legend has it that many of these foods came over to the New World via a clandestine method. The romantic tale says captured Africans hid seeds of their favorite foods—okra and black-eyed peas, for example—on their persons before the brutal boat ride into slavery.

But folklorists and historians dispute this version of history. They make the good point that most slaves did not know where they were going when they got on the slave ships. And they had no reason to believe the same foods and plants they'd always known would not be found on another shore. Plus, most slaves were transported naked. So where would they have hidden the seeds?

If the slaves did not import the African foods, then who did?

Historians point to slave traders and plantation owners. Okra, the slave traders and owners knew, was the perfect food to feed slaves, as it made for meals that were cheap yet nutritious. So, the slavers brought okra over to the New World and planted it along with other robust African food plants. In the end it was the perpetrators of slavery—the slave traders and the plantation owners themselves—who carried African foods to the New World.

Southern cooking is, like all American cooking, the product of the veritable "melting pot," albeit with an extra heavy dose of African flavoring. Collard greens, for example, come from a northern European plant related to broccoli. But the method of cooking collard greens with port and sopping the "pot likker," or cooking juices, comes directly from slave cooks.

My Affinity for Pumpkins

Another uniquely American food is that greatest of all squashes: the pumpkin. In this respect I speak both historically and culturally.

When Europeans first landed at Plymouth Rock, Indians taught them how to prepare and eat the pumpkin. When 17th century blue laws decreed that male New Englanders had to have their hair cut round, they sometimes used the half shell of a pumpkin instead of a bowl as a guide for trimming the edges. Cliff-dwelling Indians used dried pumpkins for bottles and receptacles to hold feathers and cotton down for spinning. Stems were preserved and used for stoppers. And even some of our greatest writers and philosophers have spent time contemplating the pumpkin. "The custom of planting it in the front yard with the shrubbery is fast going out of vogue," wrote Mark Twain, "for it is generally conceded that the pumpkin as a shade tree is a failure." And Thoreau said, "I would rather sit on a pumpkin and have it all to myself than be crowded on a velvet cushion."

Pumpkin pie is the most quintessential American dish I can think of. No Thanksgiving is complete without it.

My own affinity for pumpkins dates back to 1973 when, as a 17-year-old kid, I became involved with an organization that used pumpkins as a way to clean up the then badly polluted Hudson River. Actually, pumpkins were just a part of it. The bigger part was a boat (Figure 4-1).

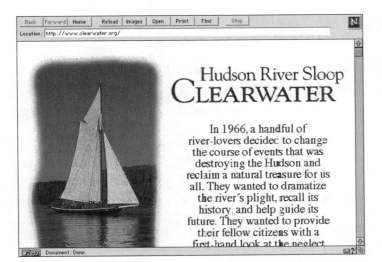

Hudson River Sloop
CLEARWATER

In 1966, a handful of river-lovers decided to change the course of events that was destroying the Hudson and reclaim a natural treasure for us all. They wanted to dramatize the river's plight, recall its history, and help guide its future. They wanted to provide their fellow citizens with a first-hand look at the neglect

FIGURE 4-1

The Hudson River Sloop Clearwater *pumpkin transport (**http:// www.clearwater.org/**)*

She was (and is) a gorgeous vessel. She is called *Clearwater*. And she is a working replica of the beautiful sloops which once dominated river commerce during the 19th century, and which can be noticed in so many paintings of Thomas Cole (**http://watt.emf.net/wm/paint/auth/cole**), Asher Durrand (**http://berniann.com/maplewood/murals/durand1. htm**), and others of the Hudson River School.

Clearwater is a floating environmental classroom. She is also a rallying point for those who do not think the Hudson River (or any waterway) should be a sewer or a chemical dump. In the autumn, usually around the end of October, she becomes something else: a cargo ship carrying pumpkins from upriver farming communities down to the city. In the Bronx and Manhattan, large waterfront festivals are held. City kids get fresh pumpkins from the country. Neighbors get to meet each other and as well meet the river. And a splendid time is enjoyed by all.

At one point we even had an official *Clearwater* pumpkin recipes cookbook. The one recipe from that little book which I remember best is that for preparing pumpkin seeds. This is a recipe that I and my family still use every autumn.

It is unfortunate that so few people take advantage of the seeds, which constitute the tastiest treat the pumpkin has to offer. (As a bonus, the seeds are good for your prostate—or so said Robert Rodale.) Are you one of the many people who use pumpkins to make jack-o'-lanterns, save the "meat" for pie making, and then simply throw away the seeds? Wrong! Wrong! Wrong!

Here is what you do: First, simply separate the seeds from the strings, but don't wash them. For every two cups of seeds add about two tablespoons of melted butter or oil and two teaspoons of salt, making sure all seeds are coated. Then spread the seeds out on an oiled baking sheet and bake them in a very slow (200-250 degrees) oven till crisp. The baking should take approximately 45 minutes. Then they are ready to eat. To store the cooked seeds, put them in clean, airtight jars.

The Most Famous American Meal Ever Eaten

The most famous meal ever eaten in American history was probably the first Thanksgiving dinner hosted by the Pilgrims (**http://media3.com/ plymouth/thanksgiving.htm**) in 1621. More than 90 Native Americans were guests. The feast lasted for three days and included not only food but games, races, and music. The Native Americans demonstrated their skills with the bow and arrow and the Pilgrims demonstrated equivalent skills with muskets. The mood was friendly, but in the weapons competition the medium was the message. Exactly when the affair took place is uncertain—probably in mid-October.

The custom of an annually celebrated Thanksgiving, held after the harvest, continued informally through the years. During the American Revolution, a day of national Thanksgiving was suggested by the Continental Congress but never acted upon.

In 1817 New York State adopted Thanksgiving Day as an annual custom. By the middle of the 19th century, many other states were also celebrating Thanksgiving. But it was not until 1863 that Abraham Lincoln codified the occasion with a formal declaration of a national holiday to be celebrated every year on the fourth Thursday of November.

Food and Cooking in the Melting Pot Called the Web

Some people detest the degree of randomness that seems to predominate American cooking. They say that all these overlapping foods from different cultures and continents do not constitute a genuine American statement of cuisine. I disagree, and I refer you to what the great American chef James Beard had to say. "While I do not overlook the grotesqueries of American cooking," he wrote, "I believe we have a rich and fascinating food heritage that occasionally reaches greatness in its own melting pot way. After all, France created French cuisine over centuries, and I daresay some of it was purely experimental cookery. Italian, Austrian, and Scandinavian cookery, as well, have had generations of change and tradition. We are barely beginning to sift down into a cuisine of our own."

Come to the Web for a cornucopia filled with rich samples of what Beard was talking about. Visit the Web for fabulous recipes and guides to great American restaurants nationwide. The recipes are for such American originals as Maine lobster, Tex-Mex combination platters, Thanksgiving turkeys, apple and pumpkin pies, and Alaskan King crab legs. And the restaurants are among the best the planet has to offer.

The Web also features some excellent resources related to American spirits, wine, and microbrewery beers. All told, there is quite a bit for us to get through. So by all means, let us begin.

American Apple Pie

   http://www.butterball.com/
butterball/appl-pie.html

The apple was one of the fruits most easily and most quickly available to the New England settlers. Thus apple pies were an early staple of the American diet. The fore-runners to today's apple pie had names like Apple Jonathan, Yankee Apple John, Apple Betty, and Apple Pandowdy. Sometimes these oven-baked sweets had stale bread as a base and some used biscuit dough. Maple syrup or sugar was usually used for sweetening. And nutmeg and cinnamon were contributed for flavor. At this Web page you get a most traditional American recipe.

American Wine on the Web Archives

   http://www.2way.com/food/wine/
daily/apr96/archives.html

Everything you always wanted to know about American wines and were afraid to ask. This is your guide to wines, regions, cellers, and more.

Annie's Pumpkin Walnut Cheesecake: A Recipe

   http://www.vix.com/free/
annestuff/cheeseca.htm

Annie, I don't know who or where you are, but thank you! Here is how the process worked in the Renehan home. Dad downloaded the recipe and printed it out. Then he tromped upstairs from his basement office. Then he handed the recipe to his wife and daughter. Then shopping and cooking ensued. In the end the family had one fine desert.

The Bay Area Restaurant Guide

   http://www.sfbay.com/food

This free online guide contains details on almost 14,000 San Francisco Bay Area restaurants with 8,000+ reviews from visitors just like you. It also includes several hundred restaurant photographs.

The Bay Area Restaurant Guide can be your magic carpet to discover and explore the restaurants of Alameda, Contra Costa, Marin, Napa, San Francisco, San Mateo, Santa Clara, Santa Cruz, Solano, and Sonoma counties. Search by region, city, restaurant type, average price, or a combination of any of these variables.

Black-Eyed Peas: A Spicy Recipe

 http://www.ebicom.net/~howle/
page/blaeyep.htm

In addition to the spicy recipe, here you will also find instructions for how to pickle black-eyed peas. Pickled black-eyed peas are sometimes called Texas Caviar. You can prepare this recipe using either fresh, dried, or canned black-eyed peas.

Boston (and Boston Region) Restaurant Guides

 http://www.bostondine.com/

HubNet Communications brings you The Boston Restaurant Guide as well as The Cape & Islands Restaurant Guide and The Boston Suburban Restaurant Guide. There are thousands of restaurants to browse and search through by neighborhood, price, and type of food. The site even includes links to caterers and banquet facilities throughout eastern Massachusetts.

Buffalo Meat Is Good for You

 http://www.tradecorridor.com/
bigskybuffalo

And it tastes good, too! If you didn't know what you were eating, you'd probably think that it was the best beef you ever tasted. It has been said that "it tastes like beef used to taste," or that "it tastes like beef wished it tasted." Buffalo meat is naturally flavorful and tender. You don't need to spice up a buffalo burger with a lot of extras. Buffalo will make any recipe better, and tastes great by itself.

It's not greasy, which brings me to another point. The flavor in most meats is in the fat, but so are the calories, cholesterol, and saturated fats. With other meats, you trim off the fat (which you paid for) and try to cook it out and drain it off. Buffalo meat

is tasty without the fat. It is mostly pure, natural wholesome protein with 25 percent to 30 percent more protein than beef and, on average, that much less fat.

Of course, it is healthy too.

So what is stopping you? The fear of buffalo extinction? That's over with. Buffalo are no longer an endangered species. The slaughtered animals are surplus bulls.

And there just isn't any food more American than buffalo meat. Get more information on buffalo—and where to buy it—at this Website.

Buffalo Wings Recipe Archive

 http://www.bababooey.com/
monkey/wings.html

This site provides a great collection of recipes for the official snack of American football: buffalo wings. All of the recipes presented are much more sophisticated than my own. Wings à la Renehan are prepared simply by dumping 'em in a deep fryer (350

degrees) and leaving them there 12 minutes, or until they float. Then open a beer and proceed to input cholesterol.

Chicago Restaurant Guide

 http://www.nwu.edu/ev-chi/
chirestaurants/

Check out such great Chicago eateries as the Daily Bar & Grill, the Abbey Pub & Restaurant, Dish!, the 1000 Notes Cafe, Tulips Cafe, Cafe Margot, the Cambridge Restaurant, the Gypsy Restaurant and Wine Bar, and many, many others.

The Culinary Institute of America

 http://www.thomson.com/
partners/cia/cia.html

Located at Hyde Park, New York, the Culinary Institute of America (sometimes referred to as the CIA) is one of the premier cooking schools in the world offering associate and bachelor's degree programs in the culinary arts, including baking and pastry arts, culinary arts management, and course work for food service professionals.

The Institute's highly acclaimed faculty of more than 125 instructors from dozens of countries throughout the world teach more than 2,000 full-time students. The Institute boasts of having the world's largest concentration of American Culinary Federation-certified master chefs.

THE CULINARY INSTITUTE OF AMERICA

433 Albany Post Road
Hyde Park, New York 12538-1499
914-452-9600

For comments and/or suggestions, contact the CIA Webmaster.

- An Overview of the CIA
- CIA by the Numbers
- Learn from the Very Best

Dallas Restaurant Guide

 http://www.kerrymenu.com/
dalall.htm

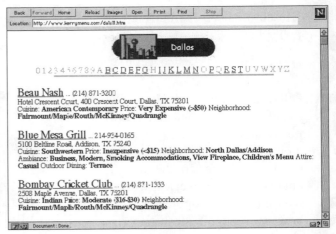

Search a rich database of restaurants in the Dallas/Fort Worth area. Another good Web resource along these lines is **http://www.dine-dfw.com/**. You've got a range of bistros from which to choose, including Tex-Mex, but also a number French, Chinese, Japanese, Portuguese, German, and Italian establishments as well.

Gumbo

 http://www.gumbopages.com

All about gumbo. This is, in fact, as close as we'll ever get to having an Encyclopedia of Gumbo. If there was ever a food saturated with the music and mood of New Orleans, gumbo is it. The scent of it is the scent of sultry Louisiana nights. It is the food you imagine the characters of Tennessee Williams always eating in between their various psychodramas of high and low life.

Hartford, Connecticut Restaurants

 http://www.wordofmouse.com/harct/

All the best eateries of one of the nicest little cities in the east. Hartford, in fact, boasts its share of four-star restaurants. It is also home to one of the premier steak houses in the country, a place that has been in business since 1870 and was one of Mark Twain's favorite eateries when he lived here a hundred years ago.

Los Angeles Restaurants, a.k.a. "Eating L.A."

 http://www.foodie.com/

Use this site's elegant, efficient search engine to search more than a thousand files and come up with just the right restaurant to fit your pocketbook and satisfy your taste buds in the neighborhood where you'd care to be. You may also like to take the L.A. "Foodie" quiz and see how you score, or browse the "chef's bookshelf," or play "restaurant roulette." What is the latter? Well, round and round and round it goes and where it stops is where you eat. Good luck.

Microbreweries of America: A Guide

 http://bmh-club.com/map.html

The Barley, Malt & Hops Club offers this graphical guide to plug you into some of the best microbreweries in the country. Start off by clicking on the map to choose microbreweries west or east of the Mississippi, then pick a brewery right off the list to read about its brews and its brewmaster.

If you're a beer lover, you may also want to check out the Barley, Malt & Hops Club that sponsors this guide. The club offers a monthly sampler pack of three craft-brewed beers, a monthly newsletter, collector cards, and as much information on beer and microbreweries as you can consume.

Another Website worth visiting, by the way, is **http://microbreweries.org/**.

Native American Recipes

 http://indy4.fdl.cc.mn.us/~isk/food/recipes.html

Here is a rich database of Native American recipes including recipes for wild rice, corn, hominy, cornmeal, squash, pumpkin, fish, waterfowl, beans, greens, and deer meat.

If you are a hunter like me you will be interested in the many recipes presented here for deer meat and venison.

New England Clam Chowder: A Recipe

 http://207.90.64.2/recipes/352.html

Here you'll find the classic recipe as perfected by Turner Fisheries of Boston Restaurant. New England clam chowder, I should say, is really the chowder of champions. It was John F. Kennedy's favorite, as well as Dwight Eisenhower's, Orville Wright's, Thomas Edison's, John D. Rockefeller's, and Cornelius Vanderbilt's. Call it "power food."

New England Culinary Institute

 http://www.neculinary.com

New England's premier cooking school is located in Montpelier, Vermont. The New England Culinary Institute has launched hundreds of notable careers. Chefs trained at New England are to be found in all the finest restaurants of New York, Los Angeles, London, and Paris. And it all started in little old Montpelier.

New Orleans Restaurants and Recipes

 http://www.compucast.com/ taste.html

The many excellent restaurants of New Orleans are noted throughout the world. New Orleans' Creole and Cajun foods have a long history and were originally "cooked up," if you will, in a thoroughly American melting pot. The Ursuline Sisters of France originally brought French cuisine to New Orleans. Then, when the Spanish came, they brought the pepper and the tomato—essential ingredients of Shrimp Creole. Finally, refugees from the West Indies and Sicily were also influential in the evolution of what has come to be considered some of the most delicious (and most spicy!) food anywhere on the planet.

At these Web pages you'll find both a restaurant guide and a great collection of Cajun and Creole recipes for do-it-yourself cooks. Be sure to consider the recipe for shrimp and andouille sausage gumbo. Send me some e-mail once you've got it cooked and I'll be right over.

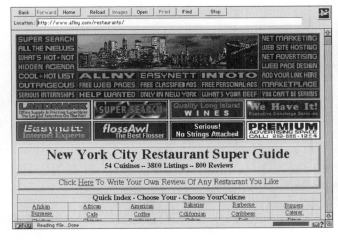

New York Restaurant Super Guide

 http://www.allny.com/ restaurants/

Here is a very large, searchable index of hundreds upon hundreds of fantastic Manhattan eateries. The index is fully searchable by any combination of parameters, including style of food, price, neighborhood, and star rating. It also includes links to many individual restaurant home pages, where you can browse menus and even make reservations via modem! If you care to, you may write a review of a restaurant you've visited and post it here with other consumer reviews. Another nice Manhattan guide can be found at **http://www.ny-restaurants.com**.

Phoenix Metro Restaurant Guide

 http://www.azmetro.com/
phxmetro.html

Designed to be the most thorough guide to Phoenix-area dining, the Phoenix Metro Restaurant Guide is completely searchable by all of the obvious parameters by which you would seek a restaurant. Each week there is a new in-depth review of a featured establishment. And you are always invited to contribute your own reviews to the database. This is a very useful feature. Not only

can you let others know which restaurants to pass up and which to visit, but you can benefit from the database of user reviews yourself and thus save yourself some unpleasantness.

Popcorn: Why Does It Pop?

 http://www.superscience.com/
popcorn.html

Learn how the Native Americans learned to pop the stuff we call popcorn. It really is miraculous. Popcorn starts off as an otherwise unremarkable small kernel of hard golden corn. In a flash, it transforms into the light, fluffy, white morsel we know as popcorn. The science behind the veritable "pop" is interesting, and fully explained in this easy tutorial.

Pumpkin Bread: A Recipe

 http://countrylife.net/bread/
recipes/3.html

Here is a recipe for Thanksgiving. The recipe given makes a 1.5 pound loaf of the tastiest bread on the planet. In the Renehan household, we always have this on Thanksgiving. The pumpkin bread is as fundamental as the turkey and the cranberries and the stuffing. The bread is the final Norman Rockwellian touch that makes the day perfect.

Pumpkin Crunch: A Recipe

 http://www.bbonline.com/~bbonline/ks/
hedgeapple/recipe1.html

And here is another recipe for Thanksgiving. You need 2 cans of pumpkin, 1 can of evaporated milk, 6 eggs, 1 cup of sugar, 1 yellow cake mix, 1/2 cup of brown sugar, 2 teaspoons of cinnamon, 1 teaspoon of ginger, and 1/4 teaspoon of cloves. Mix it all (except the cake mix) and pour into a 9" by 13" pan. Now put in the cake mix, 1/2 cup of butter, and 1 cup of pecans. Mix it up good. Bake it for an hour at 350 degrees. When it comes out, top it with whipped cream. Then call me and tell me to come over to your house for dessert.

Pumpkin Custard Pie: A Recipe

 http://www.commspec.com/
wor/page/pumpkin.htm

And another. Rumor has it here in Rhode Island that this was founding father Roger Williams' favorite dish. At Smith's Castle, less than a mile away from where I now live, Williams would often request it of Mrs. Richard Smith, the wife of his partner in Rhode Island colonial enterprise.

Pumpkin Nut Bread: A Recipe

 http://www.zia.com/tpumpkin.htm

You don't have to be a nut to like pumpkin bread, but it helps. It also helps to have

as excellent a recipe as is presented here. I remember back in 1973 the cook on the *Clearwater* made something very like this and it was a smash. The cook, Marc Weiner, is no longer a galley chef. He has moved on to host his own weekly kids' show on Nickelodeon: *Weinerville*. And that is also something of a smash.

Rhode Island Restaurants

 http://www.southcounty.com/
restaurants.htm

Here you will find all the best restaurants in my home state of Rhode Island. We have no scarcity of fine food. The Red Rooster is a four-star establishment less than three miles from my doorstep. Then we also have some of the finest seafood places in the country located at Point Judith and Galillee. These Web pages lay out all the succulent details.

Scottsdale Culinary Institute

http://www.grouper.com/culinary/

Learn to cook in Scottsdale, Arizona! Here you can learn to be a pantry cook, saucier, personal chef, line cook, assistant chef, baker, or banquet cook. All these various skills and specialties are incorporated into one stellar program that is respected throughout the world.

Seattle Restaurant Information

 http://math.washington.edu/
Visitors/restaurants.html

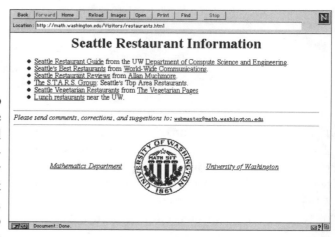

Every restaurant Seattle has to offer. Find each and every one right here. Find out where Bill Gates eats! The database, an extensive one, comes to you currently from the Mathematics Department at the University of Washington, where the Ph.D. candidates like to eat almost as much as they like to solve equations.

Tasty Maine Lobster Recipes

 http://www.maine.com/lobsters/

Here are recipes for cooking lobster the way they do it down East. The prescriptions range from your basic baked stuffed lobster to lobster Newburg supreme, grilled lobsters with champagne butter, lobster paté, lobster steamed in vodka, lobster primavera, Maine lobster stew, and even lobster mousse!

Tex-Mex Hash: A Recipe

 http://ecep1.usl.edu/cajun/ent/
10305.htm

A little of this. A little of that. Then a sprinkle of something else and you've got a uniquely American meal: a meal the southwestern cowboys probably perfected in old iron pans hung over open fires in the middle of a stark countryside. This is the type of grub I imagine cowboys in a John Ford film cooking and eating—the kind of grub John Wayne would insist upon.

Tex-Mex Home Fries: A Recipe

 http://www.reu.com/wgy/
tex_mex_homefries.html

Here's another product of the melting pot: Tex-Mex home fries! The same cowpokes would probably insist on this unique blend of flavors, don't you think? Not that they'd be too particular after a long day busting horses, herding cows, and shooting bad guys.

Turkey Trivia Game

 http://www.butterball.com/
butterball/trivia.html

Question: Which great American statesman wanted to have the turkey chosen as our national bird over the eagle? Answer: Ben Franklin. (The tougher question is: Was he right or wrong? As a nation, we've had days in recent memory when even I thought the turkey ought to be our national bird!) Question: Who first proclaimed Thanksgiving a national holiday? Answer: Abe Lincoln. Question: What percentage of American homes eat turkey on Thanksgiving? Answer: 90 percent. Question: Which state produces the most turkeys? Answer: North Carolina has that dubious distinction, but I notice Arkansas is a close runner-up. Question: How much turkey do Americans eat on Thanksgiving? Answer: 535 million pounds.

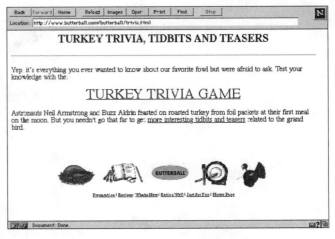

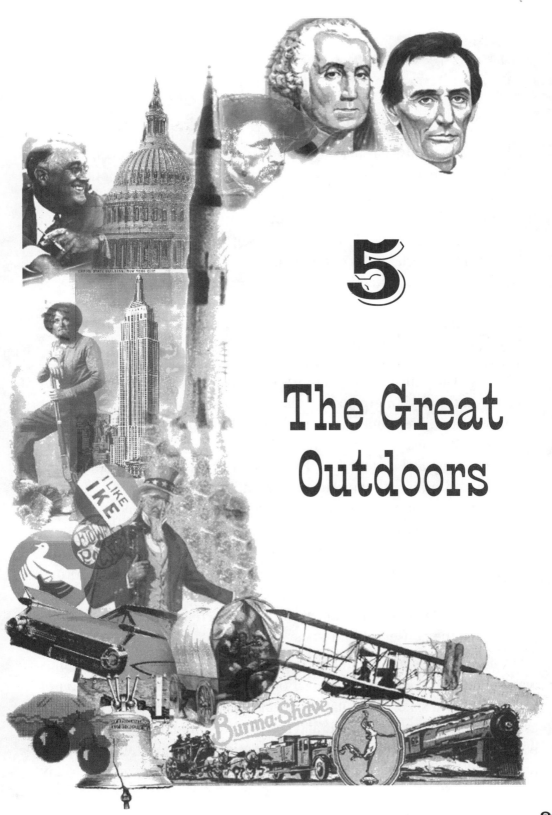

5

The Great Outdoors

A s E.B. White wrote in 1942, "People are beginning to suspect that the greatest freedom is not achieved by sheer irresponsibility. The earth is common ground and...gradually the idea is taking form that the land must be held in safekeeping, that one generation is to some extent responsible for the next." White's message lives in the interests and efforts of many today who continue the rich environmental and conservation ethic of the United States.

The Roots of Conservation

It was at the turn of the century that the federal government first became seriously interested in the idea of holding lands for their resource values. President Theodore Roosevelt (**http://www.abcland.com/~jwiedman/tr**) was the first in that office formally to declare the conservation of forest and water resources to be of prime national importance. During his administration more than 200 million acres of forests, mineral lands, and water-power sites were withdrawn from public sale. Roosevelt also appointed a number of commissions to study natural resource issues. At Roosevelt's orders, a National Conservation Commission headed by Gifford Pinchot, the first chief of the U.S. Forest Service, made a formal inventory of all natural resources in the United States. Roosevelt's actions and the reports and conferences he sponsored brought wide public attention to the conservation issue.

A new attitude about public lands and the preservation of wild lands was beginning to surface in the national consciousness. Preservation of land for its own sake, for its natural beauty, became increasingly important as more lands were developed and settled. A National Park system had been created and certain lands had been set aside by the federal government for the public to enjoy. Some states followed the federal example. Many citizens, including Roosevelt, were ardent conservationists. Many agreed with Sierra Club founder John Muir (Figure 5-1) that wilderness and wild lands have intrinsic values.

In fact, however, reserves of land for public use had existed in the United States since the mid-1600s. In 1641, the Massachusetts Colony passed a law preserving some 2,000 bodies of water for the public to use for fishing and fowling. The idea of establishing a formal park for public recreation surfaced in 1864. This was the year Yosemite Valley and a nearby grove of trees were given by the federal government to the State of California. California was charged to hold the park forever for public use.

This was a period when the frontier was suddenly evaporating, and it was no longer possible to move away from the sound of a neighbor's ax. The railroad and the barbed wire fence, two symbols of civilization, were already common fixtures of everyday life. Buffalo Bill's Wild West Show toured the nation: an exhibition of cultural antiques. For most Americans the show, enshrined within the limits of a tent, was the only glimpse they would get of what had once been wide open spaces. It was becoming obvious to many conservationists that it would be all too easy to lose all

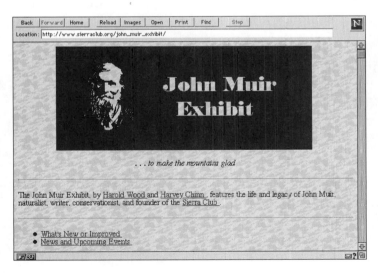

FIGURE 5-1
John Muir, nature boy
(http://www.sierraclub.
org/john_muir_exhibit/)

of the wild lands and wildlife to the plow and, eventually, to the factories and urban sprawl.

John Burroughs and the Literature of Conservation

Shortly before a war-weary Abraham Lincoln signed the 1864 legislation setting aside Yosemite to be preserved in perpetuity, he read a book by American diplomat and pioneer conservationist George Perkins Marsh (**http://www.uidaho.edu/~witt731/gpmi.html**). In *Man and Nature*, Marsh analyzed the decline of ancient Mediterranean and Near Eastern civilizations in terms of watershed abuse, and warned against a similar mistake in America.

In his book, Marsh demonstrated the way in which man had become a major technological force with a frightening new ability to change the environment drastically and permanently. His message was plain: in the face of expanding industry and population, wilderness had to be recognized as something of inherent value, the preservation of which was essential for the common good. Citing Marsh's articulation of such an important notion, my old friend and mentor Lewis Mumford, writing in *The Brown Decades*, identified the 1864 publication of *Man and Nature* as the fountainhead event of the modern American conservation movement.

Another writer of the late 19th and early 20th century—Theodore Roosevelt's good friend John Burroughs (Figure 5-2)—supplied a more philosophical argument for wilderness. During the years of 1870 through 1920, as the urban landscape sprawled and swelled, Burroughs wrote more than two dozen books of nature essays designed to provide a steady stream of encouragement, instruction, and inspiration to men and women who chose to take up hiking and other outdoor pursuits as an antidote to a society increasingly mortgaged to the advance of technology and the rise of cities.

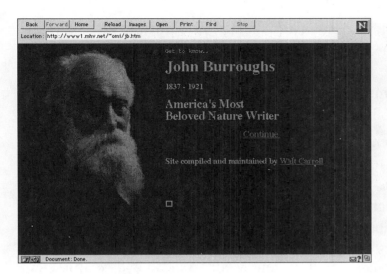

FIGURE 5-2
John Burroughs,
1837-1921
(http://www1.mhv.net/
~omi/jb.htm)

John Burroughs suggested in his writings that he thought it better for one to live in the country on a farm than in the city. He let it be known that industrial pursuits were probably not very healthy for either mind or body. And he proposed that only local, agricultural economies could be counted on to forge a way of life that honestly tended toward the good of all and did not, as Burroughs' acquaintance Henry Demarest Lloyd (**http://www.chadwyck.inter.net/mfcat/mf021.html**) put it, pit "wealth against commonwealth." At the end of his last decade, at the start of the 1920s and the dawn of the Jazz Age, the aged friend of Emerson and Whitman scanned with sad eloquence the modern American horizon of smokestacks and slums—what he'd come to call "the devil's laboratory"—and publicly mourned the fate of the world as industrial science began to outpace humankind's capacity to use its results wisely.

For Burroughs, nature and wilderness had what he called a "distinctly religious" value. His great hero Ralph Waldo Emerson had written, "The day does not seem wholly profane in which we have given heed to some natural object." The Bible said, "In Him we live and move, and have our being." In this instance Burroughs, who had rejected his own fundamentalist Baptist roots along with all other traditional notions of a personal

God, urged his readers to take the Bible literally. "How childish this talk is, that we can be nearer God, nearer heaven, in some other world, than we are here!" wrote Burroughs in 1883. "What irreligion and atheism it is! The child in its mother's womb is no nearer its mother than you and I and all men are at all times near God."

Burroughs recommended to his readers that they go to the woods to develop a personal relationship with nature that did not "vulgarize it and rob it of its divinity." Confronted with Darwin's revelations on the origin of species, Burroughs believed that thoughtful individuals of modern times required a tabernacle of worship different from that where their superstitious fathers had prostrated themselves. In the final analysis, he believed the experience of wild nature to be the embodiment of the best and most real form of prayer. "Saints and devotees have gone into the wilderness to find God," he wrote. "Of course, they took God with them, and the silence and detachment enabled them to hear the still, small voice of their own souls."

For Burroughs, the Christian tenet of sin followed by redemption found its analogy in the citizens of cities who returned to seek the pleasure and solitude of the wooded countryside. As in the stories of St. Paul and Thomas Aquinas, knowledge of God was all the sweeter and all the more profound following salvation after a fall from grace. Burroughs suggested that the idea of the city was born of fear and sin. Rude and barbarous people needed cities. The necessity of defense had built the first cities— Ur, Babylon, and Carthage. The weaker the law, the stronger the city. "After Cain slew Abel he went out and built a city," wrote Burroughs. And he suggested that it was calculated greed and a crude lack of faith that had lain the foundation for every city since.

Hence, argued Burroughs, the city was "older" than the country. "Truly, man made the city," Burroughs wrote, "and after he became sufficiently civilized, not afraid of solitude, and knew on what terms to live with nature, God promoted him to life in the country." It was only after his abdication of the forest to industrialization that man could realize the true sanctity of nature. It was only after seeing the hell of the urban that he could realize the heaven of the rural. Only after sin could he find redemption.

Burroughs' third book of nature essays, published in 1879, was titled *Locusts and Wild Honey*. In his preface, Burroughs hinted that the title of the book was an allegory. Burroughs' allusion was to another John, John the Baptist, "the voice crying in the wilderness" who "fed on locusts and wild honey." The modern prophet Burroughs proselytized for a new church of the woodlands. The new and most necessary baptism was a baptism in nature. Amid the trees, by forest streams, he believed one could find a cure for the vanity and vexation of spirit that the growing American industrial colossus doled out in such generous portions. In days of increasing urbanization and "scientific barbarism," wrote Burroughs, the woods could set one free.

And they still can.

A Word on Hunting

One of my favorite 20th century writers on nature and conservation was Aldo Leopold (Figure 5-3) of Wisconsin, who died in 1948 shortly before the publication of his classic, *A Sand County Almanac*. Like Theodore Roosevelt, Aldo Leopold was both an avid hunter and an avid conservationist/environmentalist in an age long before the present when—wrongly, I think—hunters are viewed with scorn by many environmentalists.

There is no one with a greater love for the outdoors than the hunter. There is no one with a better notion of the value of green places and wildlife than the hunter. There is no one who has observed and enjoyed these things up close in the way a hunter has. John Burroughs was a

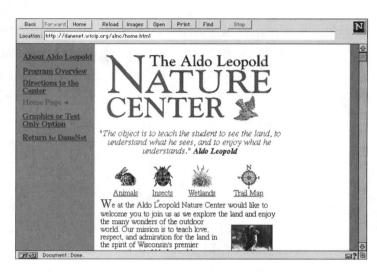

FIGURE 5-3

*Visit the home page for the Aldo Leopold Nature Center (**http://danenet.wicip.org/alnc/home.html**)*

lifelong hunter. So, too, was a man who to this day is generally recognized as one of the greatest field naturalists the United States has ever produced: Theodore Roosevelt.

One of TR's first acts as president was to launch a system of wildlife preserves modeled along the lines of those that had been pioneered by the Audubon Society since the 1880s. "I need hardly to say how heartily I sympathize with the purposes of the Audubon Society," he wrote. "I would like to see all harmless wild things...protected in every way." TR the hunter put great weight on the word "harmless," as should we. When a species was not harmless, and was not in danger of extinction or underpopulation, it was fair game.

In 1903, when Roosevelt asked permission to dedicate his new book, *Outdoor Pastimes of an American Hunter*, to Burroughs, Burroughs replied without hesitation that this would please him greatly. "I know it will be a solid contribution to natural history," he wrote the president, "as well as to the literature of big-game hunting—all your hunting books are that." In his memoir *Camping and Tramping with Roosevelt* (1907), Burroughs wrote that he had never been disturbed by the president's hunting trips. "It is to such men as he that the big game legitimately belongs," wrote Burroughs, "men who regard it from the point of view of the naturalist as well as from that of the sportsman, who are interested in its preservation."

In a letter to his son, Burroughs revealed the essence of his point of view on the subject, which represented the ultimate in natural pragmatism. "Nature does not care whether the hunter slay the beast or the beast the hunter," he wrote. "She will make good compost of them both, and her ends are prospered whichever succeeds."

A Word on Rachel

The first great literary naturalist of the modern era was, of course, Rachel Carson, who wrote the classic book *Silent Spring*. It is worth noting that in 1992 a panel of distinguished Americans declared *Silent Spring* to be the most influential book of the past 50 years. This was one of the latest in a long line of tributes to a woman who almost single-handedly alerted Americans to the dark side of science in alliance with industrial society. Her measured, carefully worded, yet passionate prose was all the more damning because she, herself, was a scientist.

It is important to remember how much controversy *Silent Spring* aroused when it was published in 1962. The pesticide industry tried to have the book suppressed, and they challenged its findings. When CBS Television scheduled an hour-long news report on Carson's condemnation of the "river of death" the chemical industry was pouring into America's water supply, two corporate sponsors withdrew. But the proverbial cat was out of the bag. The book remained on the best-seller list for months and remains in print now, 35 years later. Vice President Al Gore credits Carson's work with prompting the creation of the Environmental Protection Agency.

Park Information and Other Environmental Resources on the Web

There is no limit to the number of environmental organizations, parks, trails, rivers, and greenways represented on the World Wide Web. There are lots of them to get through, so strap on your pack and let's start hiking the mountains, valleys, and streambeds that run not far from the information superhighway.

★ ★ ★ ★ ★ ★ ★ ★ ☆

All Outdoors

 http://alloutdoors.com

All Outdoors features eight monthly magazines, eleven lively forums, daily hunting and fishing news, and over 700 archived articles from top outdoor writers. Whether you are a hunter, conservationist, environmnental activist, or hiker, you will find information here that is of value.

The American Park Network

 http://www.americanparknetwork.com/

Sponsored by Meredith Corporation, the American Park Network is without a doubt one of the most comprehensive sources of information on U.S. national parks.

Planning a trip to Yellowstone or Yosemite? A gander at the Grand Canyon or a bivouac at Biscayne? Get all of the latest information here about your destination, or find new places to visit. You can also use these Web pages to drill into your activities of interest to find parks where those activities are welcome. Activities include bicycling, boating and rafting, camping, fishing, horseback riding, photography, rock climbing, snowskiing, snowshoeing, swimming, walking and hiking, waterskiing, and wildlife viewing.

You may also want to take a look at the National Parks Service's own Web pages at **http://www.nps.gov/**.

Appalachian Mountain Club

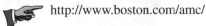 http://www.boston.com/amc/

The Appalachian Mountain Club promotes the protection, enjoyment, and wise use of the mountains, rivers, and trails of the northeast.

Founded in 1876, the Appalachian Mountain Club is a nonprofit organization with over 64,000 members. The organization is based on the idea that mountains and rivers have an intrinsic worth and provide not only recreation but spiritual renewal. The Club encourages people to enjoy and appreciate the natural world because it believes the success of conservation depends upon as many people as possible sharing the experience of wilderness.

Towards this end, the Appalachian Mountain Club maintains more than 1,400 miles of recreational trails, including 350 miles of the famed Appalachian Trail. The Club also works to develop greenways and multiple-use trails in urban and dense population areas.

Furthermore, the Club sponsors professional trail maintenance crews, shelter caretakers, ridge runners, and other programs to support healthy trails throughout the northeast. Each year Club professionals and volunteers put in approximately 40,000 hours of work to see that the northeast's hiking trails remain in good shape for the millions of people who use them.

Appalachian Trail Home Page

http://www.fred.net/kathy/at.html

The Appalachian Trail is a well-marked hiking trail that runs from central Maine to northern Georgia—about 2,159 miles. Contrary to common misconception, the trail never had anything to do with Native Americans. The Trail was created by Americans and outdoorsmen inspired by an article written in 1921 by Benton MacKaye. MacKaye's article rambles as much about social and economic injustice as the Unabomber's manifesto. But MacKaye's solution was to get back to nature and do a little hiking.

This Website is packed with information and links related to the Trail. It is *the* place to start your hike.

Rachel Carson Links

 http://www.ecotopia.org/
ehof/carson/links.html

Here are links to many of Carson's writings as published on the Web as well as the Rachel Carson Council, the Rachel Carson birthplace, and the Rachel Carson wildlife refuge. There are few questions about Rachel Carson that are not answered here.

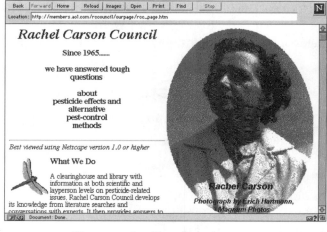

Rachel Carson Council

Since 1965.......

we have answered tough
questions

about
pesticide effects and
alternative
pest-control
methods

Best viewed using Netscape version 1.0 or higher

What We Do

A clearinghouse and library with information at both scientific and layperson levels on pesticide-related issues. Rachel Carson Council develops its knowledge from literature searches and conversations with experts. It then provides answers to

Rachel Carson
Photograph by Erich Hartmann,
Magnum Photos

Catskill Fly-Fishing Center and Museum

 http://cat1.catskill.com/flyfish/

Some of the best fly-fishing in the world is to be had in the Catskill Mountains of New York State. Come to this informative set of Web pages for much more information and learn about the place that has become a mecca for fly-fishermen from around the world.

Chesapeake Bay Trust

 http://www2.ari.net/home/cbt

Read about the efforts of the Chesapeake Bay community to encourage the protection and restoration of historic Chesapeake Bay. This Website offers a list of "10 Ways You Can Help Clean Up the Bay"—environmentally sound tips that make sense no matter where you live.

Conservation Land Trust Network (Maine)

 http://www.biddeford.com/
~mcht/cltn.htm

The Conservation Land Trust Network provides links to regional, state, and local land trusts across the state of Maine. From the interior mountains to the beautiful and expansive Maine coast, the citizens of Maine are doing much to preserve their pristine landscape. Find out more from these useful Web pages.

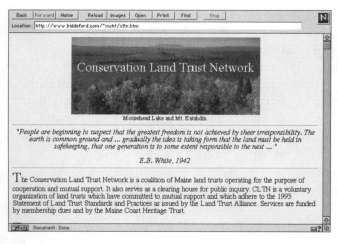

Conservation Land Trust Network

Moosehead Lake and Mt. Katahdin

"People are beginning to suspect that the greatest freedom is not achieved by sheer irresponsibility. The earth is common ground and ... gradually the idea is taking form that the land must be held in safekeeping, that one generation is to some extent responsible to the next ... "

E.B. White, 1942

The Conservation Land Trust Network is a coalition of Maine land trusts operating for the purpose of cooperation and mutual support. It also serves as a clearing house for public inquiry. CLTN is a voluntary organization of land trusts which have committed to mutual support and which adhere to the 1993 Statement of Land Trust Standards and Practices as issued by the Land Trust Alliance. Services are funded by membership dues and by the Maine Coast Heritage Trust.

Defenders of Wildlife

 http://www.defenders.org

Defenders of Wildlife is dedicated to the protection of all native wild animals and plants in their natural communities. The organization focuses its programs on what scientists consider two of the most serious environmental threats to the planet: the accelerating rate of extinction of species and the associated loss of biological diversity, and habitat alteration and destruction. Long known for their leadership on endangered species issues, Defenders of Wildlife also advocates new approaches to wildlife conservation that will help keep species from becoming endangered. The organization's programs encourage protection of entire ecosystems and interconnected habitats while protecting predators that serve as *indicator* species for ecosystem health.

EnviroLink

 http://www.envirolink.org/

All the environmental links on the planet are to be found right here, including all the U.S. ones such as the Sierra Club, Audubon Society, Friends of the Earth, *Clearwater*, Save the Bay, and many, many others.

Everglades National Park

 http://www.50years.com/

The Everglades National Park is celebrating its 50th anniversary. Join the party at this Web page which is loaded with great information, links, and pictures, and find out what you can do to help make sure the Park enjoys another 50 years of service.

Fish and Wildlife Service

 http://www.fws.gov/

The formal mission of the United States Fish and Wildlife Service is "to conserve, protect, and enhance fish and wildlife and their habitats for the continuing benefit of the American people." As a result, the Service is involved in many activities throughout the country.

The Service has a long and interesting history.

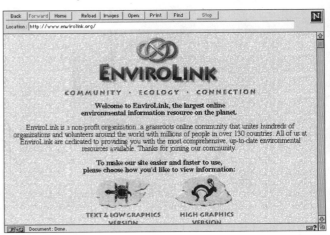

The Service's origins date back to 1871, when Congress established the U.S. Fish Commission to study the decrease of the nation's food fishes and recommend ways to reverse the decline. The Fish Commission was placed under the Department of Commerce in 1903 and renamed the Bureau of Fisheries.

Meanwhile, in 1885, Congress created an Office of Economic Ornithology in the Department of Agriculture. The Office studied the food habits and migratory patterns of birds, especially those that had an effect on agriculture. This office gradually grew in responsibilities and went through several name changes until finally renamed the Bureau of Biological Survey in 1905. In addition to studying the abundance, distribution, and habits of birds and mammals, the Survey's responsibilities included managing the nation's first wildlife refuges, controlling predators, enforcing wildlife laws, and conserving dwindling populations of herons, egrets, waterfowl, and other migratory birds.

The Bureaus of Fisheries and Biological Survey were transferred to the Department of the Interior in 1939. One year later, in 1940, they were combined and named the Fish and Wildlife Service. Further reorganization came in 1956 when the Fish and Wildlife Act created the United States Fish and Wildlife Service and established within the agency two separate bureaus—Commercial Fisheries and Sport Fisheries and Wildlife.

The Bureau of Commercial Fisheries was transferred to the Department of Commerce in 1970 and is now known as the National Marine Fisheries Service. The Bureau of Sport Fisheries and Wildlife remained a part of the Department of the Interior. In accordance with a 1974 Act of Congress, the "Bureau" name was dropped and the agency is now simply called the U.S. Fish and Wildlife Service.

Today, the Service employs approximately 7,500 people at facilities across the country including a headquarters office in Washington, D.C., seven regional offices, and nearly 700 field units and installations. Among these are national wildlife refuges and fish hatcheries, ecological field offices, and law enforcement offices.

Among other tasks, the Service runs the world's largest and most diverse collection of lands set aside specifically for wildlife: the National Wildlife Refuge System. This system began in 1903 when President Theodore Roosevelt designated three-acre Pelican Island, a pelican and heron rookery in Florida, as a bird sanctuary.

Friends of the Earth—U.S.

 http://www.foe.org/

Friends of the Earth—U.S. is a national action and political lobbying organization dedicated to environmental advocacy and activism. Read here about the organization's positions on tax law and social issues, both domestically and globally. This Website offers information on current and recent actions and alerts, as well as outlines for global action, protecting the planet, publications, and membership information.

Glacier National Park

 http://www.cs.montana.edu/cs/local/glacier.html

Glacier National Park is a national treasure located near Kalispell, Montana. Established in 1910, the park encompasses over 1,600 square miles of breathtaking country and over 730 miles of hiking trails. Come to this page for pictures (by Audrey Hagen), links, and more information.

View from the Tonto Plateau, looking down the inner gorge of the Grand Canyon.

The Grand Canyon

 http://songbird.com/gc/

On August 13, 1869, explorer John Wesley Powell wrote "We are now ready to start on our way down the Great Unknown. Our boats, tied to a common stake, chafe each other as they are tossed by the fretful river..." Come here to access Powell's words, beautiful images, and vivid reflections of the

canyons of the Colorado. Another great set of images is to be found at **http://www.west-ward.com/gallery/gcanyon.htm**. Here you'll find color photographs of Duck on the Rock, the North Rim, Powell Memorial Point, Mather Point, and more.

Grand Teton National Park: A History

 http://jackson-hole.com/parks/gtnphist.shtml

Learn about how John D. Rockefeller built a national park. As my grandmother always said: "Rich or poor, it is nice to have money." And it is doubly nice when someone with money uses it for so high-minded a purpose as this.

Hudson River Sloop Clearwater

 http://www.clearwater.org

I've mentioned this organization already once before in this book. The Hudson River Sloop *Clearwater* sails in order to insure a clean and healthy Hudson for future generations. You can, quite literally, help her stay sailing. She needs volunteer crew members. I can assure you it is a wonderful outdoor adventure. I've done it more than once myself. Find out more at the home page.

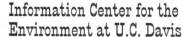

Information Center for the Environment at U.C. Davis

 http://ice.ucdavis.edu/

Here are great environmental and park links with a definite California slant. Find out about the wild places contained in one of the most beautiful states of the Union by accessing these extensive online maps, bibliographies, and articles.

LandTrust.com

 http://www.landtrust.com

Learn how to create, fund, and maintain a conservation land trust. This is not as hard a thing to do as you might at first think. All over the country, community activists are becoming involved. Find out how you can too.

The League of Conservation Voters

 http://www.lcv.org/

Make your vote count. Find out which Congressional representatives and senators have been naughty, and which have been nice. Find out who is for a healthy environment and who is for industrial profits, poisoned waters, and clear-cut logging. The contents of this set of Web pages always makes for interesting reading.

Aldo Leopold Links

 http://www.ecotopia.org/ehof/
leopold/links.html

To learn more about conservationist Aldo Leopold, who died in 1948, access the great set of links referenced on this Web page. Here you'll find Chris W. Johnson's page of Aldo Leopold quotes, the Leopold Education Project, the Aldo Leopold Nature Center, The Leopold Center, the Aldo Leopold Society, and many essays and comments on Leopold as both a man and an environmentalist.

Mohonk Mountain House, New Paltz, NY

 http://www.jlc.net/~tadd/mohonk

In the Catskill Mountains, west of New Paltz, NY, some 90 miles above New York City, there is an old resort hotel on a lake. It is a plush resort for those who like to rough it: a fine old Mountain House Inn featuring soft beds and good food but surrounded by some of the best hiking and rock climbing in the world. Take a tour of the Mohonk Mountain House via this splendid online photo essay by Tadd Torborg.

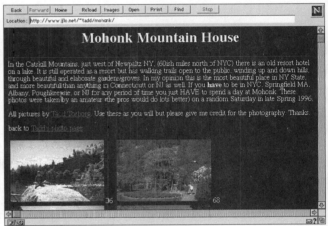

John Muir Links

http://www.ecotopia.org/ehof/
muir/links.html

Come here for links to great Web resources related to John Muir, including many of his writings available for reading or downloading online. Muir's writings available on the Web include such essays as "The American Forests," "The Earthquake," "Man's Place in the Universe," "Mt. Ritter," "Mountain Thoughts," "Steep Trails," "Stickeen," "Victorians and Meadowlarks," "The Water Ouzel," "Wild Wool," "A New View of the High Sierra," and "Snow Storm on Mount Shasta." You can also get the complete texts of the books *My First Summer in the Sierra* and *Our National Parks*. For more information on Muir go to the Sierra Club site referenced later in this chapter.

You should also be sure to check out Don Weiss' *John Muir and I* page (**http://www.mandala.co.jp/echoes/JMI/JMIhome.html**). This is a Web presentation (through words and images) of Don's solo hike of the John Muir trail. Fascinating stuff.

National Audubon Society

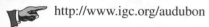   http://www.igc.org/audubon

You've heard of them. You know who they are. Well, here is their place in cyberspace which includes links to the home pages of more than 100 Audubon Society locals.

A little history: in 1886, George Bird Grinnell, an amateur hunter outraged by the senseless slaughter of birds associated with the plume trade, founded the organization and named it after his boyhood idol, John James Audubon. (Interestingly, Lucy

Audubon, John James' wife, had been Grinnell's elementary school teacher.)

The mission of the Audubon Society, then and now, is to prevent the extinction of species. Today, more than 570,000 Audubon members work on behalf of the environment in 518 communities across the United States. The organization spreads its message through a beautiful monthly magazine and many educational outreach programs.

National Park Service: ParkNet

   http://www.nps.gov/

This is the official National Park Service page with links to information concerning virtually every national park that exists. Search parks by name or region and get park descriptions, travel directions, fee information, seasonal schedules, and more.

National Parks & Conservation Association

   http://www.npca.com/

The National Parks and Conservation Association (NPCA) is an environmental activism organization offering action alerts and calls to action on political issues and bills that the NPCA believes have an impact on the environment. The NPCA also organizes Earth Day events and travel programs.

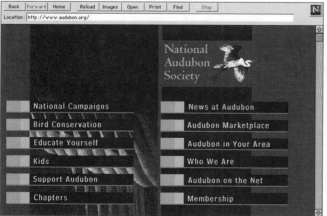

National Wildlife Federation

 http://www.nwf.org/

The National Wildlife Federation is the United States' largest member-supported conservation group. Check out their extensive, ambitious, and informative set of Web pages dedicated to preserving endangered species nationwide.

Natural Resources Conservation Service

 http://www.ncg.nrcs.usda.gov/

The Natural Resources Conservation Service (NRCS) is an agency of the federal government (part of the Department of Agriculture). Formerly known as the Soil Conservation Service, the NRCS works primarily with farmers and ranchers to promote conservation of soil and water on private and state land. Learn more about the NRCS here on its Web pages—including the organization and training of the department, technical notes and references, and volunteer programs.

Natural Resources Defense Council

 http://www.nrdc.org

The Natural Resources Defense Council (NRDC) is a membership organization comprised of 350,000

people banded together to help protect the natural environment. They stress legal action in their approach. They are lawyers and they like to sue polluters. Bravo.

The Nature Conservancy

 http://www.tnc.org/

The Nature Conservancy is an environmental organization that buys land and

properties with the intent of restoring them to their natural conditions. Often, this means burning the existing flora and fauna and starting from scratch. Some of the properties are nearly as small as postage stamps, while others cover thousands of acres. Interested in learning how The Nature Conservancy got started? You can download a Quick-Time video here that tells the tale very nicely.

Olympic National Park

 http://www.nps.gov/olym/olym.htm

With over 60 miles of wild Pacific coastline, Olympic National Park is the largest coastal national park in the continental U.S. But along with that coastline, Olympic also has snow-capped peaks and the largest remaining old-growth and temperate rain forests in the Pacific Northwest. Salmon still migrate seasonally to spawn in the clean, clear water of many Olympic rivers and streams. Ninety-five percent of Olympic National Park is designated wilderness, and over 600 miles of trails provide access to these wild areas.

Online Exhibit from the Library of Congress: The Evolution of the Conservation Movement, 1850-1920

 http://lcweb2.loc.gov/ammem/amrvhtml/conshome.html

This online exhibit documents the historical formation and cultural foundations of the movement to conserve and protect America's natural heritage. This online collection consists of hundreds of books, pamphlets, laws, Congressional resolutions, articles, excerpts, photographs, Presidential proclamations, and other documents relating to natural conservation.

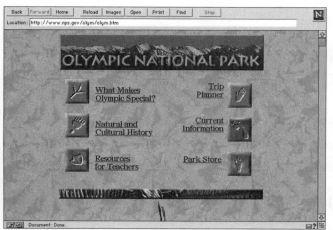

Outward Bound USA

http://outwardbound.org/

Outward Bound is an organization dedicated to helping people realize respect for nature, community, working groups, and themselves through experiencing wilderness adventures. Outward Bound offers wilderness adventure courses, professional development and contract courses, and urban education programs.

The online catalog at this Website lists wilderness adventure courses offered by the five U.S. Outward Bound schools. Courses include canoeing, sailing, wilderness survival, rock climbing, and more.

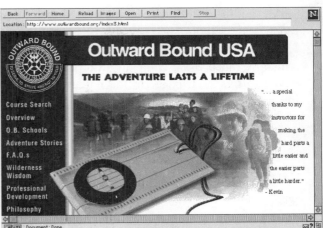

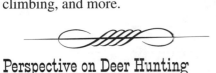

Perspective on Deer Hunting

 http://www.fcs.uga.edu/~mhulsey/
deerhunting.html

Here is a brilliant, cogently argued defense of the sport of hunting, which has gotten a bad reputation in recent years. Hunting for species that are not endangered is not only a worthwhile pursuit, it is an exercise which helps people form a bond with wild nature they could not achieve otherwise.

Petroglyph National Monument

 http://www.viva.com/nm/
cen.petroglyph.html

West of Albuquerque, New Mexico, Petroglyph National Monument is in an area known as the "West Mesa" or "Northwest Heights"—a 17-mile lava field created by volcanic activity. In 1990, Congress created Petroglyph National Monument to protect the thousands of petroglyphs inscribed in the lava escarpment—most of which are between three and seven hundred years old (although some are estimated to be two to three thousand years old). Many Pueblo Indians still consider this area to be a sacred place and journey here to worship and take place in ceremonies.

Theodore Roosevelt National Park, Medora, North Dakota

 http://www.gorp.com/gorp/resource/
US_National_Park/nd_theod.HTM

Theodore Roosevelt ranched for several years in the Badlands in the 1880s. This

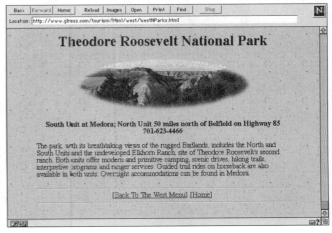

park encompasses the sites of his two cattle ranches: the Elkhorn and the Maltese Cross. Like Roosevelt himself, the Badlands in which he ranched are endlessly fascinating. Come to this Web page for the interesting history of Theodore Roosevelt National Park.

Save the Bay

 http://www.savethebay.org/

This one is near and dear to my heart. Save the Bay works to maintain the environmental integrity of a great national treasure: the Narragansett Bay. This is where I live. It is also where I sail.

Sierra Club

 http://www.sierraclub.org/

Here is the home page for the great old war-horse of environmental groups founded by John Muir in 1892. This is

loaded with rich links to historical resources, chapter home pages, news, and views concerning current environmental arguments, and much more.

Sportsman's Hunting and Fishing Guide

 http://hunt-fish.com/

With regard to hunting, this site provides detailed data on small game, big game, exotics, waterfowl, season leases, hunting ranches, and more. With regard to fishing, you've got info on saltwater and fresh water charters, outfitters, boats, piers, and tours. There are also links to equipment manufacturers and retailers as well as hunting and fishing lodges.

Utah National Parks

 http://www.surweb.org/
surweb/utah1.htm

Come here for information on Arches National Park, Bryce Canyon National Park, Canyon Lands National Park, Capitol Reef National Park, and Zion National Park. These landscapes are absolutely fabulous and uniquely American. Geologically speaking, there is no place like Utah anywhere else on the face of the earth.

Washington State Parks Home Page

 http://www.parks.wa.gov/

The signs says it all. Here is your online guide to the parks of Washington state. There are dozens of them, each one more beautiful than the next. Let the cyberguide on the Web show you around and point out your options.

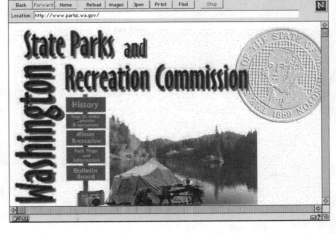

Westchester County (NY) Land Trust

 http://www.westchesterlandtrust.org/

The mission of the Westchester County Land Trust is to protect open space and promote responsible land use throughout Westchester County, New York. Their program includes not only parks but also wildlife sanctuaries and urban greenways.

Wild and Scenic Rivers

 http://www.nps.gov/ccso/
wildrivers.htm

In 1968, the Congress passed the Wild and Scenic Rivers Act. This law declares that it is the policy of the United States to preserve selected rivers and their immediate surroundings because of their "outstandingly remarkable scenic, recreational, geologic, fish and wildlife, historic, cultural, or other similar values."

Over 150 rivers are protected by the Wild and Scenic Rivers Act from the Alagnak and Allegheny to the Yellow Dog and Yellowstone. Other notable rivers include the American, Chattooga, Missouri, Pecos, Rio Grande, Rogue, and Verde river. These Web pages offer an index into the rivers of the Act by state, as well as the text of the law itself.

Yosemite National Park

☞ http://www.yosemite.org/

The Yosemite Valley was first sighted by non-Indians in 1833 by Joseph Rutherford and his group of explorers. Twenty years later, another expedition visited. Soon word spread of the grandeur. Reading about this wonderland in San Francisco newspapers, James Mason Hutchings organized the first tourist party in 1855. Artist Thomas Ayres was on that trip and his sketches helped spread the word all the more. At first tourists arrived on foot and on horseback. Wagon roads came next. Hutchings operated the first hotel and became Yosemite's first publicist and entrepreneur.

In the 1860s pioneer conservationists Frederick Law Olmstead (the landscape architect who later designed New York's Central Park) and I.W. Raymond petitioned Congress for a bill to preserve Yosemite. Such a bill was passed, with then-President Abraham Lincoln signing the legislation on June 30, 1864. History has since told us this was a landmark event. Never before had any government anywhere set aside a parcel of land for its natural beauty to be preserved for public use for all time.

In addition to the home page of the Yosemite Association, elucidated earlier, also check out the beautiful collection of Yosemite images to be found at **http://www.talamasca.com/~cuccia/photos/yosemite**.

6

Great
Patriots

There are some men and women who loom above all others in our history. These men and women—great American patriots—have contributed significantly, above and beyond the call of duty, to make the United States a better place.

We all, depending on our varying political agendas, have different lists of who the great patriots of the United States actually are. To members of the John Birch Society, for example (**http://www.jbs.org**), Senator Joseph McCarthy is the great modern saint of American patriotism. To others he is nothing but a twisted and evil buffoon.

My own convoluted—perhaps naïve—idea of what constitutes a great American patriot is simply this: a patriot is someone who pursued what he or she perceived to be the right thing for the country despite all odds and despite all obstacles. My pantheon of American heroes, therefore, includes people who sometimes worked at cross-purposes. It includes slaveholders such as Thomas Jefferson and antislavery activists such as Frederick Douglass. It includes advocates of western expansion such as Theodore Roosevelt and the Native American heroes who fought that expansion, such as Sitting Bull and Crazy Horse.

Similarly, my list includes a relatively obscure collection of folks who dedicated their lives to making great contributions for the betterment of the United States, but whose names do not routinely get trotted out alongside those of Jefferson, Adams, Lincoln, and Roosevelt: people like A. Philip Randolph, Grace Hopper, and Hyman Rickover.

Looking for Crazy Horse

To my mind, one of the greatest Americans in every sense of the word is the chief of the Lakota Sioux, Crazy Horse (Tashunkewitko). Crazy Horse was born on the Republican River in the Black Hills about 1845.

He was noted for his lifelong opposition to the coming of white settlers to the northern plains. He fought against U.S. soldiers in the Fetterman Massacre of 1866 and the 1867 Wagon Box fight, which were both episodes in Red Cloud's War of 1866-68. Crazy Horse was the victor in many raids, among them the 1876 battles of the Rosebud River and Little Bighorn.

One of the last Sioux chiefs to surrender, he did so on May 6, 1877. In September of that year, Crazy Horse (Figure 6-1) was fatally stabbed by a reservation guard at Fort Robinson, Nebraska. After the murder, his people hid his body somewhere in the Black Hills, where it rests today undisturbed, its location known only to a few tribal elders.

Finding Crazy Horse on the World Wide Web is almost as hard as finding him in the Badlands. His name has been co-opted for so many beers, topless clubs, and strip joints that a word search using "Crazy Horse" yields hundreds of results that are completely unrelated to the great chief. It is an education, however, to see how names of great Americans who happen to be Native Americans can be abused routinely, while the names of other heroes are kept sacred. There are no topless discos named after Theodore Roosevelt.

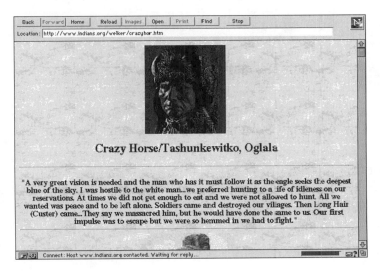

FIGURE 6-1
All about Crazy Horse
*(**http://www.indians.org/**
welker/crazyhor.htm)*

Faces in Stone

Theodore Roosevelt does, however, crown the ridge of Mount Rushmore (**http://www.state.sd.us/tourism/rushmore/album.htm**) in the Black Hills along with Abraham Lincoln, Thomas Jefferson, and George Washington. This monument to white men in the middle of the sacred Black Hills is thought by most Native Americans to be nothing less than an abomination.

As a counterbalance, Crazy Horse is slowly getting his own memorial in stone. In the town of Crazy Horse, South Dakota, a dedicated family has spent most of the past 50 years carving a mountain into what will eventually be the world's largest sculpture: Crazy Horse astride a stallion, pointing to his sacred lands (Figure 6-2).

But it could take another 50 years to finish the monument, which is so big that all four presidents from Mount Rushmore could easily fit inside Crazy Horse's head. Crazy Horse's outstretched arm will be almost as long as a football field. A five-room house could fit inside the nostril of the warrior's nose. At 563 feet high and 641 feet long, it is taller than

FIGURE 6-2

*All about the Crazy Horse sculpture (**http:// www.state.sd.us/ state/executive/tourism/ 20reason/crzy_hrs.htm**)*

the Washington Monument and almost twice the size of the Statue of Liberty.

The project was begun in 1948. It arose as a possibility when Sioux Chief Henry Standing Bear suggested it, telling Korczak Ziolkowski (a self-taught sculptor who worked on Mount Rushmore), "My fellow chiefs and I would like the white man to know the red man has great heroes, too."

Ziolkowski wound up buying the mountain along with 328 surrounding acres from the federal government. He died in 1982, but his wife and seven of the couple's ten children (along with their wives and children) today live at the bottom of the mountain and work year-round to pursue his dream. At the foot of the enormous sculpture they run the Indian Museum of North America, which attracts more than one million tourists a year and in so doing supports the sculpture project.

So far, 8.5 million tons of rock have been removed from the mountain. Crazy Horse's face is almost done.

Looking for Eleanor

One of the greatest Americans I can think of is not represented on the Web at all. Not only can I not find pages dedicated to Eleanor Dulles, but there are hardly any resources dealing with her equally remarkable brothers John Foster Dulles (Secretary of State under Eisenhower) and Allen Dulles (Director of the CIA). The Dulles who has the highest profile on the Web is Father Avery Dulles, SJ, son of John Foster Dulles and one of the most remarkable Catholic priests of our era. The closest we can get to any substantive cybermemory of Avery's father, uncle, and aunt, however, is the Web page of the Washington airport named in John Foster Dulles' honor (Figure 6-3).

FIGURE 6-3
Dulles Airport
(http://www.metwash airports.com/Dulles)

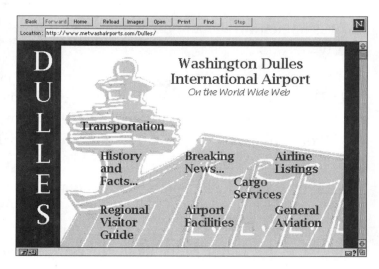

John Foster Dulles, the architect of "brinksmanship" in American foreign policy, died in 1959. Allen Dulles passed away in 1969. Eleanor, however, lived a long, long life and died just this past year, in late October of 1996, at the age of 101.

Mrs. Dulles was, by any measure, a formidable individual. A Bryn Mawr graduate with a Harvard doctorate in economics, she was the author of some dozen books including a study of international banking, a history of the French franc during the 1920s, and a charming memoir of her and her brothers and the way their lives were influenced by their grandfather John Foster (Secretary of State to Benjamin Harrison—**http://www2. whitehouse.gov/WH/glimpse/presidents/html/ww28.html**) and their uncle "Bert" Lansing (Secretary of State to Woodrow Wilson—**http://www2.whitehouse.gov/WH/glimpse/presidents/html/bh23.html**). Eleanor had no pretensions. She put on no airs. She held a variety of jobs: everything from teaching at Bryn Mawr (**http://www.brynmawr.edu**) to serving as payroll clerk for a hair net maker on Long Island to mastering the complexities of Cold War diplomacy at the State Department.

Eleanor joined the State Department in the 1940s and, by the end of that decade, was the resident expert and advocate for Berlin. Recognizing the strategic importance of the German capital in the Cold War, she maneuvered vast quantities of U.S. aid to the beleaguered city, and worked wonders in reducing unemployment and increasing production. She promoted the career of the socialist Mayor Willy Brandt as a symbol of West Berlin's all-party resistance to Communist tyranny.

She was indispensable. Nevertheless, John F. Kennedy (**http://www2. whitehouse.gov/WH/glimpse/presidents/html/jk35.html**), who did not like the Republican Dulles clan and who was noticeably uncomfortable in the presence of any woman who was not a bimbo, disposed of her. On one memorable afternoon, after Eleanor had served for more than twenty years, Secretary of State Dean Rusk (**http://www.cfcsc.dnd.ca/links/ bio/rusk.html**) walked into her office and announced, "The White House has asked me to get rid of you."

For anyone who knew her in her later years, Eleanor was a welcome reminder of another more tidy, proper, sensible age. She spoke with a precise, old-fashioned, upper-class diction. She bore a striking physical resemblance (including steel-rimmed glasses) to her brother John. She was a woman of historic talents and achievements but, as a casual victim of Camelot, has never been accorded the honors she deserved. One of these days maybe she'll make it onto the Web.

The Limits of the Web

What follows is an entirely subjective exercise. As I mentioned, we all have our different lists of exactly who the greatest patriots of the United States are. This is mine. It is predicated by my instincts and prejudices. It is also, however, predicated by what is available on the Web.

Of my great Americans, there are a number I cannot find anywhere on the Web. Not only is Eleanor Dulles anonymous in cyberspace, so too is turn-of-the-century naval historian and strategic theorist Alfred Thayer Mahan (one of the most important Americans of the last 150 years, although most Americans have never heard of him). Neither, surprisingly, can I find Paul Revere on the Web—at least there is no information on him of any measurable depth.

With these limitations in mind, let us see if those from my list of truly great Americans have managed to establish a presence in cyberspace.

✶ ✶ ✶ ✶ ✶ ✶ ✶ ✶

John Adams

  http://grid.let.rug.nl/~welling/
usa/adams.html

John Adams, the second president of the United States, was born in Massachusetts in 1735 and graduated from Harvard in 1755.

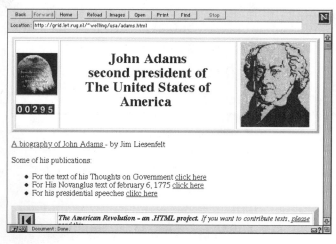

A lawyer, he opposed the Stamp Act and the Boston Port Act, was a delegate to the first Continental Congress (where he aided in drafting a petition to the king and a declaration of rights), and returned to the second Congress, during which he proposed Washington for military commander, all the while hoping to draw Virginia into greater support of Revolutionary policies.

He worked for independence, but disliked Tom Paine's plan of government suggested in *Common Sense*. In response to Paine, Adams set forth his own ideas in *Thoughts on Government* (1776).

From 1777 to 1779 Adams was a commissioner to France, and in the latter year also consulted the French government concerning peace negotiations with England. In 1782-83 he accompanied John Jay and Ben Franklin to England, where they negotiated the treaty of peace, and in 1785 he was appointed envoy to the Court of St. James (i.e., Ambassador to England).

Upon his return in 1788, he was elected the first Vice President of the United States. Although the office was no more demanding then than it is now, Adams occupied himself by working to further the fortunes of the Federalist agenda, a cause to which his old friend Jefferson was hostile. The old friendship turned cold for a while, indeed, throughout Adams' presidency and Jefferson's subsequent term in the same post. It was not until each man was in his dotage, in the 1820s, that their relationship revived.

Clara Barton

 http://oakview.fcps.edu/~jackson/html/ projects/barton.html

Here are pages devoted to the great American nurse of the Civil War and founder of the American Red Cross. She was born in 1821 and died in 1912. She served as the first president of the Red Cross for 23 years. In 1898, though more than 70 years old, she went to Cuba to help nurse American soldiers during the Spanish-American War. Nine years later, she went personally to help flood victims in Galveston, Texas.

Daniel Boone: Myth & Reality

 http://xroads.virginia.edu/~HYPER/ HNS/Boone/smithhome.html

Daniel Boone. Who is he? Well, of course, he is the man who made Fess Parker famous. Or is it the other way around? Where does the reality of the historical Boone converge with the legend, and where does he diverge from the legend? This insightful set of Web pages explores these questions.

Ralph Bunche

 http://www.kaiwan.com/ ~mcivr/bunche.html

Come to this page to consider the life and career of Ralph Bunche, African-American diplomat, United Nations official, and winner of the 1950 Nobel Peace Prize. With regard to the Nobel Prize, Bunche was the first black ever to receive it.

George Washington Carver

 http://www.invent.org/book/
book-text/23.html

George Washington Carver was born a slave in Diamond Grove, Missouri in 1860. While an infant during the Civil War, Carver was rescued from Confederate kidnappers. At 27 years of age, Carver entered Simpson College in Indianola, Iowa. Later, Carver transferred to the Iowa Agricultural College (which is now known as Iowa State University) where he earned graduate and post-graduate degrees in agriculture.

Carver served as the director of agricultural studies at the Tuskegee Institute where he developed methods for rotating crops to preserve and replenish the soil's nutrients and nitrogen content. Carver encouraged the production of peanuts and other legumes as rotation crops because of their beneficial effect on replenishing soil content. To further this end, Carver developed many different uses for peanuts—among them synthetic rubbers, paving materials, peanut oils, printing ink, and others.

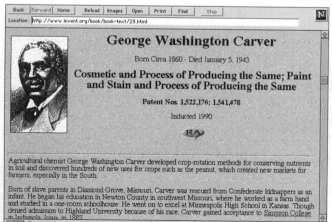

Another very good link for information on Carver is that of the national monument of Carver's birthplace: **http://www.coax. net/people/LWF/carver.htm**.

William Ellery Channing

 http://gamma.is.tcu.edu/~wells/
wecc/indexwecc.htm

Born in Rhode Island in 1780, William Ellery Channing became pastor of a Boston Congregational church in 1803. In his famous sermon at the ordination of Jared Sparks (1819), he clearly broke with orthodox Calvinism. From this date he was considered an apostle of Unitarianism and the leading opponent of Calvinism in the northeast. As a stimulating force in the intellectual life of Massachusetts, he did much to prepare the way for Transcendentalism and other advanced social and cultural movements. His idealism and opposition to dogmatism may be observed in his sermons, many of which are available here at this Website in digital reprints.

Clarence Darrow

 http://www.brokersys.com/
~corny51/darrow/darrwpic.htm

Visit this Web page to learn about the famed early 20th century attorney of the Scopes Trial and the Leopold and Loeb murder case. Darrow was also a terrific orator and often toured the country debating with a man whom I knew fairly well in his old age, Scott Nearing.

Frederick Douglass

 http://education.ucdavis.edu/
new/stc/lesson/socstud/
railroad/Douglas.htm

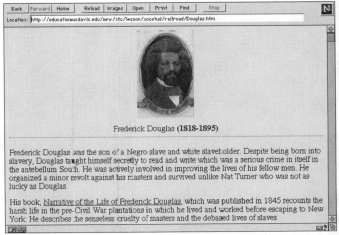

Frederick Douglas (1818-1895)

Frederick Douglas was the son of a Negro slave and white slaveholder. Despite being born into slavery, Douglas taught himself secretly to read and write which was a serious crime in itself in the antebellum South. He was actively involved in improving the lives of his fellow men. He organized a minor revolt against his masters and survived unlike Nat Turner who was not as lucky as Douglas.

His book, Narrative of the Life of Frederick Douglas, which was published in 1845 recounts the harsh life in the pre-Civil War plantations in which he lived and worked before escaping to New York. He describes the senseless cruelty of masters and the debased lives of slaves.

This informative set of pages on black abolitionist Frederick Douglass includes the complete text of the first of his three autobiographies, entitled *Narrative of the Life of Frederick Douglass*. The one problem with these Web pages is that whoever put them up—someone at U.C. Davis, I presume—has no idea how to spell the name "Douglass."

Born into slavery in 1817, Douglass escaped into Massachusetts in 1838 where he was employed as a lecturer by antislavery societies. He published *Narrative of the Life of Frederick Douglass* in 1845 after which, fearing capture as a fugitive slave, he spent several years in England and Ireland, returning to purchase his freedom and establish the antislavery newspaper *North Star*.

Douglass organized two regiments of blacks during the Civil War, although he himself did not fight, and continued to labor for his people during the Reconstruction, later serving as secretary of the Santo Domingo Commission (1871), marshal of the District of Columbia (1877-81), recorder of deeds for the District (1881-86), and minister to Haiti (1889-91). Although his first book is his most famous, he wrote

two other autobiographies: *My Bondage and My Freedom* (1855) and *Life and Times of Frederick Douglass* (1881).

W.E.B. DuBois

 http://www.erols.com/tdpedu/
dubois/dubois2.htm

An outstanding writer, critic, historian, and social critic, W.E.B. DuBois was born in Massachusetts in 1868 and received a Ph.D. from Harvard in 1895, after which he became a professor of economics and history at Atlanta University (1897-1910).

DuBois was a leader of various social reform movements designed to improve the condition of black citizens of the United States. In 1909 he was one of the organizers of the National Association for the Advancement of Colored People, which in 1948 he disavowed as being too conservative and lethargic.

Through it all, he wrote books—dozens of them. His significant contributions include *The Suppression of the African Slave*

Trade to the U.S.A., The Philadelphia Negro, John Brown, The Negro, and the novels *The Dark Princess* and *The Dark Flame: A Trilogy*.

In 1958, frustrated by the failure of the United States to deal with the problem of race, DuBois accepted the Lenin International Peace Prize in Moscow. Later, in 1961, he joined the Communist party. In 1962, the year before his death at age 95, he moved to Ghana, where he died.

This Web page, dedicated to a full biography of DuBois, contains tremendous resources through which you can get to know a great, if often neglected, American.

Dwight David Eisenhower

 http://www.dmi.usma.edu/ike.htm

Dwight David Eisenhower was my father's great hero: the warrior statesman under whom my father and so many others served during World War II. Dad considered Ike to have been as good a president as he'd been a general. This is a sentiment with which most historians are beginning to agree. Another excellent Eisenhower site, by the way, is on the White House server—**http://www2.whitehouse.gov/WH/glimpse/presidents/html/de34.html**.

Grace Hopper: Mother of Computing

 http://www.sheridan.org/~win95gal/grace.htm

After graduating from Vasser Phi Beta Kappa, Grace Hopper went on to receive M.A. and Ph.D. degrees in mathematics from Yale. In 1943 she entered the U.S. Naval Reserve and was commissioned as lieutenant. At the same time, as a senior mathematician at Sperry Rand, she worked on the first commercial computer. After be-

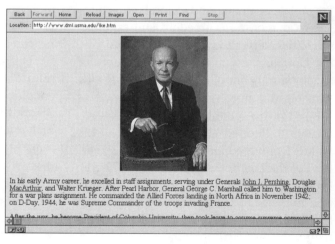

In his early Army career, he excelled in staff assignments, serving under Generals John J. Pershing, Douglas MacArthur, and Walter Krueger. After Pearl Harbor, General George C. Marshall called him to Washington for a war plans assignment. He commanded the Allied Forces landing in North Africa in November 1942; on D-Day, 1944, he was Supreme Commander of the troops invading France.

After the war, he became President of Columbia University, then took leave to assume supreme command

ing promoted at Sperry to the newly-defined post of Director of Automatic Programming, she published the first paper on compilers in 1952. Throughout her long, parallel military and civilian careers, Grace Hopper remained at the forefront of the development of American computer technology. She was born in the gas lamp days of 1906 and died in the cyberworld of 1992: a world she did much to help illuminate.

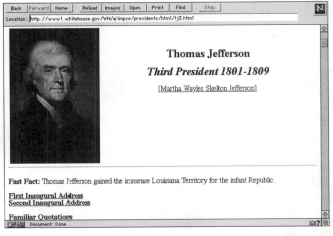

Thomas Jefferson
Third President 1801-1809
[Martha Wayles Skelton Jefferson]

Fast Fact: Thomas Jefferson gained the immense Louisiana Territory for the infant Republic.

First Inaugural Address
Second Inaugural Address
Familiar Quotations

Thomas Jefferson

 http://www1.whitehouse.gov/WH/glimpse/presidents/html/tj3.html

Born in 1743, Thomas Jefferson was the son of a prominent Virginia family. In his early manhood he studied at William and Mary College, practiced law, and served in the Virginia House of Burgesses. From the outset of his public life he associated himself with the aggressive anti-British factions, and he made an important contribution to the Revolutionary cause in *A Summary View of the Rights of British America* (1774), a brilliant exposition contending that Parliament had no authority in the colonies, whose only bond with England was allegiance to the same king.

As a member of the Continental Congress (1775-76), Jefferson was almost wholly responsible for the spirit and phrasing of the Declaration of Independence. In the Virginia House of Burgesses (1776-79) and as governor (1779-81) he attempted to translate the ideals of this document into reality by advocating laws which would make impossible the maintenance of a landed aristocracy or an established church. His revision of the state laws and constitution embodied liberal policies, not all of which could be made effective, concerning education, religious freedom, economic equality, antislavery, and other humanitarian reforms.

He went on, of course, to serve as our third President and to found the University of Virginia. He died on the same day as his friend and sometime political adversary John Adams: July 4, 1826.

Barbara Jordan

 http://www.kaiwan.com/~mcivr/jordan.html

Who can forget Barbara Jordan, with her low gravelly voice and her uncompromising intelligence, sitting on the House Judiciary Committee panel looking into the Watergate affair? After Sam Ervin's, hers is the personality that stands out the most from that affair.

Martin Luther King, Jr.

 http://www.seattletimes.com/mlk/man/MLKtimeline.html

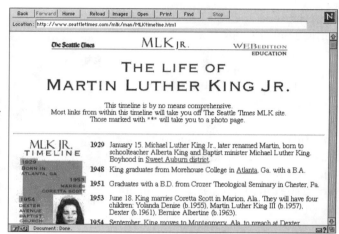

This excellent Web page presents a hypertext timeline of Martin Luther King, Jr.'s life, complete with clickable links to related resources where appropriate. Here you get a complete biography of Dr. King, many photographs, speech transcripts, and much more.

Abraham Lincoln

 http://www1.whitehouse.gov/WH/glimpse/presidents/html/al16.html

Come to the official White House pages for our sixteenth president and access a detailed biography, great image files, as well as links to Abraham Lincoln quotes and speeches. There is also a clickable link to

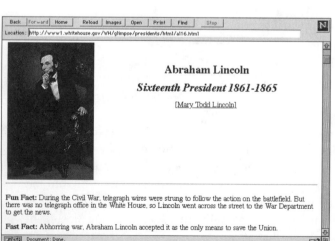

details about Mary Todd Lincoln, the president's irascible and sometimes irritating wife.

Thurgood Marshall

 http://www.kaiwan.com/~mcivr/marshall.html

Thurgood Marshall was the first black associate justice of the Supreme Court. Before being appointed to the Court in the mid-60s, he served two years as Solicitor General of the United States.

Rosa Parks

 http://www.kaiwan.com/~mcivr/parks.html

She was too tired, after a long day at work, to get up from her seat in a Montgomery, Alabama bus, so she started a revolution instead. When she refused to give up her seat to a white passenger, she was arrested and jailed. The rest is history.

A. Philip Randolph

http://www.kaiwan.com/~mcivr/
randolph.html

Born in 1889, A. Philip Randolph is most famous for organizing the Brotherhood of Sleeping Car Porters, a union which he led in a fight against the powerful Pullman Company for better wages and working conditions. He also worked diligently to end racial discrimination in the federal government and military.

Hyman Rickover

http://www2.gdi.net/~rjtree/
submarine/rickover.htm

Hyman Rickover, the father of the nuclear Navy, served for over 63 years under 13 presidents and died in 1986. In a dangerous world where strategic prowess on the high seas is absolutely necessary, Hyman Rickover was the man who spearheaded the drive to bring the United States Navy (sometimes kicking and screaming) into the technology of the modern era.

Sally Ride

http://sdphul.ucsd.edu/dept/pr/
faculty/cssr.html

Sally Ride was, of course, America's first woman in space. She also served on the Presidential Commission investigating the explosion of the Space Shuttle Challenger. Dr. Ride is today a physicist on the faculty of the University of California, San Diego. She is also Director of the California Space Institute, a research institute of the University of California.

Franklin Delano Roosevelt

http://www2.whitehouse.gov/WH/
glimpse/presidents/html/fr32.html

FDR served as President from 1932 until his death in office in 1945. He will always hold the honor of having been elected

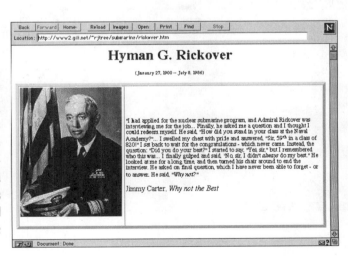

to the Presidency more than any other man ever had, or ever will. The first amendment to the U.S. Constitution to be ratified after FDR's death was the twenty-second amendment which set the maximum number of presidential terms at two.

Prior to serving as President, Roosevelt served as a New York State Senator, Assistant Secretary of the Navy, and the Governor of New York. He took the office of President at the depth of the Great Depression and launched copious social programs and policies—many of which persist to this day.

Among those programs and policies were an enormous workfare program that helped the country pull itself out of the Great Depression, the abandonment of the gold standard, deficit federal spending, the Social Security system, the progressive tax system, and government regulation of commerce.

Canonized by some and disdained by others, FDR will always be known as one of the most influential and controversial Presidents of the 20th century.

He died on April 12, 1945 at Warm Springs, Georgia, and is buried at Hyde Park.

Theodore Roosevelt

 http://www.abcland.com/
~jwiedman/tr/

Administered by the indomitable Jim Wiedman, this remarkable set of pages contains links to the rich resources of the Internet devoted to one of the greatest Americans who ever lived: Theodore Roosevelt.

I must admit I have a bias here. I have just finished a book about TR and his family during the First World War. I am a member in good standing of the Theodore Roosevelt Association. And a few of the Roosevelts are friends of mine, most notably Tweed Roosevelt, a great-grandson of TR.

That being said, however, who can argue that TR—naturalist, hunter, cowboy, Civil Service Commissioner, New York Police Commissioner, Assistant Secretary of the Navy, Rough Rider colonel, Governor of New York, Vice President and President of the United States, historian, and author—was not a dynamic personality? When he died in 1919, he left as his legacy a ringing example of just how life should be lived—to the fullest.

Theodore Roosevelt, Jr.

 http://www.matinecock.org/trjr.htm

The achievements of Theodore Roosevelt, Jr. have long been overshadowed by those of his illustrious father. Ted served with distinction in World War I and attained the rank of Brigadier General in World War II. In between wars he was Governor General of the Philippines, Governor of Puerto Rico, Assistant Secretary of the Navy, an editor at Doubleday, and Chairman of American Express. He died of a heart attack in 1944 at age 57, just weeks after he landed at Normandy with one of the first assault teams on D-Day.

Sitting Bull

 http://www.indians.org/welker/sittbull.htm

Born in Grand River, South Dakota, Sitting Bull (1831-1890), the Lakota Sioux medicine man and chief, is generally considered to have been the last Sioux to surrender to the United States government. Known among the Sioux as "Tatanka Iyotake," Sitting Bull, along with fellow chiefs Crazy Horse and Gall, bravely defended his homeland.

In 1876, Sitting Bull, Crazy Horse, and Gall attacked and defeated General George Custer at Little Bighorn. After the battle, Sitting Bull fled to Canada where he spent

"Sitting Bull"

nearly five years until his return in 1881. Upon his return, Sitting Bull spent two years in prison for the battle of Little Bighorn—which was clearly in violation of the treaty between the U.S. and the Sioux.

In 1885, Sitting Bull joined Wild Bill Hickock's (Buffalo Bill's) Wild West Show and toured Europe with Hickock and the company. Sitting Bull was killed in 1890 by Indian tribal police during a political scuffle.

Read on here for much more detail about the colorful life of Chief Sitting Bull.

Harriet Tubman

 http://www.kaiwan.com/~mcivr/tubman.html

Did the fabled Underground Railroad have a more famous conductor than Harriet Tubman? I think not. She was born circa 1820 in Maryland. In 1848 she escaped to Philadelphia, where she embarked on a long slave-saving career during which she rescued thousands. At one point the reward offered for her capture totaled $40,000. She died in 1913.

Booker T. Washington

 http://www.asc.edu/
archives/famous/
b_wash.html

This page chronicles the life and career of Booker T. Washington, who rose from humble beginnings to found the Tuskegee Institute.

Booker T. Washington was the first black to be entertained formally at the White House. When President Theodore Roosevelt issued the invitation, he knew full well that he was making a statement that the country as a whole would notice.

A few weeks after Washington's visit to the White House, he sent President Roosevelt a newspaper clipping. The article reported on Washington's meeting with an old Southern Colonel, a proud son of the Confederacy.

"Suh, I am glad to meet you," the Colonel said to Washington. "I've always wanted to shake your hand, suh. I think, suh, you're the greatest man in America."

Washington replied, modestly, that he thought President Roosevelt was the greatest man in America.

"NO suh!" roared the old man. "Not by a jugful. I used to think so, but since he invited *you* to dinner, I think he's a scoundrel."

1856-1915
Educator

Roosevelt loved the story. "I think that it is one of the most delightful things I ever read," he told Washington. "It is almost too good to believe."

George Washington

 http://www.history.org/people/
washhdr.htm

He was our first warrior-president. He led the nation not only out of domination by the British, but also towards constitutional democracy. He is aptly known as the father of our country. Come to these Web pages for a biography of the man who died in December of 1799, along with copies of his first and second inaugural addresses, portraits, and more.

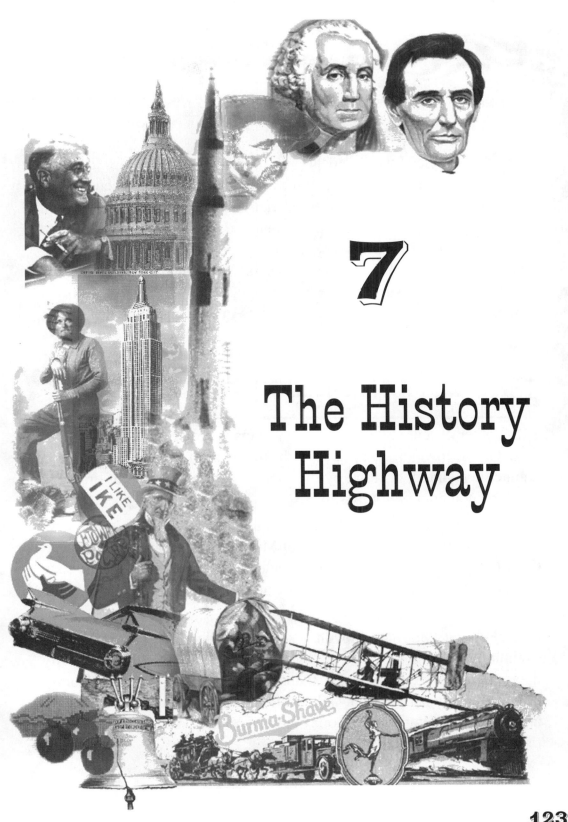

7

The History Highway

In this chapter I want to deal with the haunted places of our shared American past. These are places where battles have been fought, where treacherous deeds have been transacted, where shots have been fired. These are places where great men and women have walked, and where some lie buried. Some of these sites have been mapped and sanctified and made into museums. Others, just as interesting, have been largely lost to us: such as the building in Washington, D.C., now a Chinese restaurant, where the conspirators in the Lincoln assassination met and plotted.

A Macabre Lincoln Story

Another obscure place of history is a mausoleum in Oak Hill Cemetery, Georgetown: a tomb owned by cousins of mine. I know it is haunted—haunted, at least, by the shadows and memories of dramatic moonlit moments, if not by spirits.

As I've mentioned elsewhere in this book, on my mother's side I am descended from the Carroll family of Maryland which included Charles Carroll, signer of the Declaration of Independence. Another of this clan, William Thomas Carroll, was a clerk of the Supreme Court during the Civil War and a friend of Abraham Lincoln's.

In February of 1862, Lincoln's son Willie died. The family planned eventually to bring the body of the boy back to Springfield, but initially they wanted to keep him near them in Washington. William Thomas Carroll, who owned a burial vault (Vault #292, overlooking Rock Creek), at Oak Hill Cemetery, offered one of the crypts in the tomb as a temporary resting place for Willie (Figure 7-1).

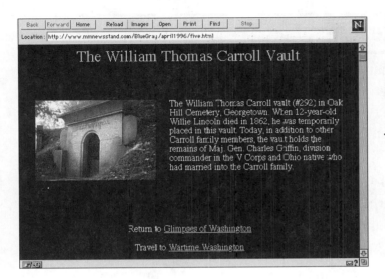

FIGURE 7-1

The William Thomas Carrol vault, Oak Hill Cemetery, Georgetown (http://www.mmnewsstand. com/BlueGray/april1996/ five.html)

The funeral was held in the East Room (**http://www.whitehouse. gov/WH/glimpse/tour/html/east.html**) of the White House, after which Willie was interred in the Carroll vault. As this was a temporary interment, the crypt in which he lay was not sealed. It was simply covered over with a board and then the gate was closed and locked.

Soon, rumors began to float around Washington that Lincoln had been back to the tomb twice to have Willie's coffin opened so that he could look upon him. It seemed he could not bear the idea of his boy being left alone in the dark isolation of the cold tomb. Lincoln only stopped the nocturnal visits after Dr. Francis Vinton, of New York's Trinity Church (**http://www.theinsider.com/NYC/Photos/trinity2.htm**), visited the White House and criticized the President for behaving "like a heathen." He would not be so concerned with his son's crypt, said Vinton, if he truly believed that Willie now lived with God in Paradise. After that, Lincoln's moonlit visits to the tomb stopped.

Three years later, after Lincoln's assassination, Willie was taken from the Carroll family vault and placed aboard the funeral train that would carry both father and son back to Illinois.

Finding Uncle Jimmy

In an earlier chapter of this book on American sports resources I mentioned that my great-uncle Jimmy Torrens, former Congressman, was buried at Gate of Heaven Cemetery in Hawthorne, New York, not far from Babe Ruth and Jimmy Cagney.

Before writing that paragraph, I verified my memory of where Uncle Jimmy was planted by using *The Political Graveyard: A Database of Historic Cemeteries* (Figure 7-2), created and maintained by Lawrence Kestenbaum and found on the World Wide Web.

The site is fantastic. No matter how esoteric the politician you are looking for, he or she is bound to be here. Sure, of course you've got all your majordomos: all your presidents and supreme court justices and so forth. But even the fringe politicians are here in abundance (for example, Uncle Jimmy!).

You can search the database by name, by state and country, or by cemetery name. You can search by specific political families, or by birth

FIGURE 7-2

The Political Graveyard
(*http://polygon.intranet.org/tpg/*)

or death years. This is your resource for finding more than 12,000 political graves nationwide—most of them lost, lonesome, windswept remnants of history.

Enough of Graves

There is, of course, much more to history than tombs and graves. There are places, as I indicated at the start of this chapter, that are haunted in a much more sophisticated manner than your standard tomb, crypt, or grave. There are places that are haunted by the passion of great historic events.

We know all the standard historical sites across the country: the Alamo, Ford's Theater, and so on. Most of these have Web pages, which I will elucidate later in this chapter. But first let's consider some more obscure historical places and personalities.

I am always intrigued by forgotten, lost places where history happened—places a few hundreds yards from where cars on a highway zip by, their owners not realizing they are within a stone's throw of where John Wilkes Booth died or Theodore Roosevelt once hunted.

Consider Troutbeck, a rural inn and conference center in Amenia, New York. The editor and social critic Joel Springarn once called this place home, and it is where the NAACP was founded. Guests here through the years included W.E.B. DuBois and Sinclair Lewis, the latter of whom called the huge lawn of the estate not a lawn at all but rather "a grass grown cathedral." Before Springarn, the place was owned by poet and farmer Myron Benton, who often entertained his friend John Burroughs here. Far from the house, in a distant field, there is a forgotten boulder that can hardly be seen today it is so covered with mulberry bushes. Here, in the early 1860s, Benton and Burroughs first read the poems of Walt Whitman. Here, a few years later, Benton entertained Oscar Wilde with a picnic lunch. Today's visitors at Troutbeck, attending conferences and business seminars, have no clue of the place's fascinating history. At least, there is no hint of it on the inn's Web page (Figure 7-3).

Consider also a shopping mall on Long Island called Roosevelt Field. It is your typical shopping center: a crowded collection of shops and stores surrounded by acres upon acres of parking spaces. It is the quintessential hallmark of suburbia.

One might assume that the shopping center is named in dubious honor of either Theodore or Franklin Roosevelt. One might assume further that it is more likely named after Theodore. After all, Theodore lived on Long Island and there is twisted tradition on Long Island of naming shopping centers after famous native sons. (Another shopping center is called the Walt Whitman Mall.)

But in fact, Roosevelt Field is named for neither Theodore nor Franklin Roosevelt. During World War I, there was an airfield on this spot where young pilots were trained for combat. One of the trainees was Quentin Roosevelt, the youngest son of Theodore Roosevelt, who used

FIGURE 7-3
*Troutbeck (**http://www.
troutbeck.com**)*

to commute down here every day from the family home at Sagamore Hill, in Oyster Bay. After Quentin died in aerial combat in July of 1918, the field where he trained was named in his honor. When the field was later given over for a shopping center, the name lingered. Brave Quentin, however, has been lost in the shuffle.

Another largely forgotten place in history is the home of the terrorist and martyred abolitionist John Brown (Figure 7-4). This is in the Adirondack Mountains at North Elba, New York (near Lake Placid—**http://www.lake-placid.ny.us**). Few people visit this lonely spot. When I was a child, my history-loving father occasionally brought me to this haunted place from our nearby summer cabin on the shores of Lake Champlain at Westport, New York.

It is to those silent brooding trips, including stops at the nearby gravesite of Brown and many of his men, that I attribute my interest in history. The second history book I ever wrote—*The Secret Six*—was a study of the six wealthy abolitionists of Boston and New York who bankrolled John Brown's doomed 1859 raid at Harpers Ferry, Virginia.

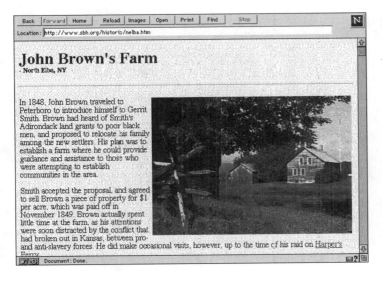

FIGURE 7-4

*John Brown's Adirondack farm (**http://www.sbh.org/ historic/nelba.htm**)*

The Secret Six were a fascinating crowd.

Most Americans know that John Brown's raid on Harpers Ferry—a raid Brown believed would ignite a bloody slave revolution—was one of the events that sparked the Civil War. But few know the story of how Brown was covertly aided by a circle of prosperous and privileged northeasterners who supplied him with money and weapons and, before the raid, even hid him in their homes while authorities sought Brown on a murder charge.

The Secret Six included Thomas Wentworth Higginson (minister and author), Samuel Gridley Howe (world famous physician and husband of poetess Julia Ward Howe, author of "The Battle Hymn of the Republic"), Theodore Parker (the Unitarian minister whose rhetoric helped shape Lincoln's Gettysburg Address), Franklin Sanborn (educator and close friend of Emerson and Thoreau), George Luther Stearns (a wealthy Massachusetts manufacturer and importer), and Gerrit Smith.

Smith was the son of Peter Smith (Figure 7-5), the partner of the first John Jacob Astor. As such, Gerrit was one of the richest men in North America.

FIGURE 7-5
Gerrit Smith
Virtual Museum
(**http://www.sbh.org/ historic/gsmith.htm**)

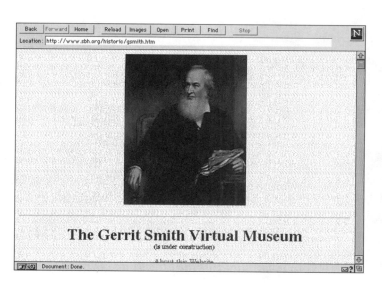

It is men like Smith and places like the John Brown farm—esoteric people and equally esoteric places that linger at the frayed edges of great historical events and achievements—that sometimes form the most interesting elements of the American saga. Thank goodness we can find so many of them on the Web.

The History Highway

There are lots of fascinating sideroads off the history highway that is the Web. This chapter is your map to them. We've got plenty of gasoline in the modem. We've got a box lunch packed. Let's go explore some forgotten—and some not so forgotten—trails.

Adams Memorial

 http://www.valley.net/~stgaud/adams.html

One of the most haunting sites in Washington, D.C. is the bronze funerary sculpture by August Saint-Gaudens commissioned by Henry Adams for his wife Clover after her suicide. Located in Washington's Rock Creek Cemetery, it is sometimes called "Nirvana." Adams called it "The Peace of God."

Adams National Historic Site

 http://www.nps.gov/adam/

Located in the City of Quincy, Norfolk County, Massachusetts (approximately ten miles south of Boston), the Adams National Historic Site was the home of John Adams, Abigail Adams, and John Quincy Adams (and the childhood home of Henry Adams). The place is comprised of 12 historic structures on 12.59 acres.

The Alamo

http://www.dcci.com/San_Antonio/Alamo.html

Learn all about the building and the battle. As we all remember, among the martyrs of this fight was none other than the legendary Davy Crockett. Another interesting footnote: Theodore Roosevelt's Rough Riders trained within sight of the Alamo in 1898.

American Memory at the Library of Congress

 http://lcweb2.loc.gov/

American Memory, according to its advertising, "consists of primary source and archival materials relating to American culture and history. These historical collections are the key contribution of the Library of Congress to the National Digital Library. Most of these offerings are from the Library's unparalleled special collections." Now you can search through thousands of prints and photos, documents, motion pictures, and sound recordings.

American Museum of Natural History

 http://www.amnh.org/

Natural history is history also. Of course, the American Museum documents natural history all around the globe, but there is

no shortage of information about American wildlife to be found here.

Boston African-American National Historic Site

 http://www.nps.gov/boaf/

At the heart of Boston's prestigious Beacon Hill is the Boston African-American National Historic Site. This park contains fifteen buildings dating from before the Civil War relating to the history of Boston's 19th century black community. The buildings include a meeting house—which is the oldest standing black church in the U.S. The buildings are connected by the Black Heritage Trail: a nearly two-mile trek whereupon stands Augustus Saint-Gaudens' memorial to Robert Gould Shaw and the all-black 54th Massachusetts Regiment.

Boston National Historical Park

 http://www.nps.gov/bost/

Walk Boston's Freedom Trail and discover the heroic and famous Bostonians who fought for American independence. This Website describes in detail the sixteen historic sites which make up the 2.5-mile trail, including Boston's Old State House, the Old South Meeting House, Faneuil Hall,

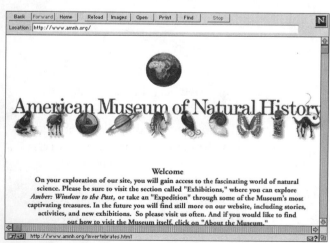

the Paul Revere House, the Old North Church, the Bunker Hill Monument, and the Charlestown Navy Yard.

Bulloch Hall, Roswell, GA: Home of Theodore Roosevelt's Maternal Ancestors

 http://www.ethom.com/roswell/ hisites.htm

Built in 1840 in Roswell, Georgia, Bulloch Hall was the home of Maj. James Bulloch, his wife Martha, and their children. Bulloch was the grandson of Georgia Revolutionary Governor Archibald Bulloch. Among the Bulloch children was the daughter, Mittie, who married Theodore Roosevelt, Sr. in the dining room of the home in December of 1853. Little did those at the wedding suspect that the union would produce a United States President, Theo-

dore Roosevelt. The wedding is reenacted each year in the month of December, and the building is on the National Register of Historic Places serving as a museum open to the public.

Bunker Hill Monument

 http://charlestown.ma.us/ monument.html

Learn about both the monument and the battle via these informative Web pages. Of course, this was a turning point in the Revolution. Today the site forms a vital part of the Freedom Trail in Boston which includes the home of Paul Revere, the site of the Boston Massacre, and other important locations.

Civil War Center: Louisiana State University, Baton Rouge

 http://www.cwc.lsu.edu/ index.htm

This is one-stop shopping for links to *everything* that is relevant about the American Civil War on the Internet. I mean everything. Here you'll find bibliographies, battle histories, data on uniforms, and much more.

Custer and the Little Bighorn Home Page

 http://pages.prodigy.com/custer/

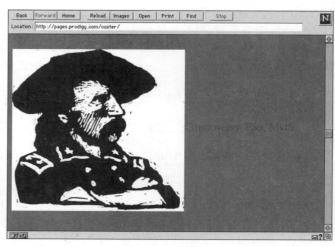

Here you'll find complete biographical details on Custer, details of the battle, Sioux accounts of the fight, and more. Another excellent page devoted to the famous battle is that of the Custer Battlefield Historical & Museum Association at **http://www.tntmedia.com/custer/**.

Dead Presidents Tour

 http://www.csn.net/~mhand/Presidents/index.html#index

Manus Hand has an interesting hobby. He ferrets out the gravesites of our presidents and has himself photographed with the various Chiefs of State, or at least on top or beside or near them. With each grave photo he also provides links to resources for the president in question.

Ford's Theatre Virtual Tour

 http://www.nps.gov/foth/index2.htm

On the night of April 14th, 1865, President Abraham Lincoln was shot in Ford's Theatre by John Wilkes Booth. The President died in the early hours of April 15th in the small back bedroom of a boarding house across the street. The theater in which Lincoln was shot and the house where he died are preserved today as Ford's Theatre National Historic Site.

Gettysburg Battlefield

 http://www.gettysbg.com/

Make a virtual visit to the site of the greatest battle ever fought on the continent of North America. This impressive Website is nearly as expansive as the battlefield itself, reflecting hundreds of images and stories from that fateful altercation.

The Ulysses S. Grant Network Home Page (and Grant's Tomb)

 http://www.css.edu/mkelsey/gppg.html

A number of historians—myself included—as well as numerous descendants of U.S. Grant have a crazy idea. Our proposal is that the final resting place of U.S. Grant on the west side of Manhattan not be a place where junkies swap needles and hobos squat in the hallways to relieve themselves. Call us crazy. Call us Puritans. Call us intolerant. We don't care. We still think a presidential gravesite should be no less sacred than any other gravesite. Via these Web pages you can find out lots of information about Grant the general and president while at the same time learning what you can do to help insure the integrity of the tomb—which has its centennial in 1997. This year also marks Grant's 175th birthday.

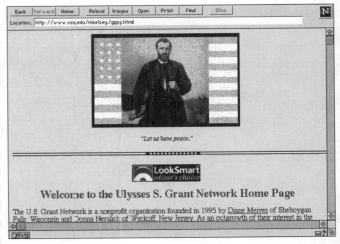

"Let us have peace."

Welcome to the Ulysses S. Grant Network Home Page

The U.S. Grant Network is a nonprofit organization founded in 1995 by Diane Meives of Sheboygan Falls, Wisconsin and Donna Neralich of Wyckoff, New Jersey. As an outgrowth of their interest in the

Harpers Ferry, West Virginia

 http://www.nps.gov/hafe/hf_visit.htm

Located at the confluence of the Potomac and Shenandoah rivers in the states of West Virginia, Virginia, and Maryland, Harpers Ferry National Historical Park is ensconced among our sacred national treasures for more than the single event for which it is best known. In fact, Harpers Ferry is historical for a number of events that have shaped our nation's history. Besides John Brown's famous raid in 1859, Harpers Ferry was the site of historic manufacturing technological innovations, the first successful American railroad, the largest surrender of Federal troops to the South during the Civil War, and other historic firsts.

Herbert Hoover Presidential Library

 http://sunsite.unc.edu/lia/president/hoover.html

He is one of the most underrated presidents in history, and he is one of my favorites. Hoover was not only a great president, he was also a great humanitarian. And, to his credit, he was of absolutely no relation to the FBI's J. Edgar Hoover.

Stonewall Jackson Home

 http://www.nps.gov/frsp/js.htm

The home of Stonewall Jackson, in Lexington, Virginia, is now a museum open to the public. Jackson is the Confederate general who got his nickname for his brave stand at First Manassas and who is best known for his leadership in the Valley Campaign of 1862. He died in May of 1863 as a result of wounds received at the Battle of

Chancellorsville, during which he was mistakenly shot by his own men. The house where he died is now the Stonewall Jackson shrine administered by the National Park Service.

John F Kennedy Birthplace

 http://www.nps.gov/jofi/

This is the birthplace of John F. Kennedy: 83 Beals Street, Brookline, Massachusetts. The home is preserved as it was when Kennedy was a young child there with original furnishings and memorabilia.

Lincoln Home, Springfield

 http://www.netins.net/showcase/
creative/lincoln/sites/home.htm

This is the home of Abraham and Mary Lincoln in Springfield.

This beautiful Greek Revival-style house has been carefully restored to its 1860 glory. Abe and Mary bought the home in 1844 for $1,200 from the man who had married them just two years earlier—the Rev. Charles Dresser.

During the seventeen years that the Lincoln's owned the home, they enlarged it from a single story to two full stories. Upon winning the 1860 Republican presidential nomination,

Lincoln received a delegation of Republican Party officials in the parlor of the home, and until the Lincolns left for Washington, the house was used for all manner of parties and celebrations.

The place is now owned by the National Park Service, which maintains yet another Website dedicated to the structure: **http://www.nps.gov/liho/**.

Lincoln Log Cabin

http://www.state.il.us/HPA/
LINCLOG.HTM

No, I'm not talking about the cabin in Kentucky which is said to be the birthplace of Abraham Lincoln, which it isn't. And I'm not talking about the Illinois cabin where he purportedly spent his childhood. I'm talking about the Goosenest Prairie cabin where Tom and Sarah Lincoln (Abe Lincoln's stepmother) lived after Abe was grown and gone. They came here in 1840, when

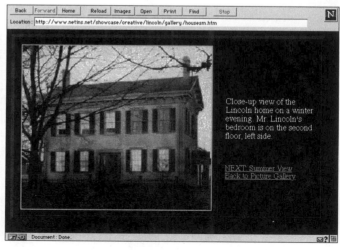

Close-up view of the Lincoln home on a winter evening. Mr. Lincoln's bedroom is on the second floor, left side.

NEXT: Summer View
Back to Picture Gallery

Lincoln was already in Springfield lawyering. Thomas lived here until his death in 1851, and Sarah was here until her death in 1869, four years after the demise of her stepson.

In 1845, while Abe lived in a fine home in Springfield, the two-room Goosenest Prairie home of his parents was home to as many as eighteen people, including Sarah's son John D. Johnston, his wife Mary, their six children, Sarah's daughter Matilda, her husband Squire, and their six children. The scene was one of abject squalor, and it was one Lincoln was ashamed of. He took no pride in his humble roots. He never allowed his wife or sons to meet their humble kin who lived only fifty miles away from them. In fact, on regular trips to visit Mary Lincoln's family in Kentucky, the Lincolns came within five miles of Goosenest Prairie, but never once did Lincoln propose to stop there so that his children could meet their grandparents.

For many years, historians blamed Mary Lincoln for the distance between the Lincolns of Springfield and the Lincolns of Illinois. However, late evidence shows that it was Abe himself who insisted his sons not visit Goosenest Prairie. He himself, however, was in the habit of stopping by there on occasion, often bearing gifts. In the years after Lincoln's death, Mary Lincoln voluntarily continued Lincoln's habit of sending money and gifts to Sarah Lincoln. When Robert Lincoln came to Springfield for his father's funeral in 1865, he met for the first time many of his Hanks and Johnston cousins who'd come to town for the occasion, and subsequently traveled to Goosenest Prairie to make the acquaintance of Sarah.

The cabin at this site is not original. The original cabin was taken apart and brought to the Columbia Exposition in Chicago in 1892, after which it was lost. The cabin at the site today is a reconstruction based on photographs. It is furnished with items which are genuine to the period during which the Lincolns lived on the homestead, but none of them are known to have been owned by Tom and Sarah.

The Lincoln Tomb

http://www.state.il.us/HPA/
LINCTOMB.HTM

When Lincoln was laid away in a Springfield tomb in May of 1865, he was not to rest in peace. For starters, the modest receiving tomb at Oak Ridge Cemetery, Springfield, was just a temporary stopping-off place. Everyone knew from the start that Lincoln—and his son Willie—were just to tarry here for a few years while a new, enormous mausoleum was built at the top of the hill above the receiving tomb.

Six years later, the new memorial was close enough to completion that Lincoln's body was moved there, without ceremony and with little fanfare. Along with Lincoln went three of his sons: Edward (who died in 1850), Willie (of whom we've already spoken, who died in Washington in 1862), and Tad (who died in 1871). In 1876, the still-unfinished tomb of Lincoln was broken into by grave-robbers who intended to snatch

Lincoln's body and hold it for ransom. They almost succeeded. Lincoln's coffin was half out of the door when lawmen accosted the thieves.

Afraid of similar body-snatching attempts in the future, Lincoln's old Springfield friends who oversaw his mausoleum now hid his remains not in the crypt of the tomb, but rather in the bowels of the mausoleum's basement, where they buried it beneath a pile of lumber. When Mary Lincoln

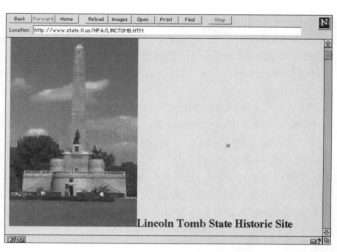

Lincoln Tomb State Historic Site

died in 1882, she too was placed beneath the boards in the basement of the tomb. Over the next two decades Lincoln and his family were exhumed, buried again, and exhumed yet once more during ongoing construction and repairs to the Monument.

In 1901, however, there was one last profanity before all the profanities ceased. At the instructions of Robert Todd Lincoln, the only surviving son, a hole thirteen feet deep was dug below the main floor of the crypt. Into this there was laid a four-foot base of cement. Before the coffin of Lincoln was lowered into the cage and cement poured down onto it, encasing it forever, the assembled aged friends of Lincoln decided to look upon his face one more time.

A hole was cut into the casket, just where the face would be. A pungent odor arose, and then there was the famous face. The embalmers had done their work well. There was Lincoln, clearly recognizable. There was the little black bow tie in place, and the suit of black cloth Lincoln had worn at his

second inauguration, now withered with mildew. There was the head, fallen to one side, on a sunken pillow.

For more information on the tomb of Lincoln, access this interesting Web page.

Jack London Historic State Park

http://parks.sonoma.net/JLPark.html

Besides being one of the most prolific novelists of the early 20th century, Jack London was a rugged individualist, an outdoorsman, and an adventurer. Upon her death, London's widow donated part of their beloved ranch near the small town of Glen Ellen in Northern California to the State of California. Later, the State acquired more of the ranch from descendents and through other means. Today, Jack London State Historic Park includes more acreage and most of the buildings in which Jack London lived and worked, writing his more than fifty books. Visit this Web page for more information on Jack London and the efforts to restore this historic ranch.

Longfellow National Historic Site

 http://www.nps.gov/long/

Find out about the home of Henry Wadsworth Longfellow in Cambridge, Massachusetts, now open to the public. Along with information on the house, the Website also provides details on the life of Longfellow, a guide to his papers, a bibliography, and more.

Lowell, Massachusetts, National Historic Park

 http://www.nps.gov/lowe/

Lowell National Historical Park preserves the vestiges of the early industrial revolution. The Boott Cotton Mills Museum contains 88 fully-functioning power looms in its weave room. Other structures are "mill girl" boarding houses, and the Suffolk Mill Turbine Exhibit. Read about this historic park and the guided tours they offer that illustrate our country's evolution from a farm-based economy to an industrial economy.

Minute Man National Historical Park

 http://www.nps.gov/mima/

Covering 900 acres, the Minute Man National Historical Park is the site of the historic battle between Colonial militiamen and British Regular troops on April 19, 1775—the first battle of the Revolutionary War. The historic North Bridge is the actual scene of the "shot heard around the world." Read here about the park, the battle, and how it helped shape the war.

Mount Vernon: Home of George Washington

 http://www.mountvernon.org/

Take a cybertour of the beloved home of our first president on the banks of the Potomac River. Washington was not born

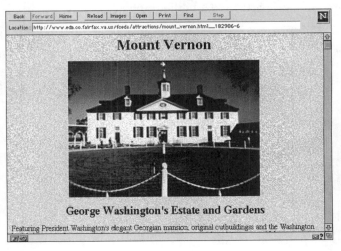

Featuring President Washington's elegant Georgian mansion, original outbuildings and the Washington

here, by the way. He was born at nearby Ferry Farm, on the site of which Wal-Mart recently tried to build one of their stores. Local preservationists, I am happy to say, were able to fight them off.

National Register of Historic Places

 http://www.cr.nps.gov/nr/nrcollec.html

The National Register of Historic Places home page gives you documentation about the buildings, sites, districts, structures, and objects nationwide listed in the National Register of Historic Places since 1966. Currently there are more than 65,000 listings in the National Register documenting nearly a million individual resources. The collection represents a tangible link to our heritage at the national, state, and local levels. Each online registration form includes a physical description of the property, information about the history and significance of the property, and a bibliography.

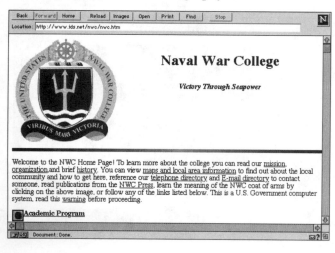

Naval War College Museum, Newport, RI

 http://www.ids.net/nwc/museum.htm

Tradition has it that on a late October's day in 1884, Commodore Stephen B. Luce, USN, was rowed from the flagship of the North Atlantic Squadron anchored off Newport, to Coasters Harbor Island two miles north of the center of the city, a location designated earlier that month by the Secretary of the Navy as the site for a new kind of college. Once ashore, Luce walked up the hill to the large stone building on the island, the former Newport Asylum for the Poor, climbed the rickety stairs and, opening the front door, solemnly announced to his few companions and the empty grounds, "Poor little poorhouse, I christen thee United States Naval War College."

Today that "little poorhouse" is a well-preserved, stately white structure, a National Historic Landmark and home to the Naval War College Museum. Named Founders Hall in honor of the founding fathers of the College, it is uniquely suited for its current use. In addition to being the original site of the College, Founders Hall is where Captain Alfred Thayer Mahan, USN, second president (1886-89) of the college and subsequently renowned naval historian, first delivered his lectures on sea power, lectures which were published in 1890 as the epochal *The Influence of Sea Power Upon History, 1660-1783.*

Today, the museum focuses on the history of naval warfare (particularly as studied at the College), and the naval heritage of Narragansett Bay—a tale that begins with the nation's Colonial roots. Its collection consists of items relating to these subjects that are perceived of value to scholarships, and it forms the core for exhibits throughout the College and for educational outreach projects. Besides permanent exhibits on the College, the genesis of the Navy in the region and the evolution of permanent installations from the late 19th century to the present, the Museum features short-term presentations dealing with College curriculum topics and special anniversaries.

For example, 1997 marks the centennial of Theodore Roosevelt as Assistant Secretary of the Navy. The museum will mount a special exhibit dedicated to the performance of TR in that job. Also in the same connection, the Theodore Roosevelt Association will hold its annual meeting and awards dinner at the Naval War College during the last weekend of October 1997. How do I know? I'm helping run it! Find out more: **http://members.aol.com/EJRen/ tra. html**.

a cybertour of gorgeous and dramatic images from the American past.

Peabody Essex Museum

 http://www.pem.org/

The roots of the Peabody Essex Museum can be traced back to 1799, when Salem, Massachusetts was America's largest and

Old American Prints

  http://www.oldprints.com/

This is a beautiful online gallery of old American prints, from Currier & Ives and others, many of them addressing historical themes such as Lee's surrender at Appomattox. Take

richest port. Ship captains, investors, and other New Englanders were among the nation's earliest global entrepreneurs—and among the first Americans to experience the tremendous diversity of people and cultures around the world. The Peabody Essex Museum documents this rich past.

Zadock Pratt Museum, Prattsville, NY

 http://www.bearsystems.com/pratt/pratt.html

The Zadock Pratt Museum in present-day Prattsville, New York preserves the legacy of Zadock Pratt—a 19th century industrialist. Pratt took a few settlers and built an industrial community complete with a tannery, a saw mill, a grist mill, a cabinet shop, a machine shop, a hat factory, three wool mills, a match factory, and glove, iron, and chair factories. Pratt also got into banking and developed real estate which he sold to his employees. Read here about this fascinating man and his life.

Sagamore Hill

 http://www.liglobal.com/highlights/saghill/sag1.html

Built by Teddy Roosevelt in 1884, Sagamore Hill became his home for the rest of his life. According to TR, "there could be no healthier or pleasanter a place in which to bring up children," he wrote, "than in that nook of old-time America around Sagamore Hill. Certainly I never knew small people to have a better time or a better training for their work in afterlife than at...Sagamore Hill." T.R. lived here until his death in 1919. His wife Edith remained here until her death in 1948. The mansion and grounds are now owned by the National Park Service.

Carl Sandburg Birthplace

 http://www.state.il.us/HPA/CARLSAND.HTM

Born in a small cottage in Galesburg, Illinois in 1878, Carl Sandburg became one of America's favorite author/poets. Sandburg's ashes lie behind the home in a small wooded park. This late 19th century middle-class home has since been granted State Historic Site status. Read here about Sandburg, his birthplace, and the State historic site.

Another interesting place to visit, both virtually and in person, is Carl Sandburg's North Carolina farm, Connemara, where he lived for the last 22 years of his fascinating life. Check it out at **http://outside.starwave.com/npf/ NC/3.html.**

Savannah & America's Black History

 http://www.savcvb.com/african.htm

The exploration and settlement of Savannah, Georgia is due in large part to the efforts of African-American explorers and settlers. This is documented in these informative Web pages, where you will find all sorts of information about the American slave trade, and much more.

Slabsides: The Cabin of John Burroughs

 http://199.0.0.2/~omi/
slabside.htm

The great naturalist John Burroughs entertained presidents and kings in this tiny log cabin in the hills above West Park, New York. Now you can visit too. Just point and click and soon you will be in the woods with old J.B.

Smithsonian Online

 http://www.si.edu

Among the remarkable things you'll find at the Web pages for the Smithsonian Institution are the Institution's "American Memory" Web resources, which provide a rich array of resources related to the American past. These include links to pages for the various Smithsonian museums, as well as much of the Smithsonian's archival material.

South Street Seaport Museum, NYC

 http://www.southstseaport.org/

Step into the 19th century and take a cybertour of the fabled "street of ships" on New York's lower east side. The place is a living slice of the American maritime heritage. It is a fun spot to visit, both in reality and in virtual reality. Check it out.

Springwood: Home of Franklin Roosevelt

 http://www.pojonews.com/enjoy/
stories/0919962.htm

Springwood, adjacent to the Franklin D. Roosevelt Library at Hyde Park, N.Y., is the home F.D.R. was born in. F.D.R. donated the home on the Hudson to the American people in 1943, on the condition that his family be allowed to use it after his death. It was transferred to the Department of the Interior on November 21, 1945, after the family relinquished their lifetime rights.

James Roosevelt (F.D.R.'s father) bought this home in 1867. Even at that time, it was an old farmhouse dating from 1800. The Roosevelts in their time turned it into something grander through several reconstructions.

F.D.R. was born here. He spent his childhood here. It was the place he loved most on the planet. And when he died, he was buried here in his mother's rose garden.

aspects of the military history of the United States. This includes Revolutionary history, the War of 1812, the Civil War, the Indian Wars, and every other military move of the United States throughout more than 200 years of nationhood.

U.S. Army Center for Military History

 http://www.army.mil/cmh-pg/

The sign says it all. Come here for extensive resources and links related to all

Valley Forge

 http://www.libertynet.org/iha/valleyforge/

Valley Forge: for six months Washington camped here with his men—nearly 12,000 of them. The grueling winter they endured here has become legend. "Naked and starving as they are," wrote Washington in February of 1778, "we cannot enough admire the comparable patience and fidelity of the soldiery."

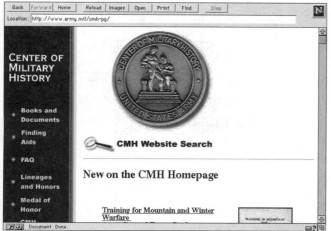

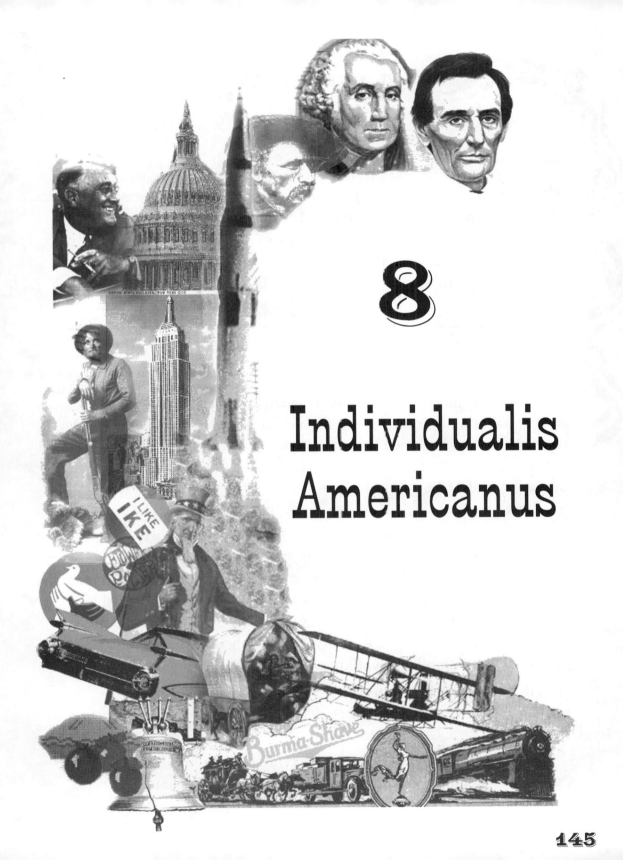

8

Individualis Americanus

Here I speak of Americans—some of them great, some of them not so great, some of them heroes, some of them anti-heroes—who were and are remarkable individuals. These are men and women who, in their individualism, reflect the true essence of independent Americanism. Consider, for example, the fascinating, succeeding generations of the Villard family, friends of mine.

The First Henry Villard

The very first Henry Villard (1835-1900) came to the United States from Germany in 1853. As soon as he had mastered the English language he began writing for newspapers. He met Abraham Lincoln, a man with whom he was to become close friends, while reporting on the Lincoln-Douglas debates (**http://www.altonweb.com/visitors/lincdoug.htm**) in the summer of 1858.

Later, Villard accompanied Lincoln to New York during the president-elect's roundabout journey to Washington for inauguration. Villard subsequently served the president as a war correspondent. It was Villard, for example, who brought Lincoln the first authentic and reliable account of the condition of the Army of the Potomac after the battle of Fredericksburg. (For Villard's full story of his relationship with Lincoln as published in *The Atlantic Monthly* of September 1904, go to the URL **http://www.theatlantic.com/atlantic/issues/95nov/lincoln/vilinc.htm**.)

Villard also participated in the Pike's Peak Gold Rush (1859) and subsequently wrote a bestselling guidebook entitled *The Past and Present of the Pike's Peak Gold Regions* (1860).

Villard went on to become a leading railroad financier and newspaper publisher. He not only wound up controlling the Oregon and California railways but was president of the Northern Pacific (1881-84). He bought the New York *Evening Post* in 1881 and was an original partner, with Thomas Edison, in the General Electric Company (1889).

In case you haven't noticed a pattern by now, I'll point it out. Whatever Villard did, he did big. When he wanted to build a home in Manhattan, he hired the architects McKim, Mead & White to design it for him. The Villard Houses, built in 1882, remain an architectural landmark in New York City to this very day. (They form the first floors of the New York Palace Hotel at 50th Street and Madison Avenue.) When Villard married, it was to Fanny Garrison, the beautiful daughter of noted abolitionist William Lloyd Garrison (Figure 8-1).

When Villard died in 1900 he left an estate worth many millions of dollars. His heirs perpetuated both his fortune and the good works of their Garrison forebears. And they did so with a gusto, style, and panache that was all their own. A baby born to the family the year the first Henry died was made his namesake. More on this Henry Villard, who was a friend of mine, in due course. First, however, we must meet the indomitable Oswald Garrison Villard, the baby's uncle and one of the first Henry's sons.

FIGURE 8-1
William Lloyd Garrison
(http://clio.nara.gov:70/l/
inform/dc/audvis/still/
civwar/civil131.jpg)

Oswald Garrison Villard

He is largely forgotten now, but Oswald Garrison Villard (1872-1949) was one of the most dynamic and dedicated people of his era. Villard was educated at Harvard and began his journalistic career in Philadelphia (1896). He was later an editorial writer for the New York *Evening Post*, of which he became owner and president after his father's death. In 1908 Villard purchased *The Nation* which, during his editorship until 1933, was established as the leading journal of liberal opinion in the United States.

Like his grandfather William Lloyd Garrison, and his mother Fanny Garrison Villard, Oswald Garrison Villard was an avowed pacifist and anti-imperialist (Figure 8-2). He was also a staunch advocate for women's suffrage and equal rights for blacks. He was a friend of W.E.B. DuBois and was a founding member of the NAACP.

Oswald Garrison Villard's books include *John Brown, 1800-1859—A Biography Fifty Years After* (1910), *Some Newspapers and Newspaper Men* (1923), *Fighting Years* (1939), and *The Disappearing Daily* (1944).

FIGURE 8-2
Oswald Garrison Villard and American Anti-Imperialism *by Jim Zwick* (*http://web.syr.edu/ ~fjzwick/ail/villard.html*)

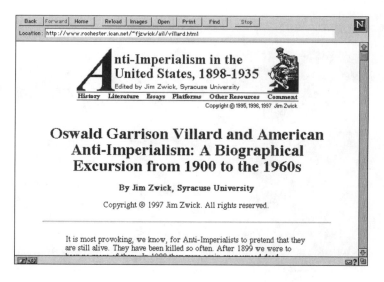

His son, Oswald Garrison Villard, Jr., is Emeritus Professor, Electrical Engineering at Stanford University with a home page located at the URL **http://www-star.stanford.edu/people/villard.html**.

The Second Henry Villard

A few years ago, when I began researching my book about Theodore Roosevelt and his sons during the First World War, I beat the bushes for someone who had experienced Harvard at the start of the war just as had the younger sons of TR. I needed a witness. I needed firsthand accounts. But as you can guess, the ranks of those who were undergraduates at Harvard in 1917 had thinned a bit through the years, and it was not easy for me to find my witness.

Thank God when I finally found him it was someone as fascinating and urbane and willing as Henry Villard, who at 94 was a retired diplomat of Ambassador rank living in Los Angeles. We hit it off immediately. He was interested that I was the biographer of John Burroughs, who'd been a hero to him in his youth. "He was one of my boyhood icons," Villard wrote me. "I remember meeting him at Onteora Park in the Catskills, where my family spent the summer months. His views as a naturalist seemed close to my own and eventually Clifford Osborne's book *The Religion of John Burroughs* became sort of a Bible for me." He also liked that I had recently written a book about the abolitionist John Brown, of whom his uncle Oswald had also written at length and with whom his great-grandfather William Lloyd Garrison had been associated, albeit at arm's length.

Our friendship was sealed when I sent him a copy of the Burroughs biography. "I have taken far too long," he wrote, "to tell you how much I enjoyed your book on John Burroughs. From a child's half-remembered icon, you have increased his stature for me to a full-bodied world figure whom I can appreciate as never before." Subsequently he also enjoyed my book about John Brown entitled *The Secret Six*. "I was brought up on John Brown," he wrote, "because of frequent visits to my grandmother's home at Dobbs Ferry [NY] at a time when Uncle Oswald and his loyal assistant Katherine Mayo had virtually taken over the top story of the house as a workshop for the Brown biography. Naturally, the chief topic of family conversation was the work in progress and its abolitionist ramifications."

Later, when we spoke on the phone and exchanged letters about Henry's time at Harvard at the start of Word War I, we discovered we had something else in common: our shared acquaintanceship with a brilliant woman who was dead by the time Henry and I encountered each other. She had lived in a beautiful apartment of an ugly building in the east sixties of Manhattan. She was an exceptional journalist and a great friend of the Canadian publisher Lord Beaverbrook. But despite all her talents, what little fame she had came more from the man she married than how brilliantly she wrote. Mary Hemingway was, after all, the last of several women who married... well, why don't you take a guess whom she married.

In Love and War

In May of 1918 Henry Villard (at 18 years of age) took a sabbatical from his studies at Harvard and went with 37 other undergraduates—mostly freshmen and sophomores—to work with the American Red Cross as an ambulance driver on the Italian front. All the boys were posted together with the Monte Grappa ambulance unit at Bassano during the last great Austrian offensive. They were back in Cambridge in time for the fall semester. One of those who traveled with Villard was Charles W. Eliot, II, grandson of the legendary Harvard president.

Shortly after he arrived at Bassano, Villard fell ill and was sent to the American Red Cross Hospital in Milan where he was befriended by another young ambulance driver. You guessed it: Ernest Hemingway.

Then only 19, Hemingway had been wounded by a shell and was recovering in the hospital. There he was also carrying on a romance with one of the American nurses, Agnes von Kurowsky. The experience later became the basis for the novel *A Farewell to Arms*. Henry Villard makes a cameo appearance in the book (Chapter XVII) as "a nice boy, also thin, from New York, with malaria and jaundice."

Henry was full of stories about "Ernie."

"As soon as I was well enough to get out of bed, they introduced me to my next door neighbor," Henry wrote me. "It was Hemingway. We hit it off immediately. He was a very attractive fellow in those days: very magnetic, very good-looking, congenial—attractive to both men and women. We spent hours and hours chatting; since he couldn't move. I spent a lot of time in his room with him. We talked a lot about his favorite subject which was baseball."

Hemingway, Henry told me, drank in the hospital more than anyone else. "He'd ring the janitor to bring him up bottles, which he hid under the pillow. When I came into the room he'd offer me a drink out of the bottle. It was strictly against the rules and the subject of great animosity between the superintendent and him. When she [the superintendent] found out about his drinking, he became Enemy Number One. Of course, he was already a kind of bull in the china shop in the hospital. He had an authoritative way about him. He'd boss the nurses around; he was rather demanding and difficult. He was different from the other patients; he was thought of as something of a character. But people enjoyed him. He didn't ever mention the idea of writing fiction."

Stuck at the hospital for several weeks, Henry became a first-hand witness to the developing relationship between the 19-year-old Hemingway and the 27-year-old American nurse Agnes von Kurowsky. "I had a crush on her," wrote Henry. "We all did. People joked about it a little, that Agnes was paying more attention to Ernie than to any of us. He wanted her by his bedside whenever he could think of any excuse. Agnes later on denied that it was anything more than a girlish flirtation, but I suspect that her feelings ran deeper than she admitted."

Henry read *A Farewell to Arms* when it came out in 1929. "The names were different," Henry wrote me, "and the girl was English instead of American, but essentially it was the story of Hemingway's love for Agnes. In my opinion, he never got over the early love affair. I'm convinced that if circumstances had allowed it, he would have gone back to her and married her. The only part of his portrait of her that was inaccurate was the extreme sexual permissiveness—there was nothing like that. She later said to me, 'I wasn't that kind of girl.' That was the truth; the affair was never consummated in any way."

Henry went on to have a long and distinguished career with the State Department, winding up as the ambassador to several developing African nations where he was loudly advertised as the great-grandson of the strident American abolitionist William Lloyd Garrison. Agnes got married, settled down, and led a relatively unremarkable life after the war. In the 1970s, when he was living in Switzerland, Henry wrote Agnes at her home in Florida and asked how she'd fared since those memorable days. They subsequently visited on several occasions.

In time, after Agnes was dead, Henry wrote a book about the experience entitled *Hemingway In Love and War*. Subsequently, film producer Dimitri Villard (Henry's son) decided the story—the real story, not the novel—should be translated into a film (Figure 8-3), which he has called simply *In Love and War*. "Unfortunately," Dimitri writes me, "my father did not live to see *In Love and War* although he was very much involved in the preparation and had read the script." The movie stars Chris

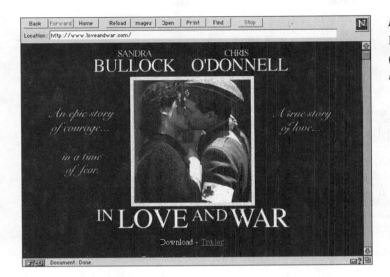

FIGURE 8-3
In Love and War
(*http://www.*
loveandwar.com/)

O'Donnell and Sandra Bullock. Produced by Dimitri, it is directed by Richard Attenborough.

The film, by the way, is excellent. It is highly dramatic, beautifully photographed, and superbly executed in every respect. It is well worth seeing. There is, however, one thing to keep in mind. For dramatic effect, in order to bring the film to both a figurative and a literal climax, the film-makers have arranged for the filmic Hemingway and Agnes to consummate their relationship—something that, as is mentioned earlier, never actually happened.

Henry and Mary and Me

Henry didn't know Mary Welsh Hemingway, the last Hemingway wife, very well. "The last time I saw her," he wrote, "was over a drink in her New York apartment looking at her collection of photos of Ernie." I, in turn, met Mary on several occasions. In my library I have a personally inscribed first edition of Mary's superb memoir, *How It Was*. One of my professors in college—a leading authority on both Hemingway and Faulkner—was a very close friend of hers. I met her on several occasions when she spoke at my college and once drove her home to Manhattan after a lecture, for which the reward was the inscribed book just mentioned. She was a very fine, very open, very gracious woman whom I shall always remember fondly.

Individualis Americanus

So I hope you see the type of people I am going to be getting at in this chapter—Americans who are unique and have made a difference in their eras: witnesses to great events, actors in great events, creators of great (if sometimes obscure) lives, and so on. In the end, all we are talking about are Americans who as individuals are, well, *interesting*. At least I hope you'll find them interesting. Some are social critics, some are scientists. Some are liberals, some conservatives. Some are dead and some are living. All are intriguing. Let's start meeting them.

Johnny Appleseed

 http://www.msc.cornell.edu/~weeds/
SchoolPages/Appleseed/welcome.html

For nearly five decades, Johnny Appleseed (John Chapman) wandered the eastern U.S. planting apple trees and entire orchards throughout Illinois, Indiana, Kentucky, and Pennsylvania. A few of his trees are still bearing fruit today.

Chapman was a vegetarian and a pacifist. His religion was Swedenborgian, and he regularly reported back to his church fathers in Sweden. Chapman was a hearty soul, but pneumonia finally took him at the ripe old age of 70 in a friend's home near Fort Wayne, Indiana.

People had always thought the ragged wanderer penniless. But upon his death it was discovered he in fact owned vast tracts of land on which he'd planted (you guessed it!) apple trees.

John Perry Barlow

 http://www.eff.org/~barlow/barlow.html

Here is the home page of a unique American: John Perry Barlow, the former Grateful Dead lyricist and current philosopher of free speech in cyberspace who makes his views clear here in a large collection of essays and other comments.

John Barrymore

 http://www.mdle.com/ClassicFilms/ PhotoGallery/jbarry.htm

John Barrymore was at once one of the best actors ever to stalk across American stages and one of the truly unique personalities ever seen in this country on or off the stage. And of course he is Drew's grandpa. This outstanding photo archive provides you with dozens of rare and otherwise unpublished photographs of Barrymore in his many guises. There is also an excellent biography of John Barrymore to be found at **http://www.turner.com/ tcm/pressroom/johnb.htm**.

Alexander Graham Bell

 http://jefferson.village.virginia. edu/albell/homepage.html

Here you have it: everything you need and want to know about Alexander Graham Bell, the inventor of the telephone. Bell was born in 1847 in Scotland and died in 1922 in Nova Scotia. Throughout his life Bell was interested in the education of deaf people. This interest lead him to invent the microphone and, in 1876, the "electrical speech machine" which we now call the telephone. By 1878, Bell had set up the first telephone exchange in New Haven, Connecticut. By 1884, long distance connections were made between Boston and Manhattan.

Bell imagined great uses for his telephone, but would he ever have imagined telephone lines being used to transmit video images? Since his death, the telecommunications industry has undergone an amazing revolution. Today, non-hearing people are able to use a special display telephone to communicate. Fiber optics are improving the quality and speed of data transmission. Actually, however, our sophisticated ability to access multimedia information on the Internet relies upon the basic technology of Bell's "electrical speech machine." It was Bell who paved the way for the information superhighway.

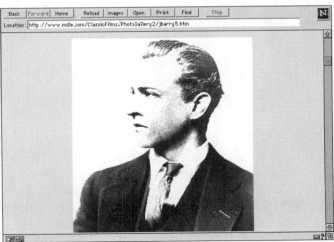

Bishop Berkeley

 http://www.ci.berkeley.ca.us/
bishopb.html

George Berkeley, Bishop of Cloyne, a British philosopher and writer after whom Berkeley, California is named, was an American in spirit. Born in Dysert Castle in Ireland in 1685, he was educated at Trinity College, Dublin, and appointed an Episcopal prelate. Berkeley was devoted to literature and to his altruistic work to establish a college in America to educate and convert Indians to Christianity. In his spare time, he was a renowned mathematician.

For a time, he lived in a place quite near to my home in Rhode Island, but returned to England when the British government declined to deliver funds promised for the start of the college. He was impressed with the New World, however. In fact, he was so powerfully impressed with the promise of America that he wrote the now-classic poem, "Destiny of America" with its famous line "Westward the course of empire takes

its way..." Berkeley's good friend Alexander Pope declared the poem a masterpiece.

Berkeley died January 14, 1753 at Oxford, England.

William F Buckley, Jr.

 http://www.heritage.org/townhall/
columnists/i-buckley.html.cgi

One of the most charming and indomitable figures of the American Right, William F. Buckley, Jr. served in the Army during the Second World War. After the war, Buckley attended Yale University and graduated in 1950. In 1955, Buckley founded *The National Review*—a popular conservative magazine with which he is still affiliated. In 1962, he inaugurated his syndicated column "On the Right," and in 1966 began airing the weekly television program *Firing Line*. His more than thirty books include political analyses, sailing memoirs, and the Blackford Oakes spy novels. Now at an age when most people are in their dotage, Buckley proceeds furiously onward at cruising speed RPM.

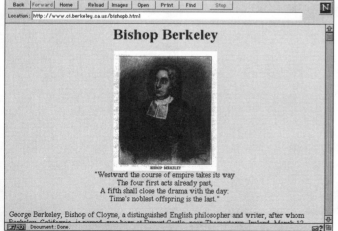

Back	Forward	Home	Reload	Images	Open	Print	Find	Stop

Location: http://www.ci.berkeley.ca.us/bishopb.html

Bishop Berkeley

BISHOP BERKELEY

"Westward the course of empire takes its way
The four first acts already past,
A fifth shall close the drama with the day:
Time's noblest offspring is the last."

George Berkeley, Bishop of Cloyne, a distinguished English philosopher and writer, after whom

Document: Done.

Buffalo Bill Cody

 http://www.historybuff.com/
library/refbuffalo.html

Buffalo Bill Cody was the man who, through his Wild West Show of the Gilded Age, brought the West—or at least one man's romantic view of the

West—to a generation of Easterners and Europeans. In so doing, he left an indelible imprint upon our culture.

Cody was born on February 26, 1846 near LeClaire in Scott County, Iowa. In 1853, his family moved to the Salt Creek Valley in Kansas, where they were among the first settlers.

Young Cody began his colorful career at the ripe old age of 11, when he signed on as an ox-team driver for 50 cents a day. Two years later, he hired on as an "extra" or messenger boy with a westbound bull train. In 1858 he became assistant wagon master on a bull train headed for Fort Laramie, where he joined a party of trappers on the Chugwater River.

In 1859 Cody joined the gold rush to Pikes Peak, Colorado. Then in 1860 he became a Pony Express rider, one of the youngest on the line at age 14. He once rode 322 miles in 21 hours and 40 minutes, exhausting 20 horses in the process.

While too young to enlist in the Army during the early years of the Civil War, Cody served the Union forces as ranger, dispatch bearer, and scout in Missouri and Kansas, and on the Santa Fe trail. In 1864 he enlisted in the Kansas Volunteer Infantry and served until the end of the war.

In 1867-68 he was hired to provide buffalo meat for workers on the Kansas Pacific Railroad. He was paid $500 per month and is said to have killed 4,280 buffalo in eight months. Cody claimed the title of "Buffalo Bill" in a buffalo hunting contest near Sheri-

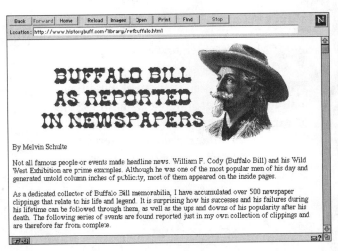

Back Forward Home Reload Images Open Print Find Stop

Location: http://www.historybuff.com/library/refbuffalo.html

BUFFALO BILL AS REPORTED IN NEWSPAPERS

By Melvin Schulte

Not all famous people or events made headline news. William F. Cody (Buffalo Bill) and his Wild West Exhibition are prime examples. Although he was one of the most popular men of his day and generated untold column inches of publicity, most of them appeared on the inside pages.

As a dedicated collector of Buffalo Bill memorabilia, I have accumulated over 500 newspaper clippings that relate to his life and legend. It is surprising how his successes and his failures during his lifetime can be followed through them, as well as the ups and downs of his popularity after his death. The following series of events are found reported just in my own collection of clippings and are therefore far from complete.

dan. Kansas, during which he outshot another buffalo hunter, Bill Comstock, shooting 69 buffalo to Comstock's 46.

As a government scout in 1868, headquartered at Fort Larned, Kansas, he performed remarkable endurance rides, once covering 355 miles in 58 hours of day and night riding. From 1868 to 1872, he served with the Fifth Cavalry in various expeditions against the Indians.

In 1872 Cody guided Grand Duke Alexis of Russia on a hunting trip and was almost elected to the Nebraska legislature on the Democratic ticket at age 26. In November of the same year Cody went East to act in a stage play about the frontier. It was Cody's first taste of performing for the public, and he "cottoned to it" right off.

Nevertheless, Cody returned to the West and participated in the last of the Indian Wars before starting his wild west show. The story of his career as a performer is legend. Cody died in January of 1917, just before his 71st birthday.

Esther Dyson

 http://www.eff.org/homes/dyson.html

Esther Dyson is an individual on the cutting edge of technological and freedom-of-expression issues. She is the president of EDventure Holdings, a small but diversified company focused on emerging information technology worldwide. She is the daughter of noted scientist Freeman Dyson.

Thomas Alva Edison

 http://edison-ford-estate.com/ed_bio.htm

One of the great geniuses in the history of technology, Thomas Edison earned patents for more than a thousand inventions, including the incandescent electric lamp, the phonograph, the carbon telephone transmitter, and the motion picture projector. In addition, he created the world's first industrial research laboratory. He was born in 1847 and died in 1931, leaving behind a world profoundly different from the one into which he'd been born. Another very good Thomas Alva Edison site is located at the URL **http://www.antique-radio. org/bios/edison.html**. And one more is to be found at the URL **http://hfm.umd.umich. eduhistories/edison/tae.html**.

Walker Evans

 http://photoarts.com/banning/gallery/evans.html

Walker Evans, who died in 1975, was an extremely important photographer whose work spans five decades. He is perhaps remembered most as the photographer who collaborated with James Agee on the Depression-era classic, *Let Us Now Praise Famous Men*. This set of pages provides a remarkable collection of Evans' photographs—mostly architectural photographs—in a splendid cybergallery.

Richard Feynman

http://web.mit.edu/awhoward/www/feynman.html

Richard Feynman was something extraordinary under the sun. It is no accident that James Gleick, in writing his biography of Feynman, entitled it simply *Genius*. He was the youngest scientist at Los Alamos in the

1940s—the *enfant terrible* of the atomic bomb project. He was also a brilliant architect of quantum theories, the most caustic critic to sit on the committee investigating the disaster of the space shuttle *Challenger*, a Nobel Prize winner for work that gave physicists a new way of describing and calculating the interactions of subatomic particles, and a beloved husband and father on the side. He died in 1988. Learn about him through this splendid set of Web pages.

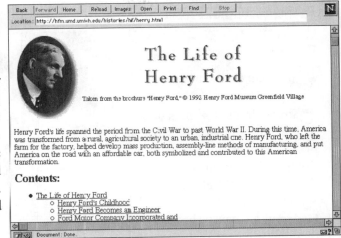

The Life of Henry Ford

Taken from the brochure "Henry Ford," © 1992 Henry Ford Museum Greenfield Village

Henry Ford's life spanned the period from the Civil War to past World War II. During this time, America was transformed from a rural, agricultural society to an urban, industrial one. Henry Ford, who left the farm for the factory, helped develop mass production, assembly-line methods of manufacturing, and put America on the road with an affordable car, both symbolized and contributed to this American transformation.

Contents:

- The Life of Henry Ford
  - Henry Ford's Childhood
  - Henry Ford Becomes an Engineer
  - Ford Motor Company Incorporated and

W.C. Fields

 http://www.louisville.edu/~kprayb01/WC.html

John Cleese has called him "the greatest of all comics." Fields described himself as a "rogue." We remember him as "Mr. Macawber" and other great characters. This useful set of Web pages includes images, a complete biography, a searchable index of famous Fields quotes, and much, much more. You even get a pic of his headstone with the famous phrase: "All things considered, I'd rather be in Philadelphia."

Henry Ford

 http://hfm.umd.umich.edu/histories/hf/henry.html

Born in 1863, Henry Ford is the man who made the automobile affordable for the average American.

Ford himself was an amazing, complex individual, and often a study in contrasts. For example, he was both a genius in many respects and a foolish anti-Semite. Another of Ford's inherent contradictions was his fundamental distaste for the urban and industrial landscapes he did so much to spawn. Ford preferred the woods.

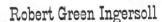

Robert Green Ingersoll

 http://www.codesh.org/ingersoll/bio.html

Robert Green Ingersoll was a great reform politician of the late 19th century. He was a supporter of women's suffrage, an activist in the reform movement of the Republican Party, and an avowed agnostic. This fascinating figure is little remembered today, although he ought to be made more of.

Patricia Ireland, President of the National Organization for Women

 http://www.now.org/
officers/pi.html

Patricia Ireland is president of the most important, most vibrant, and effective women's rights organization in the world: the National Organization for Women. Learn more about Ireland, and the cause she leads, via these informative Web pages.

**Patricia Ireland
President**

- See information on her book, *What Women Want*

NOW President Patricia Ireland leads the largest, most visible and most successful feminist organization in the United States. Ireland's major contributions thus far include organizing NOW activists to: defend women's access to abortion, elect a record number of women to political office, work more closely in coalitions with other social justice and civil rights groups and champion international feminist issues.

Ireland takes on anti-abortion terrorists in the streets, in the Congress and in the courts. Out of concern over threats to women's reproductive health, particularly the imminent threat to abortion rights, Ireland developed NOW's Project Stand Up for Women. It has included: training thousands of activists in direct clinic defense; and major lobbying and litigation successes. The most recent victory came in a January

Charles Lindbergh

 http://www.150.si.edu/chap8/
8charp.htm

On a cold and wet May morning in 1927, Charles "Lucky" Lindbergh pushed in the throttle of his rickety single-engine Ryan NYP named the "Spirit of St. Louis" to begin the first solo, nonstop flight across the Atlantic ocean. His destination was Paris, France—nearly 4,000 miles to the east. The trip would take Lindbergh 33.5 hours to make. After his historic flight, Lindbergh donated his plane to the Smithsonian museum where you can see it today.

Charles Lindbergh

Cotton Mather

 http://www.gty.org/~phil/
mather.htm

Cotton Mather (1663-1728) was the most famous minister in New England at the close of the 17th century. Toward the middle of the 1600s, the Puritan revival in America had begun to wane and the social order of the Puritan society had begun to degenerate.

By the time Mather began his ministry, the original Puritan community had vanished, leaving behind heirs to its land and fortunes, but not to its spirituality. Thus, every sermon that Mather wrote can be seen as a call to defend the old order of church authority against the encroachment of an increasingly secular world. As an apologist for the old New England ways, there is no doubt that Mather left himself open to attack, and by the end of the 17th century he had become a scapegoat for the worst in Puritan culture.

S. Christa McAuliffe

 http://www.flatoday.com/space/amf/christa.htm

Sharon Christa McAuliffe was born in Boston in 1948 and died in the *Challenger* explosion of January 1986. She was a dedicated teacher, an outstanding mother, and a brave explorer.

H.L. Mencken

 http://www.geocities.com/CapitolHill/1414/index.html

Mencken (1880-1956) was a great American journalist, editor, essayist, linguist, lexicographer, and critic. He was the man who, when he heard Calvin Coolidge had died, asked "How can they tell?" Fanny Butcher called him the Voltaire of his time.

Mencken was perhaps the most influential American editor, essayist, and social critic of the first half of the 20th century. A biting satirist and a daring prose stylist, Mencken enjoyed his greatest fame and power in the 1920s, during his editorship of *The American Mercury*, during which he championed such new American writers as Theodore Dreiser and Sinclair Lewis.

He was a classic wit. Here are a few choice lines:

"Democracy is the theory that holds that the common people know what they want, and deserve to get it good and hard."

'Courtroom—A place where Jesus Christ and Judas Iscariot would be equals, with the betting odds favoring Judas."

'No one has ever gone broke underestimating the intelligence of the American people."

"Puritanism is the haunting fear that someone, somewhere may be happy."

The H.L. Mencken Homepage

"Not associated with the estate of H.L. Mencken, the Libertarian or Republican Parties, or anyone else"

Lucretia Mott

 http://www.quaker.org/mott

Lucretia Mott was an important figure of the 19th century. A Quaker, she was active in the abolitionist movement, the early peace movement, women's suffrage, and the Free Religious Association of which she and Ralph Waldo Emerson were founding members.

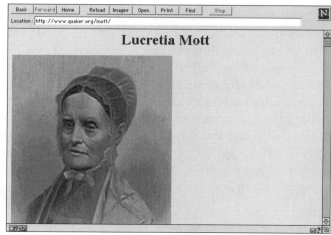

Lucretia Mott

Ralph Nader

 http://www.realchange.org/nader.htm

Most people think Ralph Nader is just peachy keen. And there are times when I do also. But he has his down side. He takes money from the trial lawyers' lobby. He busted a union among his own workers. He's made a small fortune in the stock market. I like to quote Dave Barry who once said: "Big business never pays a nickel in taxes, according to Ralph Nader, who represents a big consumer organization that never pays a nickel in taxes."

Ralph Nader's Skeleton Closet

Ralph Nader has done a lot of good for consumers. He has also led attacks on such evils as Volkswagen cars, the American Automobile Association, whole milk, colored toilet paper, fluoridated water, and the Elvis stamp. Through it all he has manipulated the press brilliantly and built himself a comfortable and powerful niche without need for election, even within his own consumer groups.

For 30 years, Ralph Nader has proclaimed himself to be "Saint Ralph", the only honest man in Washington, and the only friend of the average citizen. If that doesn't make you puke already, then click on the allegation of your choice:

a HUGE hypocrite -- just another politician -- Anti-democratic authoritarian -- secret luxury house --

Annie Oakley

 http://www.maturityusa.com/Features/A.Oakley.html

She was "little miss sureshot." That is the popular memory. But she was also a practiced, calculated performer: an exacting professional. And she was a shrewd businesswoman. Her career lasted more than 40 years and when she died in 1926 she was a wealthy woman.

J. Robert Oppenheimer

 http://www.glue.umd.edu/~enola/dvel/oppie.html

J. Robert Oppenheimer was the physicist who led the Los Alamos effort to build the atomic bomb during World War II. He was also in on the decision to use the bomb. In May 1945 Oppenheimer ("Oppie") sat on a panel of four scientists looking into the case for the military use of the bomb against Japan. Joining Oppenheimer on the panel were A.H. Compton, Enrico Fermi, and E.O. Lawrence. The consensus was that a demonstration of the bomb would not convince the Japanese to surrender, and that in the interest of ending the war the bomb should be used on a real target.

Robert Peary

 http://www.biddeford.com/~eagle/home.html

Robert Peary, Arctic explorer, is generally regarded as the first man to make it to the North Pole, which he did in 1909. This set of pages holds an interesting biography of Peary written by his son, as well as lots of information about the family home on Eagle Island, in Casco Bay, Maine.

Jacob Riis: Muckraking Journalist

 http://tenant.net/Community/Riis/contents.html

Jacob Riis, muckraking journalist and photographer of turn-of-the-century New York, dedicated himself to improving the living conditions of urban slum dwellers. Come to this set of Web pages for a dramatic, illustrated hypertext edition of Riis' classic *How the Other Half Lives,* first published in 1890 by Charles Scribner's Sons.

Will Rogers

 http://www.willrogers.org/

Will Rogers was a true American original. Rogers, who died in 1935 in an airplane crash, was not only a comedian, actor, and rodeo performer, but also a distinguished political and social satirist and a great champion of the working man. Here you can download a Rogers biography. You can also make a cybervisit to his birthplace and the ranch where he lived with his wife and family in Santa Monica.

Elizabeth Cady Stanton

http://www.nps.gov/wori/ecs.htm

Elizabeth Cady Stanton was the driving force behind the 1848 Seneca Falls Con-

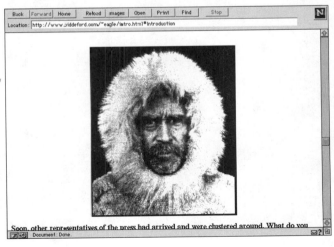

vention calling for women's suffrage. For more than 50 years she played a leading role in the suffrage movement along with Susan B. Anthony and Lucretia Mott.

Henry Stimson

 http://www.clark.net/pub/stimson/ stimson/henry.htm

As an old man, serving as Secretary of War under Franklin Roosevelt, Stimson oversaw the development of the atomic bomb. As a little boy, he was entertained by his grandmother with her reminiscences of her childhood friendship with the elderly George Washington.

He also served as Secretary of War under Taft in the years 1909-1912. During World War I, Stimson (then age 49) volunteered his services again and served as a colonel of artillery in France. In 1930, as Secretary of State in the Hoover

administration, Stimson single-handedly negotiated the London Naval Treaty.

A remarkable man? You bet.

The Wright Brothers

http://hfm.umd.umich.edu/histories/ wright/wrights.html

Come to this set of Web pages to learn all about the two Ohio lads who taught the world how to fly. Their machine first left the ground on December 17, 1903 at Kitty Hawk, North Carolina, and the world has been getting smaller ever since.

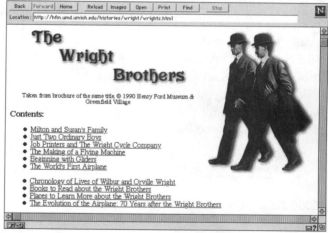

9

Kingdom of Kitsch

One of the most remarkable things about the United States is how very low its culture can sometimes go. From ceramic hula girls on the dashboards of our cars to American eagle hood ornaments and flag-decorated bowling balls, the United States is awash in a veritable sea of commercial kitsch.

Who can say when we will touch bottom? How low can we go? I once saw a convertible on Route 95 with a portrait of Elvis (**http://www.rockhall.com/induct/preselvi.html**) on its hood. On the trunk were scrawled the words, "In Memoriam." I read a story in the newspaper about a man in New Hampshire who has spent 20 years assembling the world's largest collection of gumball machines. He did it, he said, so that his life would have meaning.

The dictionary tells us that kitsch is "pretentiousness and lack of good taste in art, and art that results from this pretentiousness and lack of good taste." The term *art* in this context means all handmade artifacts of mankind—not just paintings and sculpture but also architecture, ornaments, and decorations of every type.

In short, kitsch is to art what karaoke is to music. Kitsch is a painting of Elvis Presley on the broadside of a van. Kitsch is in the art of soft drink cans which some among us think collectible. Kitsch is classic junk TV of the type that is lionized in public-access cable programs dedicated to extolling the complexities and deep hidden meanings of *Lost in Space* and *Gilligan's Island*. Kitsch is in the trivial Barbie doll collections some grown women (and, indeed, some men) fixate on instead of devoting their hours to something more profound—say, human rights.

Kitsch Is Fundamentally Useless

The one thing all forms of kitsch have in common is a fundamental uselessness.

This is true of the pink plastic flamingoes on the brief lawn of the mobile home, collectible Patsy Cline paper dolls, cute and cuddly product packaging (Figure 9-1), and the esoteric collections of Barbies and cowboy boot cookie jars with which so many Americans become fixated.

This fundamental uselessness is the great common denominator shared between all these kitschy things.

The people of the Bauhaus school taught us that form follows function. The most elegant of forms routinely evolve (almost organically, it seems) to service the most complex and elegant of functions. However, where there is no function—where there is only uselessness—the form reflects this and is the reverse of elegant: grotesque.

FIGURE 9-1

*Kitsch is for sharing. An example: Mary's Moo Moos. (**http://omni.cc. purdue.edu/~royald/ moo.htm**)*

Grotesques in Cyberspace

I am reminded of the classic stories by Sherwood Anderson (**http://www.gai.com/text/clas6.htm**), the tales of the mythical town called Winesburg, Ohio. Every half-formed provincial person, every soul limited by the horizon, was one Anderson labeled a "grotesque." He reserved the term for inward-looking people who rejected cosmopolitanism without ever realizing they had rejected it, people limited more by their imaginations than by the borders of pathetic little Winesburg.

The domain of kitsch, though it is found around the world, is a similarly limited and pathetic place. And the grotesques who inhabit it are to be found as much in cyberspace as they are in the real world.

Kitsch as it manifests in cyberspace takes two forms. First we have traditional kitsch—the flamingoes and Barbie collections of old—as documented and commented about on the World Wide Web. Secondly, we also have a new cyber-kitsch to contend with. What I speak of are the new forms of digital kitsch to be found along the cyber-roadside: flagrant exercises in trivial, banal wastes of bandwidth, publications which are to the Web what kitschy figurines are to plaster.

My favorite kitschy use of cybertechnology is the useless Camimage. There are Web Cams all over the place offering dozens of absolutely useless real-time images. Consider the Cow Cam, which shows you, to no apparent purpose other than the waste of the technological resources, two cows browsing in a field (Figure 9-2).

The cows' names are T-Bone and Filet. They wander around, eat grass, gape at the camera, then wander around, eat grass...you get the picture. At another Web Cam site the visual offered is that of the camera taking a picture of itself in a mirror.

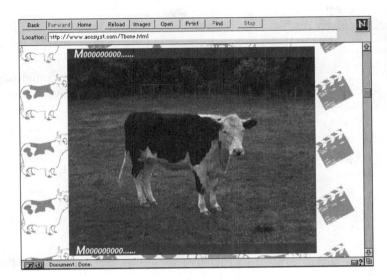

FIGURE 9-2

The Amazing Cow Cam
(http://www.accsyst.com/
cow.html)

A Celebration of Everything Lowbrow

In short, Web kitsch equals everything that is lowbrow in cyberspace: every Barbie dressed as a pilgrim, every potato chip bag collection, every database celebrating famous dogs, every online collection of cardboard yogurt tops, and so forth.

There is a lot to wade through. Pull on your hip boots, hold your nose, and let's start trudging.

Baked Frito-Lay's Potato Chips Page

 http://www.worldvillage.com/
wv/feature/bakedlay.htm

Here it is, the page we've all been waiting for, the one dedicated to the new "low-fat" potato chip introduced in 1996. Here you not only get nutritional information, but also an appreciation of the design of the Baked Frito-Lay's bag and an illustrated "day in the life" of the self-confessed Baked Frito-Lay's addict who is also the page's author.

Beavis Refrigerator Magnet

 http://www.vt.edu:10021/V/
vsawyer/pc/beavis.html

Embroider your own Beavis refrigerator magnet! What do you mean it never occurred to you? At this site you get all the instructions, an easy-to-follow pattern, and even a photo of the finished product. Every home should have one.

Camera Van

 http://www.spacelab.net/~pross/
camvan/

Why would someone cover a van with 1,705 cameras? Find out about car artist Harrod Blank and see one of his most famous creations, the Camera Van, which currently turns heads as it cruises the San Francisco Bay Area. And if the paint on your Pinto is shot, and your family's embarrassed, and you can't decide on a color, Harrod's has lots of ideas for you. Check out a few at **http://wfmu.org/Catalog/Items/c21102B.html**.

The Carpenters

 http://www.geocities.com/
SunsetStrip/Towers/9438/

Yes, long after Karen sang her last "Close to You," there are still millions of fans of the squeaky-clean brother-and-sister act. The most loyal keep the flame of mem-

ory alight in these loving pages. Link to pages describing Karen and Richard's lives, love songs, loss, legacy, and available merchandise. Link to Richard's personal page following his solo comeback. Why, you've only just begun to link.

Bill Clinton Doll

 http://fbsolutions.com/pres/

Feel like thumping Bill Clinton right on the head? Well, now you can feel his pain if you get yourself one of these great bobbing-head dolls. Complete with accessories such as a saxophone, jogging shoes, and a military uniform, there are choice sayings on the base such as "I feel your pain." Appropriately enough, the head is hollow. The doll is 7.5 inches tall. Weight depends on how often Bill has jogged to McDonald's in any given week. And in case you are wondering, there is no Paula Corbin Jones doll.

Cowboy Boot Cookie Jars

 http://www.gourmetgift.com/ 83.htm

Agh! Cowboy boot cookie jars! They are ceramic, of course, and can't actually be worn by anyone. But they look so doggone real you are tempted to imagine some cowboy wearing them for days on end before he took 'em off and filled 'em up with cookies.

Cowboy Boot Cookie Jars

Return to Designer's Kitchen
Click to Order Now

Product Number (83)
Price $41.95
Standard shipping $4.50
Standard ship time 7-10 Days

You'll get a kick out of these Cowboy Boot Cookie Jars! Rich color and detail makes these boots truly unique. These collectible cookie jars are the perfect Western gift. Makes a great centerpiece or perhaps on your hearth with fireplace matches. Choose from 4 sharp colors to fit any decor.

Measurements:
13" High

Options:
Western Flare
Bronco
Indian
Cactus

Dan's Link O'Kitsch

 http://www.america.net/~dan/ Dano.htm

Dan Hayes enjoys kitsch, especially American kitsch. He even does his own computer-generated animations of the kitschiest content. Check out his page for a tongue-in-cheek stroll along the lowbrow streets of popular art.

Debbie's Barbie Collection

 http://www.tidepool.com/barbie/ barbiedeb.html

Debbie has been collecting Barbies for a very long time. Debbie isn't a kid any more. Debbie is still collecting Barbies. Debbie has them all—the *Sound of Music* Barbie, the *Gone with the Wind* Barbie, the Civil War nurse Barbie, the American Indian Barbie, the Pilgrim Barbie, the Pioneer Barbie, Egyptian Queen Barbie, and so on.

Debbie thinks you might care about this stuff as much as she does.

Dr Pepper: The Unofficial Home Page

 http://www.wiw.org/~chris/drpepper/

Soft drinks become kitsch when one fixates on them as cultural phenomena and fixates on their cans and bottles as art. Such a fixation is prevalent at this site, which provides more information than anyone on the planet will ever need concerning Dr Pepper, including images of "classic" cans and bottles, various content formulas for the drink through the years, sales statistics for Dr Pepper going back decades, and so forth.

Here is an example of the kind of information you'll find here. Did you notice—or did you care?—that there is no period after the "Dr" in *Dr Pepper*? It is not only so on the cans and bottles, it is also acknowledged to be the case by the Associated Press Stylebook.

The period is omitted because of the italicized typeface used on DP cans and bottles in the early 1950s. Because of the font, the "r:" in the "Dr:" looked like an "i" followed by a colon ("Di:"). Dr Pepper changed the font and dropped the period altogether.

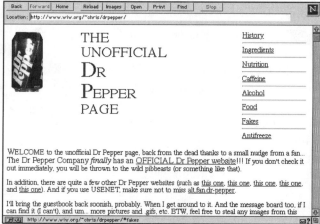

The name of the drink, by the way, comes from Dr. Charles T. Pepper, a town doctor who practiced medicine out of his own pharmacy in Rural Retreat, Virginia.

If—and that is a big *if*—you need to know more, access these Web pages. There is also an official Dr Pepper Website that is just as interesting (**http://www. drpepper. com**).

Edsels

 http://www1.usa1.com/edsel/ home.htm

Here is the mothership for owners and enthusiasts of America's all-time ugliest

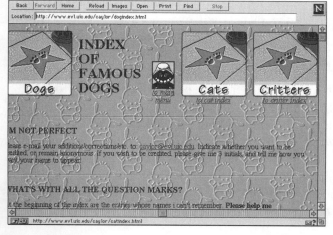

car. Check out Edsel facts, trivia, photos, and information about Ford Motor Company's "biggest loser." Join the Edsel Owners Club as it celebrates this car's 40th anniversary.

The Hepcat's Edsel Pages (**http:// uslink.net/~hepcats/edsel.html**) even include a snatch of the Edsel ad jingle for you to download. Everybody sing!

Famous Dogs, Cats, & Critters

 http://www.evl.uic.edu/caylor/ dogindex.html

There are more famous dogs than you might at first think. How about the dog who pulled the bathing suit off the kid in the Coppertone ad? How about Elliot's dog from the film *E.T.*? How about Rin Tin Tin? How about FDR's dog Fala? Here is a complete database of famous dogs, with famous cats and other critters thrown in as a bonus. Whoopee.

Figurines

 http://swdecor.cpeq.com/html/
fig.htm

Indian maidens washing clothes by the river. Happy puppies. Happy ponies. Sleeping cowboys. Happy children trotting off to school—all of them cute as buttons. Collect the entire set. Inundate your house with them. Just don't invite me over.

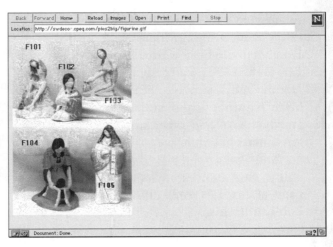

George's Matchbox Page

 http://members.aol.com/gsagi/
matchbox/index.html

George lives for classic Matchbox metal cars and trucks made from 1953-1969. If you share George's zeal, check out this site to connect with every Matchbox collector in the country and to find several fine links that will dish up all the high-resolution pictures of metal toy cars and trucks you could ever want.

Hearses in the Movies

 http://www.best.com/~border/
grimrides/movies.shtml

What hearses were in which movies? They are all here, including the 1953 Eureka Flower Car used in Arlo Guthrie's film *Alice's Restaurant*, the dual rear-axle stretch hearse in *All the President's Men*, the 1969 Superior Crown Royale Cadillac hearse used in *Beverly Hills Body Snatchers*, and...well, you get the picture.

Hippo Hat

 http://www.trix.com/effective/
hippo.html

What do you get when you combine a cute hippo hand puppet with a cowboy hat, some Velcro, and a programmable servo? A delightfully flailing hippo hat. Learn the designer's engineering secrets and admire the final product.

Howdy Doody

 http://www.odysseygroup.com/
coll796/hdvalues.htm

That happy, freckled puppet Howdy Doody and his human sidekick Buffalo Bob have been American icons since TV's infancy. Now, after almost 50 years, Howdy is firmly entrenched in the kitsch culture, with thousands of items of Howdy Doody merchandise being collected and traded. Visit this site, run by Neil Sakow, author of *Livin' in a Howdy Doody World*, for information on the availability and going rates for such vintage treasures as Howdy Doody bubble bath, a Howdy Doody Colgate Dental Cream ad display, or a Howdy Doody and Clarabell the Clown music box. Another good source of Howdy Doody books and other kitsch is **http://www.netcollectibles.com/sblenus.htm**.

And don't forget Buffalo Bob. He's still around and maintains a very friendly page at **http://www.gigaplex.com/books/bob/bsmith.htm**.

Illustrated Guide to Crackers

 http://www.netusa.net/~eli/cstuff/index.html

When I first saw the title of this page I thought it would be dedicated to monster truck drivers and country musicians. Instead it is quite literally a page dedicated to crackers, like you buy at the grocery store, all colors, flavors, shapes, and sizes. Yum yum!

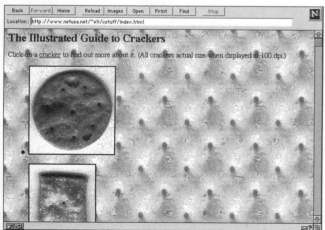

Innocent Inanimate Objects

 http://www.5sigma.com/joseph/inan/

The author of this Web page enjoys taking various inanimate objects—action figures, bananas, apples, bags of flour, and so forth—and blasting them with a .357 magnum. JPEGs and QuickTime movies of these sinister executions are then posted proudly to this Web page.

Ken's Collection of A&W Root Beer Mugs

 http://www.islandnet.com/~kpolsson/mugs.htm

You not only get a complete photo archive of Ken's extensive collection, you also get a timeline of the history of the A&W Root Beer Company, details on something called the "Root Beer Float" newsletter, and links to related (can you believe it?) sites.

Kewpie Dolls

 http://www.onenorthpole.com/ToyShop/Kewpie.html

Three generations of Americans have received these funny-looking dolls with the pointy heads as prizes at carnivals and amusement arcades. The original Kewpie was based on a drawing by

Rose O'Neill in 1912. Inexplicably, "Kewpie clubs" still exist to this day. Visit this site for links to clubs, collectors, galleries, and dealers nationwide.

Kitsch of the Month!

The Kitsch Corner: Kitsch of the Month

 http://valley.interact.nl/AV/ORG/
vg/KITSCH/kitsch1.htm

Each month, hordes of earnest kitsch chasers scan the Internet for the absolutely kitschiest item they can find. Then they submit their finds to the folks at The Kitsch Corner. The kitschiest submission wins and gets posted here. Check it out.

Kitty Kitsch

 http://www.tezcat.com/~videoc/
Kitty_Kitsch.html

How do stuffed cats in period costumes strike you? How about character kittys, such as Hansel and Gretel? Or how about cats dressed up to both watch and participate in an 1880s Punch & Judy show?

Lawn Ornament Gallery

 http://www.arch.buffalo.edu/~tasman/
virtual_cheektowaga_gallery.html

Come here for deformed dwarfs, Virgin Marys, windmills, pink flamingos, Elvis memorial mailboxes, wishing wells, and much more. The ones I like best are those fake sunflowers made out of plastic that stand tall all year, even in blizzards. I also love those blue reflecting balls that sit on concrete pedestals.

Los Angeles Cacophony Society

 http://www.alumni.caltech.edu/
~reynard/la_caco/la_caco.html

Self-described as "an open network of creative malcontents, guerrilla artists, advocates of absurdity, [and] kitsch-loving zealots," the Los Angeles Cacophony Society prides itself in subverting prime-time reality. If junk-covered "art cars" are your thing, or if indoor fireworks, stuffed animal decapitations, or an Easter egg hunt at an abandoned Nazi camp sounds like a relaxing way to spend your time, you may already be a member! If you're still curious, "Punch the klownz to enter!"

Lunch Boxes

 http://www2.ari.net/home/
kholcomb/lunch.html

Remember that Hopalong Cassidy lunch box you left on the bus when you were seven? You're sure that if you still had it it would be worth enough to put your kids through college. Well, welcome to Land of the Lunch Boxes, offering a dizzying array of square metal boxes, metal domes, even vinyl lunch boxes featuring cartoon characters, movie and TV stars, and pop icons of every description spanning five decades. You can get neat animated views of the Lunch Box-of-the-Month. And you can probably connect up with a collector who's willing to sell you another vintage Hopalong Cassidy.

Archie McPhee Catalog

 http://www.mcphee.com/

If you ever need a rubber chicken, a squeaking nun puppet, a handful of plastic ants, a voodoo doll, or a jolly rubber eye-ball, look no farther than the Archie McPhee catalog. Since 1986, the Archie McPhee Company has been offering for sale "a seemingly endless array of products so strange and indescribably fantastic they must be experienced to be believed." They continually add new kitsch to their product line, and their descriptive catalog copy is hilarious.

Marie Osmond Porcelain Doll Collection

 http://www.greenapple.com/
~lhenry/qbee.gif

There is only one doll so far, but we've been promised more to come! The first is named "Queen Bee" and is part of the forthcoming "Beauty Bug Ball" series designed by Linda Henry *especially* for the Marie Osmond collection. Accept no counterfeits!

Outhouses of America Tour

 http://www.tiac.net/users/
jloose/ohindex.htm

The line for the Outhouse Tour forms to the rear! Sorry, couldn't resist that one. These Web pages provide a complete online database directory for the Webmaster's collection of photographs of outhouses. How kitschy can you get?

Patriotic Party Supplies

 http://www.party-supply.com/
america.htm

God bless America! "The Founding Fathers built this beautiful blessed nation on faith," reads the copy of this online promotion for flag-decorated party supplies. "We need to celebrate our nation's glory." And there is no better way, says the shameless promoter, than to use his package which includes flag-decorated invitations, plates, forks, cups, and utensils along with "stars and stripes" confetti, crepe paper streamers, and a flag-decorated mylar balloon! Gosh, it makes me proud to say I'm an American.

American Celebration!

got Disney characters, Flintstones characters, Garfield, MGM characters, the Muppets, the Peanuts gang, Smurfs, superheroes, and Santa.

Pecking Chicken

 http://www.vanderbilt.edu/dotedu/
staff/cluck/

Hit this Website and get—you guessed it—"the Amazing Pecking Chicken." Somebody at Vanderbilt University evidently has way too much time on his or her hands, because an entire culture is being encouraged to grow surrounding this chicken. Read the many quotes or link, if you dare, to the Disco Chicken!

Pez Dispensers: An Online Exhibit

 http://www2.lglass.com/~kurtb/
pezdispe.html

Here they all are, every character you remember from your youth. We've

Planet Kitsch: An Audio-Visual Tour of Four Sci-Fi Camp Classics

 http://www.tvguide.com/tv/allen

Remember Irwin Allen? He is the producer who gave us all the best big-screen

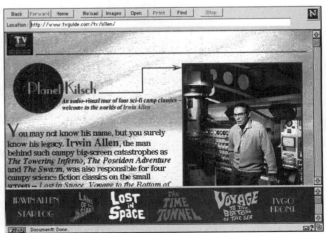

disaster flicks of our youths: *The Towering Inferno, The Poseidon Adventure*, and *The Swarm*. Allen was also responsible for the ultimate in TV sci-fi kitsch, most notably *Lost in Space* and *The Time Tunnel*. As this Web page dedicated to Allen tells us, "call him the Aaron Spelling of sci-fi TV, call him Gene Roddenberry's evil twin, call him whatever you like—there's no denying the Master of Disaster's unforgettable contributions to pop culture." If nothing else, he left us the indelible image of that robot in *Lost in Space* declaring "Danger, Will Robinson!")

Roadside America

 http://www.roadsideamerica.com

Roadside America is an amazing cyber-tour of everything kitschy along the roadside of America in towns and cities nationwide. Consider the state capitol of Utah, in the rotunda of which are statues of such Mormon immortals as Philo Farnsworth, the "Father of Television," who stands there pondering a vacuum tube. Then there is Elko, Nevada, the self-proclaimed "Best Small Town in America," featuring at its heart White King, the world's largest (stuffed) polar bear: 12 feet tall, 2,000 pounds. And of course we can't forget the statue at the Emigrant Trail Museum in Truckee, California. The statue commemorates the infamous Donner Party. The figures of four Donner Party members stand there, hands shading their eyes, gazing off into the distance. What are they looking for? Someone to eat!

There are other goodies of course: Clyde Peeling's Reptileland (Allenwood, Pennsylvania), Red Skelton's birthplace (Vincennes, Indiana), the Stonehenge Replica (Rolla, Missouri), and more. Check it out.

Route 66

 http://route66.netvision.be/

Some of the kitschiest stuff on the planet is still found along what was once "America's Highway," the old Lincoln Highway, Route 66. In the late '40s and early '50s, Route 66 became one long string of motels and tourist traps, all competing with each other to get the attention of travelers and vacationers. Life-size pink dinosaurs, imitation "Big Rock Candy Mountains," and other monstrosities lined the roadside. And the wrecks of many of them still remain. Check out some classic images of what the kitsch along Route 66 looks like today.

Rubber Band Ball

 http://www.easttexas.com/pdlg/theball.htm

Every rubber band in this ball was found, donated, or stolen. Not even one was bought! Over six years in the making, over seven pounds in weight, over eight inches in diameter and 24 inches in circumference!

Learn all about this remarkable achievement. Be amazed!

Spoon Dolls

 http://www.parrett.net/mecrean/
aa.html

Visit Annie's Attic for complete instructions on how to crochet little outfits to fit on wooden Dixie cup spoons and make your own little spoon dolls. You can make nine different dolls from Christmas Pageant Angel to Little Dutch Girl. And you wondered what to do with all those spoons you were saving.

Twinkies

http://www.twinkies.com

The Twinkie: that singular snack beloved by American children, reviled by nutritionists, and used successfully as a murder defense. For everything you ever wanted to know about Twinkies, visit Planet Twinkie, the official site complete with Twinkie trivia, Twinkie recipes (believe it or not), and the history of Twinkies and other Hostess snack products.

You might also enjoy the T.W.I.N.K.I.E.S (Tests With Inorganic Noxious Kakes In Extreme Situations) Project site (**http://www.owlnet.rice. edu/~gouge/twinkies.html**) reporting the results of scientific tests conducted

on "this incredible food." Read the findings of the Rapid Oxidation Test, the Solubility Test, the Maximum Density Test, the Resistivity Test, the Gravitational Response, the Test Radiation Test, and the Turing Test, all written in haiku.

Lawrence Welk

http://www.branson.com/branson/
welk/champan.htm

This is your connection to America's longest-running and most consciously square TV musical variety show. Stroll down memory lane with the forever-smiling, accordion-wielding maestro, Lawrence Welk, and his beloved singers, dancers, and orchestra. Catch up on the careers of perennial Welk Show favorites including the Lennon Sisters and Jo Ann Castle. Hear music clips from Welk favorites like "You'll Never Walk Alone" and "Flight of the Bumble Bee." Find out all about the Welk Resort

Center in Branson, Missouri. Wunnerful, wunnerful!

If you prefer a post-modernist view of Welk and all things Welkian, check out **http://www.zeldman.com/welk.html** for a respectful (if skewed) angle on this uniquely American performance artist. As the site asks, "Who needs Laurie Anderson when we can watch Miss Jane Brown bang out the ragtime on a beige-and-gold piano fringed with patriotic panty linings?"

What's In My Desk Drawer?

 http://cac.psu.edu/~jag164/desk.html

What's in Jen's desk drawer? Who cares! Nevertheless, here is a detailed inventory including four hi-lite markers (one green, one yellow, one orange, and one blue), and so forth. A link also brings you to a page where you can see the itemized contents of Jen's purse. The contents of these pages never change, nevertheless we are loudly informed that the pages are "Subject to Change Without Notice!"

Wonder Bread

 http://ebbs.english.vt.edu/olp/bpq/7/bread.html

Here is a poem inspired by and celebrating that blandest of all American food-stuffs: Wonder Bread. One Paul Callahan also had a disturbing dream about Wonder Bread which he felt compelled to write out and post at **http://www.retina.net/~aki/dreams/951125.html**.

Yogurt Top Collection

 http://www.natural-innovations.com/boo/yogurt-tops.html

This Web page provides a summary of the contents of the Webmaster's collection of 239 cardboard yogurt tops, most of them Dannon, from the good old days when Yogurt came in containers with cardboard tops. "Are you old enough to remember?" writes the Webmaster excitedly. "I collected these when I was a kid in New York City."

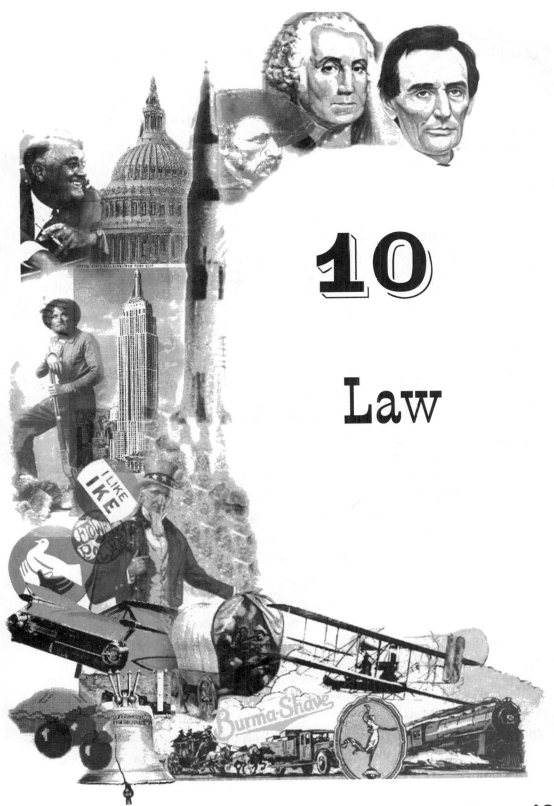

10

Law

The eminent legal scholar Grant Gilmore tells us, quite correctly, that law reflects but in no sense determines the moral worth of a society.

The values of a reasonably just society reflect themselves in a reasonably just system of law. The better the society, the fewer laws there will be. In Heaven, for example, there will be no laws at all, just order.

Likewise, the values of an unjust society reflect themselves in unjust laws. The worse the society, the more laws there are likely to be. In hell there will be nothing but laws and, writes Gilmore, "due process will be meticulously observed."

May God help us.

Law and Cyberspace

Generally speaking, I believe the less law there is, the better off we are. I am, at heart, a libertarian when it comes to many issues. In many areas of society and government, my penchant is for deregulation and elimination of bureaucracy. I absolutely despise, for example, a recent bit of federal regulation called the Communications Decency Act (otherwise known as Title V of the Telecommunications Act of 1996). In effect, by insisting that Internet publishers take technologically impossible steps to assure that "indecent" speech will not reach minors on the Internet, this act renders null and void the guarantee of freedom of expression contained in the Bill of Rights.

The Act was passed by Congress and signed by President Clinton (Figure 10-1) in early February of 1996. As I write (in the spring of 1997), the act is under consideration by the Supreme Court following a lower court decision that declared the Act unconstitutional. The free-speech

FIGURE 10-1
*Bill Clinton, against free
speech (**http://www.
whitehouse.gov/WH/
EOP/OP/html/
OP_Home.html**)*

litigators are headed by the ACLU, with additional "amicus" briefs being filed by an unlikely coalition of institutions and corporations including *Playboy*, the American Library Association, and the National Association of Broadcasters.

Saying that the Internet has "no parallel in the history of human communication," Anne Beeson, ACLU national staff attorney, has insisted that by imposing a censorship scheme unprecedented in any medium, the Communications Decency Act (CDA) would threaten what one lower court judge called the "never-ending worldwide conversation" of the Internet.

In its brief filed with the Supreme Court, the ACLU asserts that the government's efforts to end that conversation amount to a flat-out ban on constitutionally protected free speech. The ACLU's brief notes that lower courts issued 409 separate findings that comprehensively show there is no way for the vast majority of publishers of information on the Internet to distinguish between adults and minors in their audience. Thus, the effect of the CDA would be to reduce all of the communication on the

Internet to what is suitable for children, a result the Supreme Court (in previous cases regarding different mediums of communication) has repeatedly found unconstitutional.

The complete list of 20 plaintiffs in the Supreme Court case, formally known as *Reno v. ACLU*, are the ACLU, Human Rights Watch, Electronic Privacy Information Center, Electronic Frontier Foundation, Journalism Education Association, Computer Professionals for Social Responsibility, National Writers Union, ClariNet, Institute for Global Communications, Stop Prisoner Rape, AIDS Education Global Information System, BiblioBytes, Queer Resources Directory, Critical Path AIDS Project, Wildcat Press, Justice on Campus, CyberWire Dispatch, the Safer Sex Web Page, The Ethical Spectacle, and Planned Parenthood Foundation of America.

One of the lead law firms involved with filing Amici Curae ("friend of the court") briefs in the suit is the Philadelphia-based firm of Schnader, Harrison, Segal & Lewis (Figure 10-2) which represents,

FIGURE 10-2
Schnader, Harrison,
Segal & Lewis
(http://www.shsl.com/)

among other groups, my professional organization the Authors Guild (**http://www.authorsguild.org/guild/**). In a Supreme Court first, the firm is providing its brief on a CD-ROM that includes full-color illustrations of Websites with a hyperlink function that will allow Supreme Court Justices to go online to link directly to the Web pages being introduced as evidence.

Where will this end? Will the Supreme Court recognize the CDA for what it is? Will the Court understand the CDA represents a gross denial of constitutionally guaranteed rights of free speech? We can only hope so.

Where Law Is Just and Necessary: Protecting the Commonwealth

To my mind, law is not just what regulates speech, but rather the protection of the common good—the *commonwealth*, if you will. One of the areas in which I, personally, alternate my own libertarian instinct is when it comes to that most obvious of commonwealths, the natural environment.

State and national laws are absolutely necessary for the uniform protection of the vast ecosystem that is the ground we stand on: our country.

One of the most important—and most maligned—of federal laws protecting the environment is the Endangered Species Act (ESA) (Figure 10-3).

The ESA, when properly implemented and funded, is intended to save all species—including our own—from irreparable injury. The idea is to protect wildlife species not only because all life deserves respect and appreciation, but also because various species serve as indicators of the health or condition of the ecosystems upon which all life depends.

GREAT AMERICAN WEBSITES

FIGURE 10-3

Information on the Endangered Species Act (http://www.nesarc.org/ index.html)

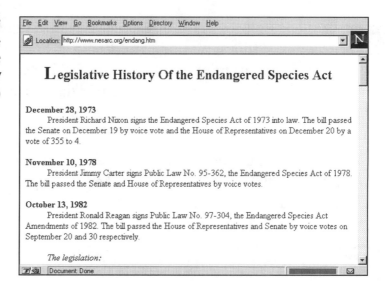

The ESA is a critically important law because it requires developers, politicians, biologists, industrialists—all citizens—to consider how their actions affect species and associated ecosystems.

Law Resources on the Web

There are a large number of resources on the World Wide Web related to American law and jurisprudence. Let's take a cyberstroll through some of them.

Advertising Law Information

 http://www.webcom.com/~lewrose/ home.html

Everything you always wanted to know about advertising law but were afraid to ask—you'll find it here. Maintained by Lewis Rose of the law firm Arent, Fox, Kintner, Plotkin & Kahn, these Web pages offer a wealth of resources and links.

American Civil Liberties Union (ACLU)

 http://www.aclu.org/

The American Civil Liberties Union (ACLU) is the nation's foremost advocate for the protection of the rights enunciated in the Constitution of the United States, most importantly those enunciated in the Bill of Rights. They are active advocates for those working toward freedom of expression, association, and religion.

The Association of American Law Schools

 http://www.aals.org/

The Association of American Law schools acts as the learned society for law school teachers. The non-profit association of 160 schools was founded in 1900 for "the improvement of the legal profession through legal education." The AALS also serves as a representative of legal education to the federal government and other societies and organizations. In addition to a quarterly newsletter, the organization publishes the *Directory of Law Teachers*, a respected guide in the field of law education.

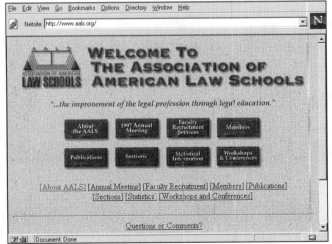

Brooklyn Law School

 http://www.brooklaw.edu/

The Brooklyn Law School was founded in 1901 with 18 students and since that time has graduated many distinguished members of the bar and the bench. Today, the school enrolls more than 1,400 students and its alumni association boasts more than 14,000 members. The school is highly ranked while at the same time not being so expensive as to be prohibitive.

Center for Law and Social Policy

 http://epn.org/clasp.html

The Center for Law and Social Policy works to improve the life and prospects of low-income families. The idea is to make sure the poor have access to the civil justice system and to use the civil justice system to work toward better housing, jobs, and wages.

Columbia Law School

 http://www.columbia.edu/cu/law/

One of the finest law schools in the country, Columbia features one of the most prestigious faculties on the continent. Its reputation commands respect not only around the country, but also around the world.

Earthlaw

 http://www.envirolink.org/orgs/elaw/

Earthlaw describes its members like this: "We sue bad guys that are hurting the environment. (And we do it for free.)"

A group of lawyers founded Earthlaw in 1993 to fight legal battles that address the environmental concerns of the West. The non-profit, public-interest organization attempts to balance the scales of justice against industry politicians and giant law firms.

"We believe we are—all of us—defined by the battles we fight," they write. "Earthlaw fights to protect endangered forests, native prairies, desert rivers, clean air, and clean water. We fight to save animals and ecosystems that cannot defend themselves. We fight on behalf of people who, without Earthlaw, would have no way of standing up to the bureaucrats and corporations destroying the natural world we hold so precious."

Check out Earthlaw's Web pages for more details.

Ecology Law Quarterly

 http://law164.berkeley.edu/~elq/

The Ecology Law Quarterly is a widely respected journal for those interested in environmental law and policy. The Quarterly is edited and produced by students at the Boalt Hall School of Law, University of California, Berkeley.

Emory University School of Law

 http://www.law.emory.edu/

Based in Atlanta, Emory University is home to one of the finest schools of law on the planet. The Website for the school includes a fantastic "Electronic Reference Desk," comprehensive resources on Georgia State law, and much more.

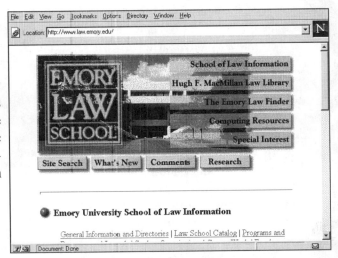

Entertainment Law Resources

 http://www.laig.com/law/entlaw/

This set of Web pages is packed with great information on how to negotiate film, television, and multimedia deals. It describes how to protect yourself legally every inch of the way and wind up with contracts that work for you rather than against you.

Federal Judiciary of the United States

 http://www.uscourts.gov

The Administrative Office of the U.S. Courts maintains this Website as a compendium of information relating to the entire Judicial Branch of the federal government. Here can be found details about the federal courts in each state, as well as the latest news from the U.S. Supreme Court itself.

The Environmental Lawyer

 http://www.gwu.edu/~envtllaw/index.html

The Environmental Lawyer Web pages are a cooperative effort between the George Washington University Law School and some sections of the American Bar Association. Come here for detailed information on all aspects of the fast-changing federal rules, regulations, and codes of which all environmental lawyers must keep abreast.

Federal Judicial Center

 http://www.fjc.gov/

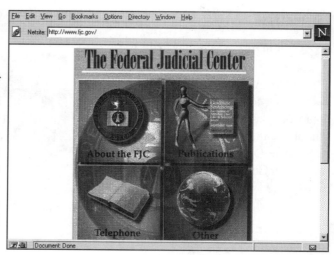

Established in 1967 by an Act of Congress, the Federal Judicial Center is the federal courts' official agency for research and continuing education. The Center's charter is to conduct and promote research on federal court organization, operations, and history. The results of this research is posted here on the Web.

Fletcher School of Law & Diplomacy, Tufts University

 http://www.tufts.edu/fletcher/

The Fletcher School of Law and Diplomacy is the oldest graduate school of international affairs and international law in the United States. It was founded in 1933 to focus its resources on teaching and research in the area of international relations. Some of our nation's best career diplomats and consular officials are products of Fletcher.

Georgetown University Law School

 http://www.ll.georgetown.edu/lc/

Georgetown University offers a full program of legal education as well as some-

thing neat called the Cyberspace Law Institute. Here you will also find the John M. Olin Program in Law and Economics, and an extensive collection of resources related to public interest law.

Harvard Law School

 http://www.law.harvard.edu/

Harvard Law School is the nation's oldest and arguably most distinguished law education institution. Founded in 1817, the school boasts the largest academic law library in the world, with collections near 1.5 million volumes. The school retains 70 full-time professors, 25 clinical instructors and attracts numerous visiting professors and lecturers. Visit the school's Web pages for many more details.

Information Law Web

 http://seamless.com/rcl/infolaw.html

The proprietor of these useful Web pages bills them as featuring "a collection of people, places, and things that can help you understand your rights in the emerging information age." The Webmaster is opposed to the so-called Communications Decency Act, as am I.

Illinois Bar Association

 http://www.illinoisbar.org/

The Web page for the Illinois Bar Association is packed with useful information. Here you'll find late-breaking news on Illinois court opinions, as well as information on law schools in Illinois, pending litigation, and much more.

Intellectual Property Law Center

 http://www.ipcenter.com/

Here are legal resources related to all aspects of intellectual property law including copyright, patents, trademarks, and more. The links include recent court rulings related to all these fields, references, citations, and courses.

Lawyer Jokes

 http://pubweb.acns.nwu.edu/~bil874/comedy/occup/lawyerjo.htm

Here are some samples copied directly from the Lawyer Jokes Web page:

★ What do you call 50,000 lawyers at the bottom of the ocean? A good start!

★ What do you call a lawyer with an IQ of 50? Your Honor.

★ What's the difference between a lawyer and a trampoline? You take off your shoes to jump on a trampoline.

★ How can you tell when a lawyer is lying? His [or her] lips are moving.

★ Why don't sharks attack lawyers? Professional courtesy.

★ What do you get when you cross the Godfather with a lawyer? An offer you can't understand.

★ Where can you find a good lawyer? In the cemetery.

★ What's the difference between a lawyer and a vampire? A vampire only sucks blood at night.

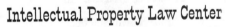

Legal dot Net

 http://www.legal.net/

This is an outstanding Web resource for attorneys and non-attorneys alike offering extensive links *and* proprietary resources for everyone doing battle in or with the legal system in any state of the union.

Milbank, Tweed, Hadley & McCloy

 http://www.milbank.com/

Based in Manhattan, the firm of Milbank, Tweed, Hadley & McCloy earned its reputation in the field of financial and corporate law more than a century ago. The firm is associated with many of the great business mergers and takeovers of the 20th century.

National Association of Patent Practitioners

 http://www.napp.org/

In its Web pages, the National Association of Patent Practitioners provides a great

deal of valuable information in matters relating to patent law, its practice, and much more. This is a "must" resource for any individual looking to patent an invention in the United States, and any attorneys representing such individuals.

National Consumer Law Center

 http://www.consumerlaw.org/

According to the mission statement on its Web page, the National Consumer Law Center (NCLC) "provides a range of unique, substantive services to legal aid and private pro bono attorneys, government officials and others." This extensive consumer law resources center has been in existence for over 25 years, but has only recently made its wealth of information available on the World Wide Web.

New York State Bar Association

 http://www.nysba.org/

With more than 60,000 members, the New York State Bar Association is the largest voluntary state bar association in the United States. At more than a century old, it is also the oldest. Throughout its history, this organization has played an important part in shaping the law, informing and educating practitioners of the law, and liv-

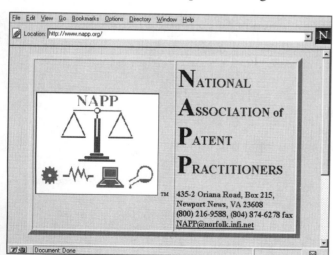

ing up to the demands a society makes of its legal professionals.

New York University School of Law

 http://www.nyu.edu/law/

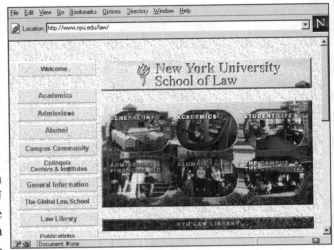

Located on beautiful Washington Square in New York City, the NYU School of Law offers a comprehensive three-year program designed to train young people for careers as distinguished lawyers and jurists. Check the Web page for more information.

Queer Legal Resources

 http://www.qrd.org/qrd/www/legal/

Here are links to reference information regarding lesbian and gay legal issues, U.S. military cases, same-gender marriages, state-specific gay rights statutes, immigration laws that pertain to gay rights, and much more.

St. John's University School of Law

 http://www.stjohns.edu/law/

St. John's University School of Law in Jamaica, Queens, NY, is a highly-respected establishment among whose graduates are numbered Governors Mario Cuomo and Hugh Carey of New York, and Governor George Deukmejian of California.

U.S. House of Representatives Internet Law Library

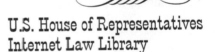 http://law.house.gov/92.htm

Here you will find hundreds of links to resources related to all aspects of American corporate, criminal, and case law. Here you'll also find state-by-state resources related to individual state statutes, and much more. All this comes courtesy of our friends in the House of Representatives. So, those guys are good for something after all.

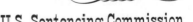

U.S. Sentencing Commission

 http://www.ussc.gov/

In an attempt to standardize sentencing in our nation's federal courts, the U.S. Sentencing Commission was created. It is an independent organization within the government's judicial branch. The agency establishes sentencing policy and issues guidelines for the form and severity of punishment of convicted felons.

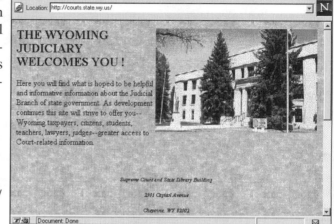

U.S. Supreme Court Decisions

 http://www.utpb.edu/library/supreme.html

Updated annually, this comprehensive database summarizes and provides backup data related to every decision handed down by the U.S. Supreme Court. You can search decisions by title or year.

USSC+: U.S. Supreme Court Database

 http://www.usscplus.com/

Here is another wonderful set of resources related to the Supreme Court. Among other things, you can download RealAudio files containing oral arguments presented before the U.S. Supreme Court. These are actual recordings of U.S. Supreme Court proceedings, including questions and answers exchanged between Supreme Court justices and case attorneys. Search the sound file database by case name or year.

Wyoming State Supreme Court

 http://courts.state.wy.us/

The Wyoming State Supreme Court Web page includes a complete online directory of court opinions, a digital law library, an overview of the Wyoming Court System, and profiles and biographies of Wyoming Supreme Court justices.

Yale Law School

http://www.yale.edu/lawweb/lawschool/ylshp.htm

Yale houses one of the finest law schools on the planet—perhaps *the* finest. It is also one of the most challenging. Here you'll find information on admissions, faculty, computer services, and much more.

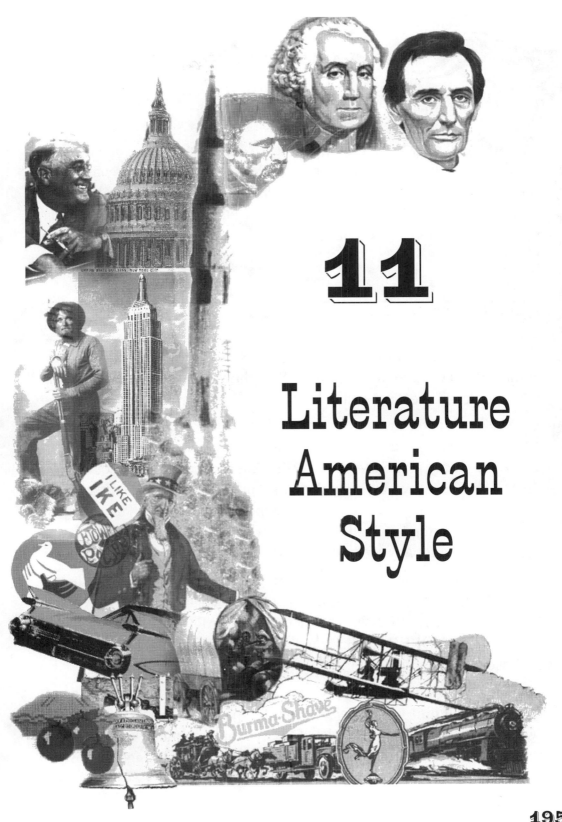

11

Literature
American
Style

My literary mecca is in Lowell, Massachusetts, in a run-down cemetery dumped in the middle of a working class neighborhood. The place is overgrown and neglected. Most of the people buried here are the types who have families who don't make the regular payments required for perpetual care. There are other bills that are more pressing.

Over the Hill and Behind the Trees

He is over the hill and behind the trees. You have to park your car, climb the fence, and walk a ways. Somehow, the rough access seems appropriate—almost poetically so.

You walk behind some tombs of old fat cats who were buried here when the burying was good and the town was rich, back in the 1890s. There are empty pint bottles of Wild Turkey tucked in the weeds behind the tombs. There are also cigarette butts and the odd condom tossed here and there. All of these, too, are somehow appropriate. The guy just wouldn't have minded at all. In fact, he would have welcomed the jovial and carefree company the booze and the condoms hint at.

Past the tombs and the condoms, behind the trees and up the hill, you have the grave. The marker lies flat on the grass—well, actually, flat on the weeds. It reads "JOHN L. KEROUAC, MAR. 12, 1922 - OCT. 21, 1969. HE HONORED LIFE." Yup. You've got it. Here lies the immortal Jack Kerouac (Figure 11-1). R.I.P.

I didn't know him at all. I was thirteen years old when he died. A friend of mine knew him well, very well, in Tampa in the '60s. Bill Osborne (well, actually, William Mayley Osborne, if you must know) was a first-class expressionist painter. I've got two of his paintings: a view of the Hudson from an area where we both once lived, in the 1970s, in Ulster

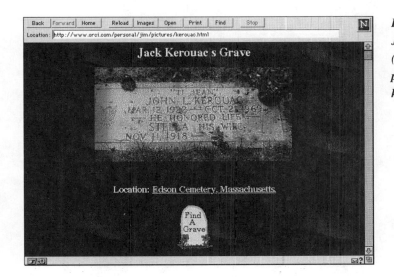

County, New York, and a waterfront scene that hints at John Steinbeck's Cannery Row near Salinas, California.

Bill used to shoot pool with Jack Kerouac in Tampa in the mid-'60s, and used to make good money doing it because Jack always insisted on betting and Jack always lost. How is that for a literary anecdote?

A Bit About Walt Whitman

Bill Osborne and I were friendly when we both lived in a town called West Park, New York, in Ulster County. The place was the former hometown of the naturalist John Burroughs of whom I've already written at length in this book. JB, of course, was a close friend of Walt Whitman. Burroughs wrote the first biography of Whitman to ever be published, *Notes on Walt Whitman As Poet and Person* (1867). It was a hotly argued defense of his friend, who was so often criticized by the press and the public.

Burroughs was never to stop defending Whitman (Figure 11-2). Through the years, as Burroughs gained substantial prestige as an essayist

and naturalist, he routinely used that prestige to advance the interests of his great mentor and friend.

In 1882, when the Authors' Club of New York was organized, Burroughs initially indicated a willingness to be among the charter members. Then he learned Whitman would not be invited to join. As soon as he heard this, Burroughs demanded his own name be removed from the rolls. "In New York there is a society of authors of which I was a member," he told a friend several years later. "Some two or three years ago they actually blackballed Whitman. They would have done themselves infinite honor had they elected him—I didn't propose him—but they showed themselves contemptible little fools by refusing him." In 1886, after visiting the club for an evening with Richard Watson Gilder, Burroughs reminded himself in his journal that this was the organization that had banned Whitman. "Think that the hope of American letters is in the hands of such men!" he commented in his journal. "I sincerely pity them. They are mostly the mere mice of literature. Such men as Gilder, Stedman, and DeKay recognize Whitman, but probably the least one of the remainder believes himself a greater man."

Burroughs vacationed with Whitman at Ocean Grove, New Jersey, in late September of 1883. They spent a week together by the sea. "Walt Whitman came yesterday and his presence and companionship act like a cordial upon me that nearly turns my head," wrote Burroughs in his journal for September 27. "The great bard on my right hand, and the sea upon my left—the thoughts of the one equally grand with the suggestions and elemental heave of the other." Whitman seemed the equivalent of—or better yet, the human personification of—the ocean. "There is something grainy and saline in him," wrote Burroughs, "as in the voice of the sea. Sometimes his talk is choppy and confused, or elliptical and unfinished; again there comes a long splendid roll of thought that bathes one from head to foot, or swings you quite from your moorings." The 46-year-old Burroughs would occasionally take off on long loops down the coast, or back inland, while the 63-year-old Whitman moved slowly along the beach or sat in some nook sheltered from the wind and sun. When alone, Whitman spent most of his time scratching a new poem in his notebook, "With Husky-Haughty Lips, O Sea!"

In a letter written at Ocean Grove, Whitman described Burroughs going "up and down long stretches of this beach every day, his pants rolled up to below his knees, his right hand saluting to shade his eyes as he scans the scene up and down. He comes back to me, sits down, and talks for half an hour of the margin of shore where the tongue of the surf slips back and forth, opening his hand to show the life he's found an inch below the damp sand." Later Whitman noticed from a distance that down on the shore Burroughs made the acquaintance of "three very little girls with buckets." Burroughs spent nearly an hour crouched on the sand with them, using a bucket to dig a deeper and deeper hole from which he pulled "shells and strange creatures that he held out for the young ladies' astonished pursual [sic] and, providing, it seemed, a running narration through the whole exercise."

Whitman wrote that Burroughs was "looking like a man who is in the healthiest of middle-ages. His beard is half gray, his head half bald, his body slim and muscled." Burroughs, wrote Whitman, "speaks much—speaks too much—about diet, a thing he is very careful of and has many theories upon. He is greatly concerned about my habits in this regard; I suffer his advice without argument, because I know it comes from love." Burroughs was then a subscriber to the dietary theories of a widely published British physician, Sir William Thompson. "[Thompson] shows very convincingly that as our activities fail by the advance of age, we must cut down in our food," Burroughs wrote to Whitman shortly after the Ocean Grove vacation. "If not, the engine makes too much steam, things become clogged and congested, and the whole economy of the system is deranged. He says a little meat once a day is enough, and recommends the cereals and fruits. I think you make too much blood. The congested condition of your organs at times shows it. Then you looked to me too fat; and fat at your age clogs and hinders the circulation. In the best health we grow lean, Sir William says, like a man training for the ring."

Burroughs was reading Darwin's *Origin of Species* (**http://www. emergentmedia.com/~madsen/origin/intro.html**) during his stay at Ocean Grove. It was an appropriate place for him to read the book, since Darwin believed the ocean to be the cradle of life on earth. The poetry of Whitman, Burroughs reminded his friend Myron Benton in a letter from Ocean Grove, was rife with suggestions of "the grand drama of evolution." Whitman's masterpiece "Out of the Cradle Endlessly Rocking" had first been published in 1859, the same year as *Origin of Species.* The poem is packed with images of man emerging from oceans of both real and psychic depths. The child emerged after nine months' gestation in the ocean of the mother's body; the race emerged from the brackish depth of the primordial sea after the long gestation of eons. The process in each case, wrote Burroughs in a letter to Edward Dowden, was "at once a birth and a baptism. Birth, in the end, is the only real baptism. You yourself are your own priest."

Such Were the Stories

Such were the tales and stories I encountered when I lived in West Park, New York, since the home of John Burroughs, occupied by some of his ne'er-do-well descendants, was right next door.

Walt Whitman had been a guest here in the 1870s. In fact, the family's kitchen table was popularly known in the family as the "Whitman table" because Whitman had written portions of *Specimen Days* on it while visiting in the 1870s (Figure 11-3).

The property and the woods near it are full of Whitman associations. Back in the hemlock forest, about three miles in from the river, is a lost and forgotten waterfall known only to a few dedicated trout fishermen. It is on a wild and beautiful stream called Black Creek. And it is a place of which Whitman wrote at length in his journal when here.

"I write this memorandum in a wild scene of woods and hills," he wrote, "where we have come to visit a waterfall. I never saw finer or more copious hemlocks, many of them large, some old and hoary. Such a sentiment to them, secretive, shaggy—what I call weather-beaten and

FIGURE 11-3

*Whitman notebooks. The one to the far right, in part composed at West Park, is now preserved at the Library of Congress (**http://lcweb2.loc.gov/ammem/8top.jpg**)*

let-alone—a rich underlay of ferns, yew sprouts and mosses, beginning to be spotted with the early summer wildflowers. Enveloping all, the monotone and liquid gurgle from the hoarse, impetuous, copious fall— the greenish-tawny, darkly transparent waters, plunging with velocity down the rocks. With patches of milk-white foam—a stream of hurrying amber, 30 feet wide, risen far back in the hills and woods, now rushing with volume—every hundred rods a fall, and sometimes three or four in that distance. A primitive forest, druidical, solitary and savage—not ten visitors a year—broken rocks everywhere—shade overhead, thick under- foot with leaves—a just palpable wild and delicate aroma."

Elsewhere in the journal Whitman spoke of the Hudson after nightfall in springtime. "The river at night has its special character beauties," he wrote. "The shad fishermen go forth in their boats and pay out their nets—one sitting forward, rowing, and one standing up aft dropping it properly—marking the line with little floats bearing candles, conveying, as they glide over the water, an indescribable sentiment and doubled bright- ness. I like to watch the tows at night, too, with their twinkling lamps, and hear the husky panting steamers; or catch the sloops' and schooners' shadowy forms, like phantoms, white, silent, indefinite, out there."

Living at that spot, walking the trails walked by Whitman and Burroughs, reading their prose and poetry, I felt a remarkable kinship to both men. And then years later, far away from the Hudson, I encountered Whitman and Burroughs once again, on the Web.

Enter Mr. Ginsberg

Of course, the most important contemporary cultural and literary descendant of Walt Whitman is beat poet Alan Ginsberg. He was born in 1926 in the town of Paterson, New Jersey, the son of a school teacher and poet. He attended Columbia University (**http://www.columbia.edu**). With the publication of *Howl* in 1957 he became noticed. *Kaddish* (1961) secured his reputation and was soon followed by *Reality Sandwiches* (1963) and *Planet News* (1968).

Allen Ginsberg is, of course, the voice of America just as much as Whitman ever was—although this is something the average American will acknowledge no sooner than will he or she acknowledge Whitman. Ginsberg articulates the real America: not just the purple mountain majesties, but the dirt under the rug as well. Cops and courts and power-figures in general don't care for Ginsberg, just as they didn't care for Whitman, because he blows the whistle on the absurdity of authority and censorship. Often, in fact, his insights make a devastating mockery of official wisdom.

In 1974 Anne Waldman and Allen Ginsberg founded a school of writing at the Naropa Institute (**http://www.naropa.edu/**) in Boulder, Colorado, where today you can earn a bachelor's or a master's degree. At Naropa, writers explore the prehistoric vestiges of ancient poetry for insights into humanity, as well as the arts of T'ai Chi and Zen archery. Where else can you take a course entitled "Beats and Other Rebel Angels?" Yes, this is the place sometimes called the Jack Kerouac School of Disembodied Poetics.

American Literature on the Web

American literature pervades the World Wide Web. There is a rich array of resources available addressing everything from early American literature to some of our very latest "stars" of the novel. Whether your interest be in John Steinbeck or Louisa May Alcott, Ezra Pound, or Edith Wharton, the Web has something for you.

Let's take a look.

George Ade

 http://www.spcc.com/ihsw/
ade.htm

Midwestern journalist George Ade (1866-1944) was known as "The Aesop of Indiana." By the turn of the century he was one of America's most widely-read columnists and had earned the admiration of the likes of Mark Twain.

Ade began working in 1890 for the *Chicago Morning News* (later the *Chicago Record*). After a stint as a reporter, Ade took the reins of a column focused on local events, and he successfully captured the pulse of Chicago through his colorful characters—Doc Horne, a gentleman liar, Artie the office boy, and Pink Marsh, a black shoeshine boy.

Ade began inserting his famous "fables" into his column. These, his best-known body of work, were collected in book form in 1899 as *Fables in Slang*. Visit this Website for a biography and photo, then find the text of *Fables in Slang* at **http://www.oed.com/cgi-bin/toc.getter?query=/u/triggs/TEXTS/TEI/AD.1899.Ade.Fables.narp**.

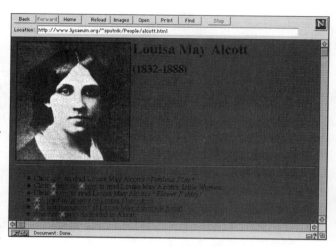

thorne, and other great literary figures. But there is only one grave that always—and I mean *always*—has flowers on it, and notes from adolescent girls expressing heartfelt *thank yous*. This is the grave of Louisa May Alcott (1832-88). At the Web pages devoted to Louisa you may read *Perilous Play*, *Little Women* and *Flower Fables* right online. You may also access a detailed biography and look at excellent photographs.

Everyone knows about Louisa. Few recall her equally interesting father. Amos Bronson Alcott (1799-1888) was a close friend of Emerson and one of the early Concord Transcendentalists. He was also a champion of educational reform.

Louisa May Alcott

 http://www.lycaeum.org/
~sputnik/People/alcott.html

There are many graves in the old cemetery at Concord, Massachusetts that are sacred. Here, on one windswept ridge, you have the graves of Emerson, Thoreau, Haw-

Authors Guild

http://www.authorsguild.org/

I am proud to say that I am a member of this, the only formal organization for published writers in the United States. The Web pages of the Authors Guild are still under development, and are sometimes slow to load, but the organization itself is first-rate.

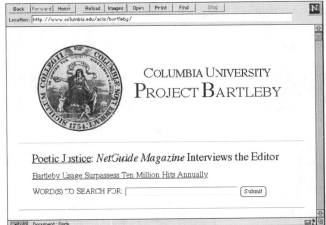

Bartleby

 http://www.columbia.edu/acis/bartleby/

Project Bartleby provides complete e-texts of the books by such great American authors as Emily Dickinson, W.E.B. DuBois, T.S. Eliot, F. Scott Fitzgerald, Robert Frost, Sarah Orne Jewett, Herman Melville, Edna St. Vincent Millay, Carl Sandburg, Gertrude Stein, Walt Whitman, and others. It will shortly include also the complete works of Theodore Roosevelt—a project in online publishing with which I am helping. The first book of Roosevelt's to hit the Web will be *The Rough Riders*, soon to be followed by more.

The mastermind behind this project is editor-in-chief Steven van Leeuwen. A formal medical editor, van Leeuwen is the main man responsible for Bartleby's evolution into the premier online library for poetry, novels, serious nonfiction, and reference materials.

Books at Bartleby include DuBois' *The Souls of Black Folk*, Fitzgerald's *This Side of Paradise*, Sandburg's *Cornhuskers*, and Thomas Paine's *Common Sense*, not to mention Walt Whitman's *Leaves of Grass*.

Madison Smartt Bell

 http://www.goucher.edu/~mbell/Welcome.html

Madison Smartt Bell is one of the finest fiction stylists at work today. At this Website you can read selections from his fiction—including portions of his latest novel, *All Souls Rising*. He has written eight novels to date.

Ambrose Bierce

http://hydra.tamu.edu/~baum/
bierce.html

Ambrose Bierce (1842-1914?) was called "Bitter Bierce" in his time. Born in Ohio, he served in the Civil War and later became a brilliant journalist in San Francisco. Working under the pseudonym Don Grile in England (1872-75) he published three collections of vitriolic sketches and witticisms: *The Fiend's Delight* (1873), *Nuggets and Dust Panned Out in California* (1873), and *Cobwebs from an Empty Skull* (1874). Returning to San Francisco, he wrote for Hearst's *Examiner*, where his wit and satire made him extremely popular.

Many of his books were mere potboilers cranked out quickly to make a dollar or two. However, in 1891 he issued *Tales of Soldiers and Civilians*, stories reminiscent of Poe's tales of horror and marked by an ingenious use of surprise endings, sardonic humor, and realistic emotions. This was followed by *The Monk and the Hangman's Daughter* (1892).

Bierce is generally believed to have died in Mexico in 1914. His most lasting memorial is *The Devil's Dictionary*, a volume of ironic definitions still popular today.

Ray Bradbury

http://www.on-ramp.com/johnston/
bradbiog.htm

Born in 1920, Ray Bradbury is one of the most highly regarded and prolific science fiction writers of our era. His books include *Dark Carnival* (1947), *The Martian Chronicles* (1950), *The Golden Apples of the Sun* (1953), *October Country* (1955), *A Mediation for Melancholy* (1959), and *The Illustrated Man* (1951).

My favorite book of Bradbury's is *Fahrenheit 451* (1953), which presents a future totalitarian state in which television presents all that people are to think and know, and the ownership of books is cause for the state to burn both the books and the owners.

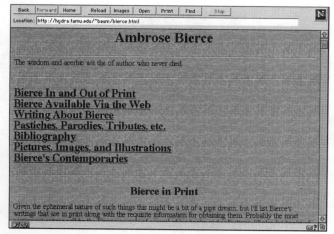

Richard Brautigan

http://www.cnct.com/home/
jen/rich.html

Bruce Cook of the *National Observer* wrote, "Brautigan is good for you. No writer you can think of is quite like him today, nor was any writer anytime—unless you can imagine the kind of things Mark Twain might have written had he wandered into a field of ripe cannabis with a pack of Zig Zag papers in his pocket. That's about as close as I can come to Brautigan, a kind of cracker-barrel surrealist whose humor is essentially 19th century Western American."

These well-crafted pages trace Brautigan and his work from his emergence in the early '60s as a hip literary visionary to his death by suicide in 1984 at the age of 49.

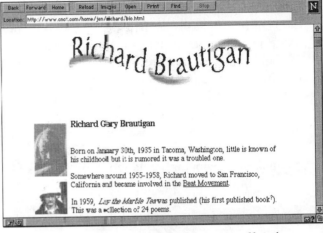

William Cullen Bryant

 http://www.vcu.edu/engweb/ eng372/bryant.htm

Come to this Web page to read William Cullen Bryant's most famous poem, "To a Waterfowl."

Bryant (1794-1878) was a poet of nature and his work is often compared with that of Wordsworth, who profoundly influenced him. But unlike Wordsworth's God, Bryant's God remained ever a Divine Being distinct from His creation.

Nature, for Bryant, was simply the visible token of God's transcendent beauty and awful power. Thus, throughout Bryant's poems, there is a pervasive sense of the transience of earthly things.

Although Bryant's themes were few and his thought not profound, he possessed a simple dignity and an impeccable, restrained style. I have several

Bryant first editions in my collection, among them *A Forest Hymn* (1860) and *Among the Trees* (1874).

Pearl Buck

 http://dept.english.upenn.edu/ Projects/Buck/

Pearl S. Buck (1892-1973) is best known for her second novel, *The Good Earth*, about the hard lives of Chinese peasants, but

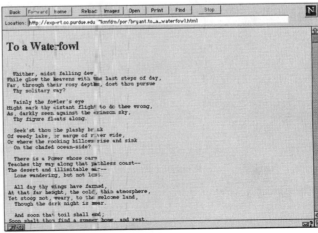

she would ultimately publish over seventy books. In 1938, Buck became the first American woman to win the prestigious Nobel Prize for literature.

Buck was equally well-known for her active role in the civil rights and women's rights movements. These pages give insight into all of Buck's accomplishments, including her establishment of the Pearl S. Buck Foundation, encouraging adoption of Amerasian children in Asia.

Edgar Rice Burroughs

 http://www.tarzan.com/

Edgar Rice Burroughs, (1875-1950) was author of the popular, fantastic adventure stories concerning Tarzan, the son of a British nobleman abandoned in the African jungle in infancy and reared by apes. *Tarzan of the Apes* (1914) is the first in the lengthy series of tales about the boy, who grows up to wed and have a son and a grandson in the

many sequels. Burroughs also wrote works of science fiction.

Truman Capote

 http://www.sgi.net/marbles/zeno/ capote.html

Truman Capote (1924-84) was born in New Orleans but made his name in New York. His writing is absolutely beautiful.

Here is a road map of the literature. Start your reading with *Other Voices, Other Rooms* (1948), the study of a homosexually-inclined boy painfully groping towards matu-rity. Then move on to *The Grass Harp* (1951), about innocent people, old and young, escaping social restraint by living in a tree house. Follow this up with *Breakfast at Tiffany's* (1958), the splendid novella about a light-hearted, amoral playgirl of New York, Holly Golightly.

To wrap up your Capote tour, try the true crime nonfiction book *In Cold Blood* (1966) or *Music for Chameleons* (1980).

Raymond Chandler

 http://www.byronpreiss.com/ brooklyn/marlowe/chandler.htm

Raymond Chandler (1888-1959) defined hard-boiled American fiction with his spine-tingling novels like *The Big Sleep*. He defined film noir with the movies based on his novels and with the original screenplays he wrote for other movies, like *Double Indemnity* and

Strangers on a Train. Visit here for links to a detailed Chandler biography, a bibliography of other works dealing with Chandler, commentary by noted mystery writers, and more.

Visit the "Shifting World of Philip K. Dick" at **http://dove.mtx.net.au/~jrowse/pkd/dick.html** for massive amounts of information and many links to other dedicated sites and interesting articles.

Stephen Crane

 http://www.en.utexas.edu/~mmaynard/Crane/crane.html

Though only 29 when he died, Stephen Crane (1871-1900) made an indelible mark on America's sense of itself when he wrote the one Civil War novel known by nearly every American schoolkid for three generations: *The Red Badge of Courage*. Get to know him better at this site.

Emily Dickinson

 http://www.jacs.com/ed.html

Emily Dickinson (1830-1886) was a spinster of Amherst, Massachusetts. Before her death at 56, she had composed well over 1,000 brief lyrics, her "letter to the world" as she called it. She wrote most of them in seclusion, and showed them to hardly anyone—only a few friends during her lifetime. Of course, subsequent generations have seen her works widely publicized.

Philip K. Dick

 http://dove.mtx.net.au/~jrowse/pkd/dick.html

Though Philip K. Dick (1928-1982) is best known today as the author of *Do Androids Dream of Electric Sheep?*, which was subsequently made into the movie *Bladerunner*, he was far more than a mere science fiction writer. He produced a large collection of novels and short stories that are a wealth of uniquely imaginative ideas. His ideas about humanity, reality, and God ring with ever-increasing relevance. With Dick, things are never what they appear to be. His finest work, *The Man in the High Castle*, is an amazing feat of philosophic speculation.

John Dos Passos

 http://www.english.upenn.edu/~afilreis/50s/aaron-chap15.html

We cannot forget John Dos Passos (1896-1970) whose bitter, highly impressionistic novels attacking the hypocrisy of materialism in the United States between the two world wars influenced several generations of American novelists. *Three Soldiers* (1921), *Manhattan Transfer* (1925), and the *U.S.A. Trilogy* comprised of *42nd Parallel* (1930), *1919* (1932), and *The Big Money* (1936)—are some of the most important American novels ever written.

Theodore Dreiser

 http://www.ihs1830.org/
dreiser.htm

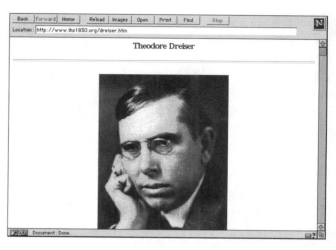

Theodore Dreiser (1871-1945) was the author of many novels, among them *Sister Carrie* (1900), *Jennie Gerhardt* (1911), and *An American Tragedy* (1925). However, it took considerable time for Dreiser's talent to become recognized. In its first year in print, *Sister Carrie* sold only 450 copies. But by the time he wrote *An American Tragedy* in the mid-'20s, Dreiser's reputation was known, and he was widely renowned as an engaging, talented, and original writer.

T.S. (Thomas Stearns) Eliot

 http://www.usl.edu/Departments/
English/authors/eliot/index.html

T.S. Eliot (1888-1965) is by far the most important poet of the 20th century. He was a reluctant American, however. Although he was born here (St. Louis) and schooled at Harvard, he soon retreated to the United Kingdom, became a subject of the Crown, and swore allegiance to the Church of England. At this Website you'll find a detailed biography of Eliot along with images and the texts of several of his most important works, including "The Hollow Men," "The Love Song of J. Alfred Prufrock," and "The Waste Land."

Ralph Waldo Emerson

http://miso.wwa.com/~jej/
1emerson.html

Born in Concord, Massachusetts in 1803, Ralph Waldo Emerson was among the country's most influential thinkers. The son of a Congregationalist minister, Emerson became one himself for a short while. Because he couldn't agree with the doctrine, Emerson left his only pastorate (Boston's Old North Church) after just three years.

As a writer and poet, Emerson developed his Transcendentalist themes through his work and lectures. Some of his best known essays are "The Over-Soul," "Compensation," and "Self-Reliance." At this excellent Website you will find a complete biography of Emerson, portraits, texts of all of his most important works, and much more.

William Faulkner

   http://www.mcsr.olemiss.edu/~egjbp/
faulkner/faulkner.html

Come to Yoknapatawpha County, Mississippi, the fictitious backdrop William Faulkner (1897-1962) used for novels and stories written over a span of five decades. From his earlier novels like *The Sound and the Fury* (1929) and *As I Lay Dying* (1930) to his last novels, *The Reivers* (1962) and the posthumously published *Flags in the Dust* (1973), Nobel laureate Faulkner brought an American sense of place to his writing every bit as magical as that of Mark Twain. These beautiful pages can point you in many directions to explore Faulkner's long and productive career. Learn about his novels, poems, screenplays, and other works, plus trivia and much more.

F Scott Fitzgerald

   http://www.sc.edu/fitzgerald/

F. Scott Fitzgerald (1896-1940) just had his centennial last year. He is, of course, the man who gave us *The Great Gatsby* and *Tender is the Night*. His earliest novel, *This Side of Paradise*, is now available online at Project Bartleby, which is referenced earlier. One of the very nice things about these Web pages dedicated to Fitzgerald is that you can access sound files of Fitzgerald reading poems by John Masefield and others.

Erle Stanley Gardner

   http://www.phantoms.com/
~phantom/gardner/

What Arthur Conan Doyle and Dorothy Sayers did to establish the quintessential British sleuths in Sherlock Holmes and Lord Peter Wimsey, Erle Stanley Gardner (1889-1970) did for American sleuths with his Perry Mason. He wrote 155 books (of which 86 are Perry Mason novels) and a total of 300,000,000 copies are out in the world. *The Guiness Book of Records* lists Gardner as second only to Barbara Cartland in the number of books in print. Want to learn more about this somewhat underrated and mysterious author and his old stomping grounds? Check out this site for some surprising and entertaining reading.

Allen Ginsberg Interview

   http://www.iuma.com/Seconds/html/
issue28/Allen_Ginsburg.html

Who were his influences? Blake, Kerouac, Whitman, Rimbaud, Poe, and

Pound. What did all those writers have in common? "Naked mind. Art for art's sake. Experimental form. Not experimental but self-invented forms. And some expansion of consciousness."

Bret Harte

 http://www.malakoff.com/bret.htm

Born in Albany, New York, Bret Harte (1836-1902) is best known for his tales of the gold rush in California, among them *The Luck of Roaring Camp* and *The Outcasts of Poker Flat*. Like many writers of his generation—among them Nathaniel Hawthorne—he supplemented his writing income by serving as a U.S. consul. Harte was first posted to Prussia (1878) and subsequently Glasgow (1880-85). He lived the rest of his life in London.

Nathaniel Hawthorne

 http://www.bnl.com/shorts/veilhawt.html

One of Nathaniel Hawthorne's greatest short stories is "The Minister's Black Veil." You can read the entire tale right here, at the URL elucidated here. Hawthorne (1804-64) was of course one of our great 19th century prose stylists and the author of such novels as *The House of the Seven Gables* and *The Scarlet Letter*.

Ernest Hemingway

 http://www.ee.mcgill.ca/~nverever/hem/pindex.html

Ernest Hemingway (1899-1961) is someone I've already written about at length elsewhere in this book. At this Web page, you'll find a fantastic biography of "Hem" along with images, links to Hemingway's prose in cyberspace, and much more.

William Dean Howells

 http://www.tiac.net/users/eldred/wdh/howells.html

William Dean Howells (1837-1920) was the author of many popular novels, among them *The Rise of Silas Lapham* (1885), *Their Wedding Journey* (1871), *The Shadow of a Dream* (1890), and *The Day of Their Wedding* (1895). This site includes the complete texts of all these novels plus images, a biography, an obituary, and criticism.

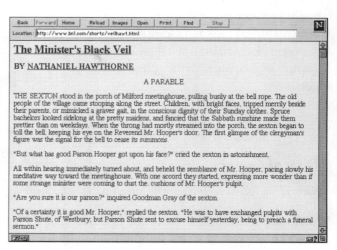

Washington Irving

http://www.en.utexas.edu/~maria/
irving/washbio.htm

Washington Irving (1783-1859) is the man who gave us Rip Van Winkle and "The Legend of Sleepy Hollow." He also wrote the excellent *Diedrich Knieckerbocker's History of New York, A Tour of the Prairies, A Book of the Hudson, Wolfert's Roost, History of the Life and Voyages of Christopher Columbus,* and numerous other books. Irving lived and died in Tarrytown, New York, where he lies buried.

Washington Irving

Location: http://www.en.utexas.edu/~maria/irving/washbio.htm

Washington Irving

Washington Irving was born in New York City April 3, 1783. He was the youngest member of a prosperous merchant family. Furthering his education, Irving traveled to Europe from 1804 to 1806. After his European tour, he continued to study law in New York. However, his interests in law slowly disappeared as his zeal for writing literature overtook him. It is here

Henry James

http://www.son.wisc.edu/~schuster/
james.htm

These Web pages not only provide biographical information on Henry James (1843-1916), but also e-texts of *The Ambassadors* and other of James' books. My all-time favorite James story is the hauntingly beautiful *A Turn of the Screw*, the best ghost story ever put to paper.

Jack Kerouac

http://www.charm.net/~brooklyn/
People/JackKerouac.html

Jack Kerouac (1922-69) was born in Lowell, Massachusetts where today he lies buried. He was the quintessential "beat" novelist. I don't know any-

one with a brain who has escaped teenager-hood without reading Kerouac's *On the Road* and *The Dharma Bums.*

Stephen King

http://www.careweb.com/king/

What? You think Stephen King is out of place on an author list with Walt

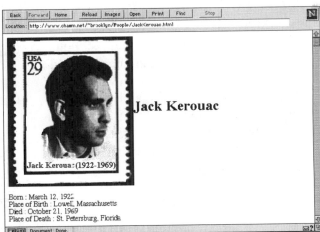

Location: http://www.charm.net/~brooklyn/People/JackKerouac.html

Jack Kerouac

USA 29

Jack Kerouac (1922-1969)

Born : March 12, 1922
Place of Birth : Lowell, Massachusetts
Died : October 21, 1969
Place of Death : St. Petersburg, Florida

Whitman and Emily Dickinson? Well, King is touching something so universal in the American psyche that he is one of the widest-read writers of all time. So, whether you're a fan or prefer to eye King nervously from a distance, now you can take a spine-tingling stroll through these pages for information on King's books and movies. There is also a biography of King, two chapters from an upcoming book called *Wizard & Glass*, and plenty of very interesting trivia. For more useful links, including how to get *Phantasmagoria,* the Stephen King Newsletter, check out **http://wwwcsif.cs.ucdavis.edu/~pace/king.html.**

Stephen King

The Master of Horror

Ring Lardner

 http://ourworld.compuserve.com/homepages/Topping/

According to the historical marker in front of his childhood home in Niles, Michigan, Ring Lardner (1885-1933) was a "sports writer, humorist, and sardonic observer of the American scene." Lardner's most popular works include his famous baseball stories and his sports reporting. Lardner was also an accomplished short story author. Find out more at this site about the man who single-handedly defined 20th century American sports writing.

Literary Kicks

 http://www.charm.net/~brooklyn

Get great profiles and other information concerning the Beats: Jack Kerouac, Allen Ginsberg, Neal Cassady, William S. Burroughs, Gary Snyder, Lawrence Ferlinghetti, Gregory Corso, and Michael McClure.

Jack London

 http://www.parks.sonoma.net/JLStory.html

As I've said elsewhere in this book, Jack London (1876-1916) is one of my great heroes. Here you'll find biographical information on Jack along with photographs. If you would like to read one of Jack's classic short stories—"To Build a Fire"—go to the URL **http://www.bnl.com/shorts/firelndn.html.**

H.P. Lovecraft

 http://nti.uji.es/CPE/ed/0.0/hpl/

Howard Phillips Lovecraft (1890-1937) was born and died in Providence, Rhode Island, and he was the author of some of the most frightening prose ever concocted. Stephen King has expressed his debt to Lovecraft many times. To learn more about this New England horror phenomenon, check out the H.P. Lovecraft home page. Another very good Lovecraftian site is located at **http://www.primenet.com/~dloucks/hpl/**.

Norman Mailer

 http://www.kersplat.com/interview/norm.htm

Norman Mailer (born 1923) is one of our most important contemporary writers. His career began with *The Naked and the Dead* (1948) and hasn't stopped since. Mailer not only writes novels but also elevates nonfiction to the highest of art forms, as in his *The Prisoner of Sex* (1971) and *The Executioner's Song* (1979).

Herman Melville

 http://www.melville.org

He's the man who gave us *Moby Dick*. Nevertheless, Herman Melville (1819-91) died in obscurity. I've spoken about Melville elsewhere in this book as being a Luddite. He was also, of course, a great genius who never ceases to amaze us. There is always something new, interesting, and complex in Melville.

This extensive site dedicated to Melville includes a biography, images, links to e-texts of his books, contemporary reviews of his books, Melville's letters to Nathaniel Hawthorne, book reviews written by Melville, Melville's obituary notices, Melville's own reflections on his life and works, and links to other Melville-related sites on the World Wide Web.

Edna St. Vincent Millay

 http://www.millaycolony.org/ednabio.html

Edna St. Vincent Millay (1892-1950) was born in Maine and graduated from Vassar (1917) having already won fame with the

publication of "Renascence" (1912), which was later the title poem of her first volume, *Renascence and Other Poems* (1917). She was also a social activist for many causes.

National Book Award Winners in Fiction

 http://www.bookbroker.com/ natbkwin.htm

Going back to 1950, this list chronicles every winner to date including John Cheever for *The Wapshot Chronicle* (1958), E.L. Doctorow for *World's Fair* (1986) and Walker Percy for *The Moviegoer* (1962).

Flannery O'Connor

 http://ruby.ils.unc.edu/flannery/ Bionotes.htm

Mary Flannery O'Connor (1925-1964) was an author from Georgia. Her Gothic

novels and short stories are chilling and hard to forget. The first of them, *Wise Blood* (1952), tells the tale of a young religious fanatic who tries to establish a church without Christ in the Georgia Mountains. Her second, *The Violent Bear It Away* (1960), is a macabre tale set in the backwoods of Georgia. It presents the fanatical mission of a boy intent on baptizing a still younger boy. Her short stories, among them "A Good Man is Hard to Find," are equally eerie although they are all, as well, infused with Christian symbolism and allegory.

Eugene O'Neill

 http://www.ucc.uconn.edu/ ~lrh95001/eopics.html

Eugene O'Neill (1888-1953) is the playwright who gave us *Mourning Becomes Electra, The Iceman Cometh*, and *Long Day's Journey Into Night*. His daughter, Oona, married Charlie Chaplin. Chaplin's actress daughter, Geraldine Chaplin, is O'Neill's granddaughter.

Dorothy Parker

 http://www.suck-my-big. org/poems/

Acid tongued Dorothy Parker (1893-1967) was a popular poet and writer. She was also, without a doubt, the wittiest member of the Algonquin Round

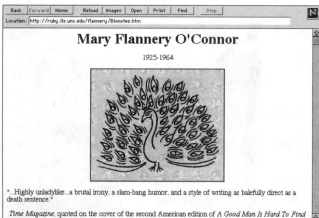

Mary Flannery O'Connor

1925-1964

"...Highly unladylike...a brutal irony, a slam-bang humor, and a style of writing as balefully direct as a death sentence."

Time Magazine, quoted on the cover of the second American edition of *A Good Man Is Hard To Find*

Table. Transcriptions of her three collected volumes of poetry are scattered around the Net, but this site is a good place to start exploring. And if you need a deadly barb for your next cocktail party, go to **http://www.users.interport.net/~lynda/dorothy.html** and study up on a few select Parker one-liners.

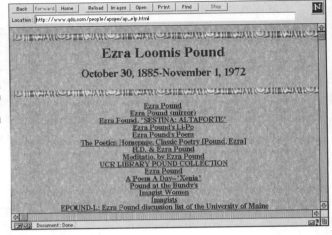

George Plimpton

 http://gyoza.com/frank/html/01plimpton.html

George Plimpton is the editor (and one of the founders) of *The Paris Review*. He is also a gifted writer in his own right. He enjoys fireworks not just as a spectator, but as a rocketeer himself. It has been my pleasure to be among the guests at his home in Wainscott—near East Hampton, New York—for the pyrotechnics of more than one 4th of July.

Ezra Pound

 http://www.qds.com/people/apope/ap_elp.html

Ezra Pound (1885-1972) was a brilliant poet. He was also an anti-Semite and a collaborator with the Nazis. He was born in Idaho, reared in Pennsylvania, and spent most of his life in Italy, where he died in 1972. He was a great admirer of Mussolini. During the war he broadcast Fascist propa-

Edgar Allen Poe

 http://www.acadiacom.net/mia23/poe.html

Edgar Allen Poe (1809-49) was born in Boston, the son of itinerant actors. His haunting prose and poetry will live forever. One of the most frightening stories I have ever read is "The Murders in the Rue Morgue." And who can forget that immortal poem, "The Raven"?

ganda over the Rome radio, and afterward was returned to the United States to face trial for treason. Adjudged to be of unsound mind, he was committed (1946-58) to St. Elizabeth's Hospital near Washington. Robert Frost and Ernest Hemingway lobbied for his release, and when the release came Pound promptly returned to Italy.

Ayn Rand

 http://www.vix.com/pub/objectivism/ Writing/RandBiography.html

A naturalized American, Ayn Rand (1905-1982) was born in Russia. Her first novel, *We, the Living* (1936) depicts young Russian individualists trapped and destroyed by totalitarian dictatorship. *Anthem* (1938) is a short novel about a heroic dissenter in a future monolithic and collectivized state. *The Fountainhead* (1943) is a long biographical novel praising the independence of an architect modeled on Frank Lloyd Wright. *Atlas Shrugged* (1957) treats

the value of a superior concept of individualism related to people who plan a new society based on the oath: "I will never live for the sake of another man, nor ask any other man to live for mine." *For the New Intellectual* (1961) collects the passages of these four novels to present Rand's philosophy of objectivism.

John Crowe Ransom

 http://www.library.vanderbilt.edu/ speccol/jcrbiog.html

John Crowe Ransom (1888-1974) was one of the major voices in 20th century American poetry. His books include *Poems About God* (1919), *Chills and Fever* (1924), *Grace After Meat* (1924), and *Two Gentlemen in Bonds* (1927). He taught at Vanderbilt (1914-37) where he was a leader of the Agrarians and an editor of *The Fugitive*. In 1937 he joined the faculty of Kenyon College, where he founded *The Kenyon Review*. So long as undergraduates may not escape their freshman year without reading Ransom's "Bells for John Whiteside's Daughter," there is hope for American civilization.

"The Ransom of Red Chief" by O. Henry

 http://www.bnl.com/shorts/ redchief.html

This classic story was written by O. Henry and was a favorite of my grandmother's. The story has been made into several films through the years, but it is best rendered by O. Henry himself. You'll find the complete text of the story faithfully reproduced on this Web page.

Gertrude Stein

 http://www.tenderbuttons.com/

Gertrude Stein (1874-1946) was born in Pennsylvania, educated in Europe and at Radcliffe, then moved permanently to Paris, where she sat in the eye of the artistic and literary hurricane swirling through the '20s and '30s. Writing both poetry and prose, her work was and is challenging and experimental. The pages maintained at **http://www.tenderbuttons.com/** provide poetry, photos, and some scholarly links, including one to the excellent Gertrude Stein Memorial Webpage (**http://www. magibox.net/~stein/**) and one to the Alice B. Toklas home page. Some more biographic information can be found at **http://www. sappho.com/poetry/g_stein.htm**.

John Steinbeck

 http://www.byronpreiss.com/ 21st/pearl/steinbec.htm

John Steinbeck (1902-1968) created fiction that combined realism and romance, but not always harmoniously. His settings are often rural areas, where people live most happily when close to nature, but where malevolent forces, such as drought or labor and market conditions or human greed, often destroy the vital relationship between man and land. In dealing with the consequent problems, Steinbeck's approach is sometimes lyric and mystical, sometimes realistic and sociological. His books include *Of Mice and Men, The Grapes of Wrath, Cannery Row, East of Eden*, and *The Winter of Our Discontent*. One of my favorites isn't a novel at all. *Sea of Cortez* was written in 1941 by Steinbeck along with his friend, marine biologist Ed Ricketts. It is a journal of their travels and marine research in the Gulf of California. Get it. Read it.

Harriet Beecher Stowe

http://www.cs.cmu.edu/People/ mmbt/women/StoweHB.html

The publication of Stowe's novel, *Uncle Tom's Cabin*, literally changed the course of American history. But there's more to Harriet Beecher Stowe (1811-1896) than one novel. Find out more about Stowe the novelist and Stowe the abolitionist at this site. And if you want to read *Uncle Tom's Cabin*, all you have to do is download the whole text from **ftp://uiarchive.cso.uiuc.edu/pub/etext/gutenberg/etext95/utomc10.txt**.

Henry David Thoreau

 http://envirolink.org/elib/enviroethics/thoreauindex.html

Henry David Thoreau (1817-1862) needs no introduction. We all know of his life at the little pond outside of Concord, Massachusetts, which he wrote up in the volume *Walden*. We are equally familiar with his *Week on the Concord and Merrimack Rivers*, *The Maine Woods*, *Cape Cod*, and *A Yankee In Canada*.

James Thurber

 http://www.phx.com/alt1/archive/books/reviews/12-95/JAMES_THURBER.html

If James Thurber (1894-1961) had written nothing besides *The Secret Life of Walter Mitty* and *The Thirteen Clocks*, his place among America's great writers would be secure. But in a long career as novelist, short story writer, columnist, and cartoonist, he tickled America's funny bone a thousand different ways and made us understand ourselves a little better for the experience. Visit this site for a biography and links to cartoons and more.

Mark Twain

 http://web.syr.edu/~fjzwick/twainwww.html

Samuel Langhorne Clemens (1835-1910) was, of course, popularly known as Mark Twain, and the author of such classics as *Huckleberry Finn, Tom Sawyer, Roughing It*, and *A Connecticut Yankee in King Arthur's Court*. It is worth remembering that no less a writer than Ernest Hemingway said all modern American literature began with *Huckleberry Finn*.

This extensive Web page has links to texts of Twain's books online, criticism, Twain maxims and quotations, Twain biographies and criticism, Twain teaching resources, Mark Twain FAQ, and much more.

Gore Vidal: Monotheism and Its Discontents

 http://opera.cit.gu.edu.au/essays/
monotheism.html

Gore Vidal (born 1925) is perhaps most noted for his historical novels, among them *Burr* (1973), a favorable fictive view of Aaron Burr. Other volumes in Vidal's American canon include *1876* (1976) and *D.C.* (1967). Vidal is the author of many other novels as well as screenplays and literary criticism. He ran unsuccessfully for Congress (as a Democrat) in Dutchess County, New York, in the 1960s. This Web page reprints a talk he gave at Harvard.

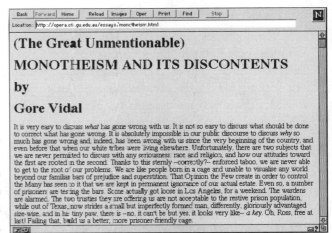

(The Great Unmentionable)
MONOTHEISM AND ITS DISCONTENTS
by
Gore Vidal

It is very easy to discuss *what* has gone wrong with us. It is not so easy to discuss what should be done to correct what has gone wrong. It is absolutely impossible in our public discourse to discuss *why* so much has gone wrong and, indeed, has been wrong with us since the very beginning of the country, and even before that when our white tribes were living elsewhere. Unfortunately, there are two subjects that we are never permitted to discuss with any seriousness: race and religion, and how our attitudes toward the first are rooted in the second. Thanks to this sternly --correctly?-- enforced taboo, we are never able to get to the root of our problems. We are like people born in a cage and unable to visualise any world beyond our familiar bars of prejudice and superstition. That Opinion the Few create in order to control the Many has seen to it that we are kept in permanent ignorance of our actual estate. Even so, a number of prisoners are testing the bars. Some actually got loose in Los Angeles, for a weekend. The wardens are alarmed. The two trusties they are offering us are not acceptable to the restive prison population, while out of Texas, now strides a small but imperfectly formed man, differently, gloriously advantaged size-wise, and in his tiny paw, there is --no, it can't be but yes, it looks very like-- *a key*. Oh, Ross, free at last! Failing that, build us a better, more prisoner-friendly cage.

Kurt Vonnegut, Jr.

 http://copper.ucs.indiana.edu/~briscott/
vonnegut.html

Vonnegut was born in 1922. The reasons I like him are summed up in this quote:

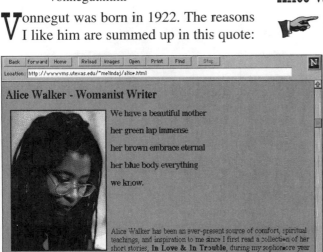

Alice Walker - Womanist Writer

We have a beautiful mother

her green lap immense

her brown embrace eternal

her blue body everything

we know.

Alice Walker has been an ever-present source of comfort, spiritual teachings, and inspiration to me since I first read a collection of her short stories, **In Love & In Trouble**, during my sophomore year of college in 1982.

"This is what I find most encouraging about the writing trades: They allow mediocre people who are patient and industrious to revise their stupidity, to edit themselves into something like intelligence. They also allow lunatics to seem saner than sane."

Alice Walker

 http://wwwvms.utexas.edu/
~melindaj/alice.html

Alice Walker is one of the most eloquent and politically involved literary voices in America today. If you only know her from her novel *The Color Purple*, you have only scratched the surface of this complex writer and activist. From the civil rights movement to the anti-nuclear movement, the environmental movement, the women's movement, and most recently the movement to protect indigenous people, their cultures, and natural environments, Walker remains an outspoken activist on issues of oppression and power, championing the victims of racism, sexism, and military industrialism, and seeking to preserve our natural heritages. Come to these expansive pages for a biography, interviews, articles, and links to other pages dedicated to Walker and her work.

Another site, **http://www-engl.cla.umn. edu/lkd/vfg/Authors/AliceWalker**, provides more biographic information, some lovely photos, and links with emphasis on repeated efforts to censor Walker's work.

Edith Wharton

 http://www.english.cup.edu/~fred/ ewharton.html

Edith Wharton (1962-1937) is perhaps best known for the short novel *Ethan Frome* (1911). She came from an affluent New York family and was privately educated in the United States and Europe. Others of her novels include *The House of Mirth*

(1905) and *The Age of Innocence* (1920). At this Web page you not only get a biography of Wharton and many excellent graphics, but also links to e-texts of Wharton's books including *The House of Mirth, Summer*, and *The Age of Innocence*.

Walt Whitman

 http://frieda.art.uiuc.edu/gd360/scrary/ usa/cont.html

Walt Whitman (1819-1892) was, of course, the author of what is perhaps the most influential book of poetry ever produced: *Leaves of Grass*. Poems in the volume include "Song of Myself, "When Lilacs Last in the Dooryard Bloom'd," and "Out of the Cradle Endlessly Rocking" among other classics. This site is packed with biographical information, illustrations, and links to e-texts of Whitman's poetical legacy.

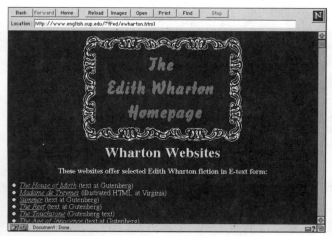

John Greenleaf Whittier

 http://www.pitt.edu/~dash/ whittier.html

John Greenleaf Whittier (1807-1892) was a Massachusetts-born Quaker with little formal education. What he did have was a profound gift for narrative verse, of which "Snowbound" and others of his poems are ample evidence. He was also a strident abolitionist and a great friend of William Lloyd Garrison. You'll find some of his more popular poems on this Web page.

William Carlos Williams

☞ http://www.library.kent.edu/speccoll/
poetry/williams.html

Physician, novelist, playwright, editor, essayist, and poet, William Carlos Williams was born in 1883 in Rutherford, New Jersey and died there in 1963.

Williams' novels include *The Great American Novel* (1923), *A Novelette and Other Prose* (1932), and *Selected Essays* (1954). He also wrote his autobiography in 1967.

Among all of his accomplishments, Williams stood out the most for his poetry. Many consider Williams among the best poets of his time. Williams' most famous poems include *The Tempers* (1917), *Sour Grapes* (1921), *Paterson* (1948), and *The Desert Music and Other Poems* (1954). *Pictures from Brueghel* (1963) won him the Pulitzer Prize for poetry.

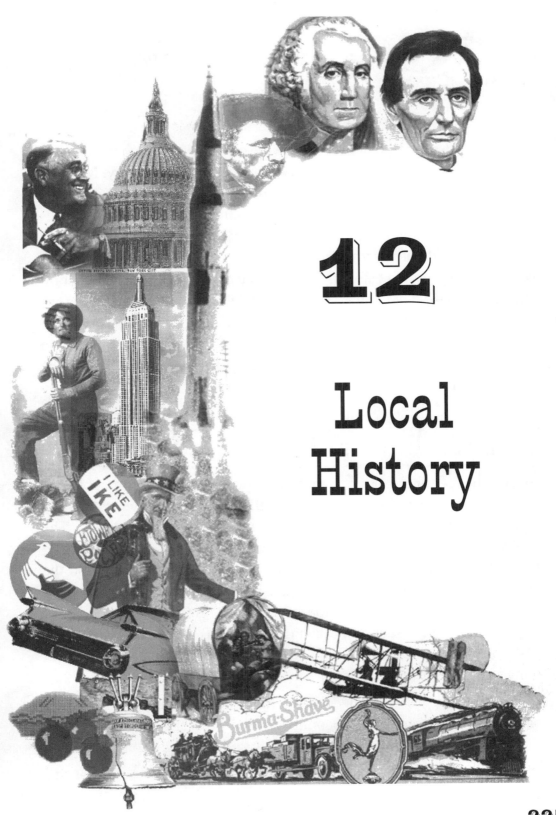

12

Local
History

Local historical societies nationwide do some of the most important historical research and preservation work in the country. Many of these local programs have impact and interest that is national in scope. For example, a small historical society in Maine saved and now preserves the home of Gettysburg hero Joshua Lawrence Chamberlain (**http://www.cfcsc.dnd.ca/links/bio/chamu.html**). In my own home town of Wickford, North Kingstown, Rhode Island (**http://www.cshell.com/nkcc/nkscenes/wick1.htm**), another small band of local history buffs has saved the site of Roger Williams' first Rhode Island trading post and the adjacent home of Williams' protégé Richard Smith. The properties in question have more than mere local interest, for they form the birthplace of practical religious freedom in America.

Saving the New-York Historical Society

Another of our most important local historical societies is that of New York (**http://www.cityconnection.com/NYHS/**). Two years ago it looked like the New-York Historical was about to go bankrupt. The endowment of the 193-year-old institution was in a mess, and dwindling fast. After a drastic restructuring, it now looks like the Society and the bulk of its collections will survive intact. But can an organization founded in 1804 with the vague mission of rescuing "from the...obscurity of private repositories such important documents as are liable to be lost or destroyed by...those into whose hands they may have fallen" successfully reinvent itself for the 21st century?

The Society was long been home to fine collections of Old Master paintings, Americana, and decorative arts. In the end it looks like the sacrifice of the Old Masters is what will save the organization and the balance of its holdings from a death sentence.

"The Historical Society must now identify its own special niche and audience among all the cultural institutions of New York City," wrote the Society's Executive Director, Betsy Gotbaum, in Sotheby's catalogue (**http://www.sothebys.com**) for one of the Old Masters sales last January. "These auctions...are one aspect of a grand plan to reinvent the New-York Historical Society, reach out to new audiences, and create permanent financial stability."

Stability drew near with the $16 million sale of Giovanni da Milano's "Crucifixion with The Virgin," and Lo Scheggia's "Triumph of Fame," among others. But with solvency came a range of well-publicized and heated debates. Perhaps the hottest response was *The New York Times'* art critic Michael Kimmelman's observation that "[the Society] is hoping to raise money, not to buy other works, as public institutions are supposed to do when they sell art from their collections, but to replenish an endowment...if this is the price the public must pay, [the Society] isn't worth saving."

From supporters came the response that the Society could no longer afford to exist as a repository for everything and anything under the philanthropic sun (costs for outside storage of the Society's collection run to $500,000 annually). Not only must the masterworks be sold to bulk up the endowment, but other less stellar holdings in the way of papers and decorative arts need to be sold as well.

And so, the auctions continue. As I write, Swann Galleries is about to begin a 30-month series of sales, estimated to bring in between $500,000 and $700,000. The sales will offer (among other things) maps, comic books, sheet music, British and Continental first editions, duplicate items, and other things judged outside the scope of the Society's mission or redundant among its holdings. The consensus is that this is the right thing to do. "Every large collection should go through this periodically," says one NYHS executive. "The research value of these materials is not great; no one would go to a historical society for [such materials as these]."

It is an interesting process. Let us just hope that it works and that the New-York Historical Society survives.

My Local History

There are no Web pages for historical societies in my neck of the woods: South County, Rhode Island. As I belong to most of them, this is probably something I should try to fix. One of these days—when I have a spare moment. For the moment, the best we can do in the way of Web pages is that of the elementary school where my children attend, Wickford Elementary, the oldest active public school in New England (**http://ride.ri.net/ schools/North_Kingstown/Wickford_El/Wickford_El.html**).

Despite the overall absence of relevant Web pages, I'd be negligent if, in this chapter on local history, I did not at least tell you a little something about the fascinating and beautiful village—Wickford, Rhode Island—that my family and I call home.

The story of the village is really the story of a great house, its rude beginnings in the land of the Narragansett Indians, its flourishing, its decline, and its final restoration. We must start with the name the Indians gave to the land here: *Cocumscussoc.*

Roger Williams and his friend Richard Smith came to this desolate spot sometime between 1636 and 1639, and from their frontier trading post emerged the first of the great slaveholding plantations of the region and its mansion house, popularly known as "Smith's Castle," which still stands and has been restored to its former glory after years of neglect.

Cocumscussoc was the focal point of the diverse forces and cross-currents—political, military, commercial, agricultural, religious, and social—that shaped the uncertain destiny of the struggling Rhode Island colony. The place played a vital role in the largest and bloodiest engagements of the Indian wars in New England: the Great Swamp fight. And it served as capitol of the Narragansett country during the prolonged boundary controversy with Connecticut.

Ben Franklin (**http://oz.plymouth.edu/~biology/history/franklin.html**) was a guest at Smith's Castle. So was Bishop Berkeley. So too was my forbear, Charles Carroll of Carrollton. Just down the road, in a snuff mill at the head of the Narrow River, is the birthplace of colonial portrait painter Gilbert Stuart, 1755-1828 (**http://sunsite.unc.edu/cjackson/stuart/**)—maker of famous paintings of Washington, Adams, Jefferson, Madison, and John Jay, among others. Stuart was born here in 1755 and christened in the Episcopal Church of St. Paul's, which still stands (though not in its original spot). The snuff mill also stands, and is protected and cherished today as it will be for generations to come.

We try not to tear down our history too quickly around here. Just as the Gilbert Stuart snuff mill is safe forever, so are Smith's Castle and the venerable St. Paul's. And I am happy to say, after exploring this topic on the Web, the same spirit of local preservation seems strong throughout the country.

Local History on the Web

There is no scarcity of local history as represented on the Web: local historical societies, local historical archives, and local history online exhibits. The resources are, in fact, voluminous and, if I may say so, heartening. For they send a message to me that the country is filled with people who care, and care passionately, about the intricacies of the American past, who know it is important, and who intend to pass on its stories and artifacts to succeeding generations.

Let's see what some of these remarkable people are up to.

Albany County (Wyoming) Historical Society

 http://www.uwyo.edu/ahc/achs/index.htm

Wyoming's Laramie Plains lie between the Medicine Bow Mountains on the west and the Laramie Range on the east. The Sioux, the Cheyenne, and the Arapaho carved out ancient trails and followed the Laramie Rivers across this basin. Then came the mountain men and the settlers. Check in with the Albany County Historical Society for more on the history of the Laramie Plains—fascinating crossroads of frontier history.

Albemarle County (Virginia) Historical Society

 http://monticello.avenue.gen.va.us/go/ACHS/

Founded in 1940, the Albemarle County Historical Society offers a variety of public programs, including exhibits, publications, lectures, walking tours, oral history interviews, and various educational programs. The Society also maintains a research library containing over 2,000 books and bound periodicals, as well as photographs, manuscripts, maps, pamphlets, newspapers, and more relating to the history of the community. And the Website is replete with links to Monticello, home of Thomas Jefferson, and many history, genealogy, and preservation resources.

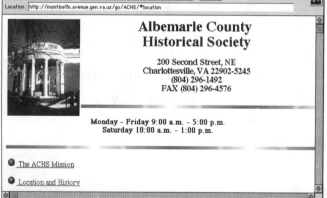

Albemarle County Historical Society

200 Second Street, NE
Charlottesville, VA 22902-5245
(804) 296-1492
FAX (804) 296-4576

Monday - Friday 9:00 a.m. - 5:00 p.m.
Saturday 10:00 a.m. - 1:00 p.m.

The ACHS Mission

Location and History

Amana Colonies

 http://www.jeonet.com/amanas/

Learn all about the German and Swiss settlers who turned seven villages on 26,000 acres in the Iowa River Valley of eastern Iowa into one of the most successful and long-lived experiments in communal living anywhere on earth. Visit these pages for information on Amana museums, tours, historical heritage, visitor information, the famous Amana crafts and industries, and more.

Arizona Historical Society

 http://emol.org/emol/tucson/ahs/ahsindex.html

The Arizona Historical Society provides a museum of Southwest history in Tucson. On its Web pages you'll find good information on the museum's ongoing exhibits, a great tutorial history on the founding of Tucson, and links to other Websites related to Tucson history, Arizona history, and southwestern history generally.

Aspen (Colorado) Historical Society

 http://aspen.com/aspenonline/
directory/ae/sponsors/artscouncil/
sponsors/histsoc/index.histsoc.html

Aspen is not just a meeting place for the rich and famous and a place to ski. The purpose of the Aspen Historical Society is to educate the public about the whole history of the Aspen region and its place in the history of the American West. Visit this site for more on Aspen and for a sample of the approximately 10,000 photos available through the Historical Society's archives for reproduction and viewing.

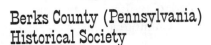

Berks County (Pennsylvania) Historical Society

 http://www.berksweb.com/histsoc.html

The Historical Society of Berks County, Pennsylvania is dedicated to collecting, preserving and fostering an appreciation for the historically important architecture of Berks County and the preservation of some 20,000 artifacts of colonial and Civil War history. Toward this end, the Society maintains a fine museum, details on which you can find here at the Society's Web page.

Besancon Historical Society

The Besancon Historical Society
15533 Lincoln Highway East

Besancon (Indiana) Historical Society

 http://cvax.ipfw.indiana.edu/www/
depts/history/historgs/besanco.html

The Besancon Historical Society exists to help interpret and pass along the history and heritage of the settlers of Besancon, Indiana. The Society promotes historical and genealogical research, conserves historic sites and structures, collects and preserves artifacts, and works to stimulate interest in the history of the region. These Web pages provide many details on the Society's varied and interesting projects.

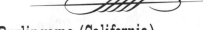

Burlingame (California) Historical Society

 http://www.spectrumnet.com/~spectrum/
history/history.html

The town of Burlingame, California has a rich past, as is documented in the official Web pages of the Burlingame Historical Society. For example, consider the town's "Wurlitzer Fountain" located on Chapin

Avenue. German sculptor Walter Schott (1861-1938) created the fountain around 1910 and named it "Three Dancing Maidens." Rudolph Wurlitzer, the organ company founder bought the fountain in Germany after it had accumulated such awards as the Grand Prize at the 1910 World Exposition in Brussels and the Great Gold Medal from the Munich Glass Palace Exhibition in 1912. Wurlitzer brought the fountain to his home in Ohio where it remained until his son moved it to Burlingame in the '50s. You can see an identical fountain in the Conservatory Garden of New York's Central Park.

Chicago Historical Society

 http://chicagohs.org/

The Chicago Historical Society presents several absolutely fabulous, permanent Web exhibits. My favorite is entitled "The Chicago Fire and The Web of Memory," which details the history (and folklore) of the fire with first person accounts and artifacts.

Welcome to *The Great Chicago Fire and The Web of Memory,* a commemorative exhibition created by the Chicago Historical Society and Northwestern University

Columbia: The Magazine of Northwest History

 http://www.kcts.org/edusvs/wshshtml/main.htm

Access great digital reprints of fine illustrated articles from Columbia, the publication of the Washington State Historical Society. Be sure to check the article entitled "Climbing Mt. Rainier with Curtis in 1909"—a splendid illustrated piece concerning the explorer and photographer Edward S. Curtis (1868-1952).

Cranford (New Jersey) Historical Society

 http://www.bobdevlin.com/crhissoc.html

Dubbed the "Venice of New Jersey," Cranford, New Jersey on the Rahway River remained relatively secluded until the late 1830's when the railroads made it accessible from New York City. Find many more details about Cranford at this Web page.

Dallas Jewish Historical Society

 http://nimon.ncc.com/dvjcc/DJHS.html

The Dallas Jewish Historical Society is committed to preserving Dallas' rich Jewish history, and to promoting research and education in Jewish culture and history.

Evanston (Illinois) Historical Society

 http://www.adena.com/ehs/ index.htm

The Evanston Historical Society was founded in 1898 to collect and preserve the history of Chicago's oldest northern suburb. Today the Society employs four full-time and five part-time professional staff members to fulfill its mission. Its offices are in the home of vice president of the United States and Nobel laureate Charles Gates Dawes, which also serves as the Society's museum.

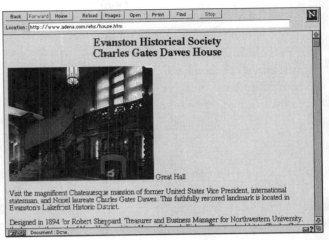

Evanston Historical Society
Charles Gates Dawes House

Great Hall

Visit the magnificent Chateauesque mansion of former United States Vice President, international statesman, and Nobel laureate Charles Gates Dawes. This faithfully restored landmark is located in Evanston's Lakefront Historic District.

Designed in 1894 for Robert Sheppard, Treasurer and Business Manager for Northwestern University,

Grand Trunk Western Historical Society

 http://www.rrhistorical.com/gtwhs/ index.html

The Grand Trunk Western Historical Society records and preserves artifacts and the history of the Grand Trunk Western Railroad—once one of the greatest railroads in the country. This was the old railroad of the northern Midwest, primarily running between Michigan and Wisconsin.

Hart County (Kentucky) Historical Society

 http://www.ovnet.com/userpages/ feenerty/history.html

The Hart County Historical Society is one of the most active of the many small, local historical societies across the country. They have a terrific set of Web pages and a great newsletter. They are currently up to their necks struggling to preserve the site of the Battle for the Bridge, fought September 14-17, 1862.

Hudson River Maritime Museum

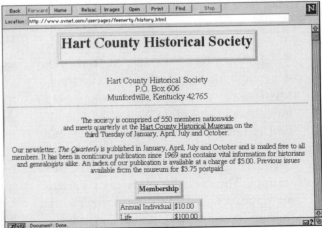 http://www1.mhv.net/~omi/hrmm.htm

The Hudson River Maritime Museum is dedicated to preserving the rich maritime

Hart County Historical Society

Hart County Historical Society
P.O. Box 606
Munfordville, Kentucky 42765

The society is comprised of 550 members nationwide and meets quarterly at the Hart County Historical Museum on the third Tuesday of January, April, July and October.

Our newsletter, *The Quarterly*, is published in January, April, July and October and is mailed free to all members. It has been in continuous publication since 1969 and contains vital information for historians and genealogists alike. An index of our publication is available at a charge of $5.00. Previous issues available from the museum for $3.75 postpaid.

Membership

| Annual Individual | $10.00 |
| Life | $100.00 |

heritage of the Hudson River, Rondout Creek, and Kingston, New York. Exhibits include coverage of the sloops of the Hudson, the great steamboats (such as the *Mary Powell*), and other related topics.

Issaquah (Washington) Historical Society

 http://www.issaquah.org/comorg/past/mpast.htm

The Historical Society of Issaquah, Washington not only has a great Web page, they also have an excellent museum dedicated to chronicling the history and heritage of this beautiful section of Washington State.

Itawamba Historical Society (Mississippi)

 http://www.network-one.com/~ithissoc/

In the town of Mantachie, located in the breathtaking Appalachian hill country of Mississippi, you will find the Itawamba Historical Society. At this Web page, you will find the Online Research Center, which contains the Society's online library of books devoted entirely to Itawamba County, Mississippi. This includes early county deeds, marriage records, Civil War documents, and links to Itawamba County family histories.

The Jewish Historical Society of Maryland

 http://www.jhsm.org/

Originally created to protect Baltimore's old Lloyd Street Synagogue, the Jewish Historical Society of Maryland today occupies and protects several synagogues and other important Jewish buildings. The site includes links to more local historical and genealogical resources.

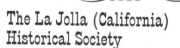

The La Jolla (California) Historical Society

http://www.iaco.com/features/lajolla/lifeinlj/history/ljhs.htm

Learn all about beautiful La Jolla, California's rich history as a center of tourism throughout the late 19th century and into the 20th century. With its more than 13 miles of rugged coastline, La Jolla has attracted some of the most notable Americans to its sandy shores. Read all about it courtesy of the La Jolla Historical Society.

Lake Erie Islands Historical Society

 http://www.leihs.org/

The Lake Erie Islands Historical Society is based on the island of Put-in-Bay, Ohio. It is dedicated to preserving lore and artifacts related to the Battle of Lake Erie, Lake Erie lighthouses, and other local history items of interest. Put-in-Bay is, by the way, where John Brown, Jr.—the son of the radical abolitionist—made his home for many years.

Lancaster County (Pennsylvania) Historical Society

 http://lanclio.org/

This rich set of Web pages includes not only historical data but also image archives, old maps, and much more. The Society's offices are in the Wilson Memorial Building in Lancaster County, located next door to Wheatland, the country home of President James Buchanan, which the Society has open to the public.

The Lenni Lenape Historical Society, Allentown, Pennsylvania

 http://www.lenape.org/main.html

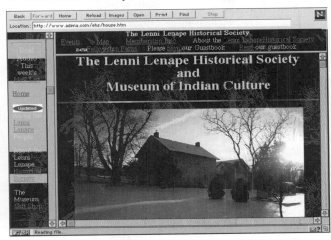

The Lenni Lenape Historical Society and Museum of Indian Culture was founded in 1980 by Carla J. S. Messinger of Allentown, Pennsylvania. Carla is a direct descendant of the home-band of the Lenni Lenape (one of the Delaware tribes). She presents multimedia programs on Lenape cultural heritage for schools, libraries, branches of the state and federal govenment, and more. These informative pages are dedicated to "unstereotyping" native Americans in eastern Pennsylvania and beyond.

Lexington (Massachusetts) Historical Society

 http://link.ci.lexington.ma.us/WWW/ LexHistSoc/lhspage.htm

The Lexington Historical Society takes responsibility for preserving and maintaining the many significant landmarks in the historic town of Lexington, Massachusetts. Lexington, of course, is where the "shot heard around the world" was fired, thus igniting the American Revolution.

The Louisville & Nashville Railroad Historical Society

 http://www.rrhistorical.com/lnhs/ index.html

Established in 1982, the Louisville & Nashville Railroad Historical Society collects, restores, preserves, and displays artifacts of the Louisville & Nashville railroad, which at its peak boasted over 6,000 miles of track in 13 eastern states.

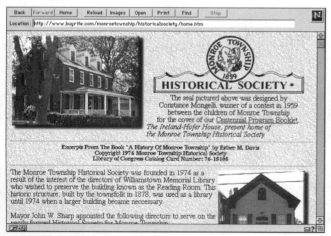

Minnesota Historical Society

 http://server.tt.net/icehousestudio/ pdgwebv1/jump/mhs.html

Chronicling the long and fascinating history of Minnesota, the Minnesota Historical Society is the home for many important archives. They also do work in the fields of historic preservation, and provide grants for research into local history. Visit the Web page for more details.

Missouri Historical Society

 http://coins0.coin.missouri.edu/ community/state-hist/index.html

The Missouri Historical Society provides an archive for state, town, and county records, genealogical publications, local histories, regional maps and atlases, and more. The Society also archives marriage records, birth and death data, census records, a photo collection, and unique resources related to early Missouri history. This is a rich source for people researching family histories or regional histories related to Missouri.

Monroe (New Jersey) Historical Society

 http://www.buyrite.com/ monroetownship/ historicalsociety/home.htm

The Historical Society of Monroe, New Jersey was founded in 1974 and is dedicated to preserving the history of this splendid little place in the New Jersey Pine Barrens. They have a museum, a rich archive of historical materials, and a first-rate Web page.

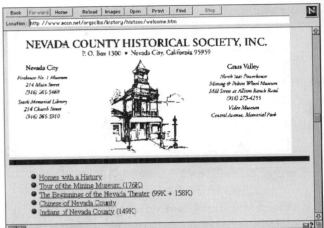

NEVADA COUNTY HISTORICAL SOCIETY, INC.
P. O. Box 1300 • Nevada City, California 95959

Nevada City
Firehouse No. 1 Museum
214 Main Street
(916) 265-5468
Searls Memorial Library
214 Church Street
(916) 265-5910

Grass Valley
North Star Powerhouse
Mining & Pelton Wheel Museum
Mill Street at Allison Ranch Road
(916) 273-4255
Video Museum
Central Avenue, Memorial Park

- Homes with a History
- Tour of the Mining Museum (176K)
- The Beginnings of the Nevada Theater (99K + 158K)
- Chinese of Nevada County
- Indians of Nevada County (149K)

Nevada County (California) Historical Society

 http://www.nccn.net/orgsclbs/history/histsoc/welcome.htm

Nevada City and Nevada County have a rich heritage stemming from the old mining days of the mid- to late-19th century. They also have a splendid architectural history. All of these remnants—all the great stories, artifacts, and buildings of the past—are chronicled and cared for by the Nevada County Historical Society.

New Bedford (Massachusetts) Whaling Museum of the Old Dartmouth Historical Society

 http://www.newbedford.com/whalingmuseum.html

The New Bedford Whaling Museum has been telling the story of this unique New England whaling port for more than 90 years. The Museum's exhibits include a one-half-scale model of a whaling ship—the largest ship model in the world at 89 feet in length—artistic artifacts such as Richard Ellis' 100-foot mural of sperm whales, and natural science artifacts like the skeleton of a humpback whale. Find out more about this splendid museum at the Web page.

New Hampshire Historical Society

 http://newww.com/org/nhhs/

Whatever your question, if it is about New Hampshire, past or present, the New Hampshire Historical Society is here to help you find the answer.

Need details on an obscure White Mountain landscape painter? Want to learn about such New Hampshire notables as Daniel Webster, Franklin Pierce, and Mary Baker Eddy? Want to do genealogical research into your family's New Hampshire roots? Start here, at the home page of the New Hampshire Historical Society.

Ohio Historical Society

 http://winslo.state.oh.us/ohswww/ohshome.html

The Ohio Historical Society is a nonprofit organization founded in 1885 to promote a knowledge of the archaeology and history of Ohio. The Society exists to interpret, preserve, collect, and make available evidence of the past, and it does so admirably.

Otter Tail County (Minnesota) Historical Society

 http://www.prtel.com/ffalls/events/ museum.htm

The Otter Tail County Historical Society is recognized by the Minnesota Historical Society as one of the best local history museums and archives in the entire state of Minnesota. The Society was organized in 1927 and houses artifacts, biographical information, photographs, and more.

Oyster Bay (New York) Historical Society

 http://members.aol.com/OBHistory/ index.html

We're not just for historians anymore! proudly trumpets the header on this page. The society has worked hard to make these pages reflect the fun-for-all-ages design of their historical museum in this Long Island town that dates back to the 1650s. They describe their historical tours as hands-on time machine trips, making regular stops in the 1740s (looking in on an Oyster Bay tradesman), the 1780s (playing with Revolutionary War period reproduc-

tion articles), and the 1830s (entertaining in the parlor of Marmaduke Earle). Oh, you don't know Marmaduke Earle? Visit these pages to learn more.

Palisades Amusement Park (New Jersey) Historical Society

 http://members.aol.com/palisades1/ index.html

What could be more local than an amusement park? The Palisades Amusement Park has been closed for over twenty-five years, but its famous Cyclone roller coaster and Tunnel of Love have a special warm spot in the hearts of many. Welcome to the main gate of the Palisades Amusement Park Historical Society, dedicated to the preservation of this uniquely American spot.

Pejepscot (Maine) Historical Society

http://www.curtislibrary.com/ pejepscot.htm

Established in the 1880s, the Pejepscot Historical Society serves the Pejepscot region of Maine and is one of Maine's oldest historical organizations. One of the Society's three museums is the Maine home of Civil War hero Joshua Lawrence Chamberlain, which the Society rescued from demolition in 1982 and is in the process of restoring.

Plymouth (Pennsylvania) History

 http://www.liu18.k12.pa.us/
~wvwmain/plymouth.html#list

Read about the history of Plymouth, Pennsylvania including such interesting gems as how the town was named, the rich Indian history of the area, as well as information on early settlers and the local industry of this coal-mining town. These pages, by the way, were put together by students at the Plymouth Elementary School, who have done a first-rate job of it.

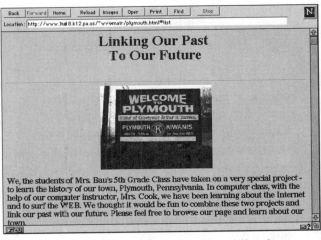

Linking Our Past To Our Future

WELCOME to PLYMOUTH

We, the students of Mrs. Bau's 5th Grade Class have taken on a very special project - to learn the history of our town, Plymouth, Pennsylvania. In computer class, with the help of our computer instructor, Mrs. Cook, we have been learning about the Internet and to surf the WEB. We thought it would be fun to combine these two projects and link our past with our future. Please feel free to browse our page and learn about our town.

The Historical Society of Princeton (New Jersey)

 http://www.princetonol.com/groups/histsoc/

Since 1938, the Historical Society of Princeton has collected and preserved materials about this university town and its environs, and has sponsored exhibitions, educational programs, and publications. Visit these pages for more information on the Historical Society, programs, collections, landmarks, four centuries of history, a spotlight on one particularly notable Princeton resident: Albert Einstein, and much more.

Puget Sound Maritime Historical Society (Washington)

 http://www.psmaritime.org/

Since 1953, the Puget Sound Maritime Historical Society has been located at Seattle's Museum of History and Industry, encouraging people to learn about the maritime heritage of the Pacific Northwest. The Society works to collect, preserve, and display all manner of maritime historical objects, relics, and data.

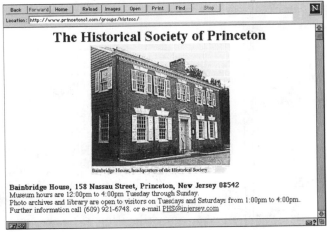

The Historical Society of Princeton

Bainbridge House, headquarters of the Historical Society

Bainbridge House, 158 Nassau Street, Princeton, New Jersey 08542
Museum hours are 12:00pm to 4:00pm Tuesday through Sunday.
Photo archives and library are open to visitors on Tuesdays and Saturdays from 1:00pm to 4:00pm.
Further information call (609) 921-6748. or e-mail PHS@injersey.com

Rhode Island History Bookstore

 http://www.aclock.com/history/

Since 1974, the Rhode Island Publications Society has published or cosponsored about 50 books and pamphlets on Rhode Island and its cities and towns. The Society also distributes the publications of the Rhode Island Historical Society, the Rhode Island Historical Preservation Commission, the Diocese of Providence, and several local history societies. They offer an extensive online catalog.

Santa Clarita Valley Historical Society Home Page

 http://felix.scvnet.com/~highlites/scvhs/index.html

The Santa Clarita Valley is nestled in the southern part of one of the transverse (east-west) mountain ranges that separate Southern California from the Great Central Valley to the north. It was in the Santa

Clarita Valley that the first documented discovery of gold in California occurred. The Valley is also home to the oldest existing oil refinery in the world and the first commercial oil field in California, as well as the third-longest railroad tunnel in the world. Learn more about the history of the valley via these useful Web pages maintained by the Santa Clarita Valley Historical Society.

Shasta (California) Historical Society

 http://www.shastalink.k12.ca.us/rmah/SHS.html

The Shasta Historical Society was formed in 1930 under the name Trails of '49. Today the Society acts as an educational, nonprofit institution to collect, preserve, and educate people about the early history of Shasta County. The Society's page shares a site with the Redding Museum of Art and History, which schedules many historical exhibits and school and community outreach programs throughout the year.

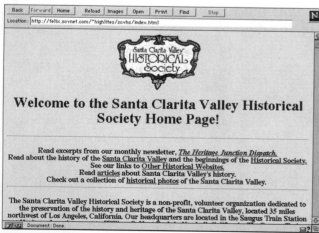

Welcome to the Santa Clarita Valley Historical Society Home Page!

Read excerpts from our monthly newsletter, *The Heritage Junction Dispatch.*
Read about the history of the Santa Clarita Valley and the beginnings of the Historical Society.
See our links to Other Historical Websites.
Read articles about Santa Clarita Valley's history.
Check out a collection of historical photos of the Santa Clarita Valley.

The Santa Clarita Valley Historical Society is a non-profit, volunteer organization dedicated to the preservation of the history and heritage of the Santa Clarita Valley, located 35 miles northwest of Los Angeles, California. Our headquarters are located in the Saugus Train Station

Smoky Mountain Historical Society (Tennessee)

 http://www.smokykin.com/smhs/

The Smoky Mountain Historical Society promotes the study of culture, genealogy, and history in and around the Smoky Mountain counties of Tennessee (primarily Blount, Cocke, and

Sevier). Visit this page for more information about the Smoky Mountain Historical Society.

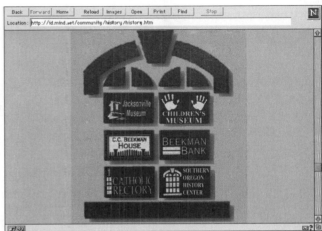

Southern Oregon Historical Society

 http://id.mind.net/community/
history/history.htm

Established in 1946, the Southern Oregon Historical Society preserves and displays historical artifacts relating to Southern Oregon—and Jackson County in particular. This page offers links to the Jacksonville Museum, a Children's Museum, the Southern Oregon History Center, and other interesting items.

Suffolk County (New York) Historical Society

 http://www.lieast.com/rmuseum.html

Having been founded in 1886, the Suffolk County Historical Society is one of the oldest local historical societies in the country. Collecting, preserving, and displaying artifacts of Suffolk County, Long Island—some of which date back more than 300 years—they maintain quite a nice museum in Riverhead, New York. They also provide extensive information about Suffolk and its rich history in these useful Web pages.

Texas Panhandle Railroad Historical Society

 http://www.webtex.com/webtex/
buscon/tprhs.html

The Texas Panhandle Railroad Historical Society is, according to its Web page, "dedicated to the preservation of the railroad history of the Texas Panhandle." This means an emphasis on the legendary Sante Fe Railroad. This site should be of interest to both railroad buffs and those interested in local Texas history.

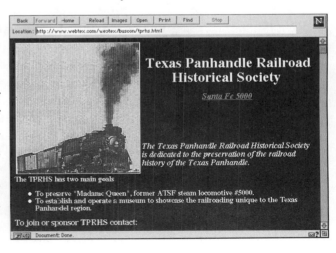

Utah History Home Page

 http://www.ce.ex.state.ut.us/history/

The Web pages of the Utah State Historical Society are a veritable gold mine of information on one of the most interesting states in the Union. The Society was founded in 1897 on the 50th anniversary of the first settlement in the Salt Lake Valley by the Mormon pioneers. The Society became a state agency in 1917.

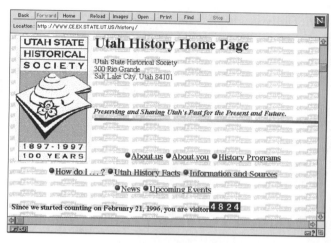

Valley Forge Historical Society

 http://www.libertynet.org/iha/valleyforge/

One of the most fascinating battles of the Revolutionary War involved not one single shot. It was the heroic battle against the elements fought by George Washington and his army from December 19, 1777 to June 19, 1778, as they waited to renew the fight against the British. This remarkable, interactive site offers fascinating insights to that historical event and how it shaped Pennsylvania and America. Learn the story of Valley Forge, take a virtual spin through the 7,000 items on display in the museum, learn more about Washington and others who served here (remember Benedict Arnold?), view maps, explore unsolved mysteries, check out links, and more.

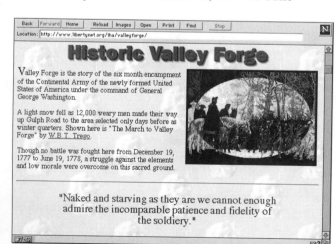

Vigo County (Indiana) Historical Society

 http://web.indstate.edu/community/vchs/home.html

The Vigo County Historical Society is the proprietor of the Sage-Robinson-Nagel House (built 1868), in which the Society stores its historical treasures in twelve rooms. The artifacts are of Terre Haute, Vigo County, and the Wabash Valley, and among the exhibits is an excellent one on novelist Theodore Dreiser and his brother, Vaudeville performer Paul Dreiser.

Western Reserve Historical Society (Ohio)

☞ http://www.wrhs.org/

The Western Reserve Historical Society serves Northeastern Ohio collecting, preserving, and displaying the artifacts and documents that illustrate the rich history of this region. The WRHS boasts of being the largest privately supported regional historical society in the country. It's also one of the oldest—having been founded in 1867.

Read here the interesting explanation about why this historical society is named "Western Reserve" instead of "Cleveland" or "Northeastern Ohio." (This may also explain part of the name of Case Western Reserve University.)

Intrigued? There's lots more interesting information on these pages.

13

Made in the U.S.A.

What isn't made in the U.S.A.? We make computers, sneakers, books, magazines, jets, submarines, yachts (yes!) and computer software. We dominate many of these industries. And if present trends continue, with the unhappy brain- and cash-drain of the 1970s finally halted, we will dominate more industries, rather than fewer, in the coming decades.

American-based firms are among some of the largest on the planet, and include such household names as Johnson & Johnson, Kodak, 3M, IBM, American Express, and Wells Fargo. All of these firms are successful. Some are successful while at the same time keeping a weather eye on their obligations to the commonwealth. Others are criminal polluters and exploiters of cheap and easy overseas labor. With our corporations as with everything else about the United States, there is good and bad, positive and negative, always at work.

Most often, buried somewhere in the pasts of these firms, there lurk the ghosts of great entrepreneurial visionaries—inspirational founders who, years ago, shot the stars of logic and plotted the fundamental courses on which these same corporate vessels voyage. I speak of people such as Bill Gates (**http://www.microsoft.com/corpinfo/bill-g.asp**).

At least one of these inspirational founders is worth looking at in some detail. Here is one who was a genius, a brilliant marketer and organization builder, a great philanthropist, and a suicide.

What's in a Name? George Eastman and Kodak

Based in Rochester, New York, Eastman Kodak was founded in the 1880s by George Eastman. It was Eastman who coined the slogan "You push the button, we do the rest" when he introduced the first Kodak camera in 1888.

There has been some fanciful speculation on how the name *Kodak* originated. The plain truth is that Eastman invented it out of thin air. He explained: "I devised the name myself. The letter "K" had been a favorite with me—it seems a strong, incisive sort of letter. It became a question of trying out a great number of combinations of letters that made words starting and ending with 'K.' The word 'Kodak' is the result." (Figure 13-1.)

A Level Playing Field

One of the beautiful things about the Web is that it creates a level playing field for business. Overall, bandwidth is cheap. It does not cost much to have a presence on the Web and to purvey your goods on the Web.

Thus, right alongside the Web pages for Fortune 500 firms such as Bethlehem Steel and Caterpillar, we also have countless Web pages for

FIGURE 13-1
The company he founded, Eastman Kodak
(***http://www.kodak.com/***)

Mom and Pop shops selling all sorts of handmade-in-America goods (Figure 13-2). There is, for example, the guy who makes and sells canes out of a workshop in rural Oregon (**http://www.houseofcanes.com/**), the family which makes and sells fine wooden clocks in Missoula, Montana (**http://205.226.96.50/dfc/page1.htm**), and the two nice ladies who make traditional porcelain dolls in Pennsylvania (**http://janellen.ptd. net/katnpat.htm**).

In commerce, as in all things, inexpensive Web access is proving to be a great democratizing tool, giving everyone an equal voice and equal shot at the large markets to be found in cyberspace. This is one of the things I find truly appealing at the Web and American commerce as defined on the Web. And that is why, interspersed with all the necessary references to the Web pages for all our largest American corporate powerhouses which follow, you'll also find a fair share of references to the Web pages of a variety of corporate midgets offering a broad array of products (from trout flies to saddles to quilts) handmade in the U.S.A..

FIGURE 13-2

*There is nothing like a level playing field. Even the smallest of buisnesses can go on the Web (**http://www. basspro-shops.com/ catalog/fishflym.htm**)*

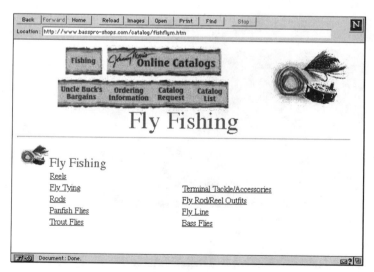

Miles to Go

There is no scarcity of Web pages representing those who produce merchandise in the United States. We lave a lot to trudge through, and miles to go before we sleep. So let's get a move on.

Amana

 http://www.raytheon.com/rap/amana/

Amana Refrigeration was founded in 1934 by George Foerstner. Foerstner took a bet from an Iowa City businessman that he couldn't build a beverage cooler that would work reliably. Now, after more than 60 years, Amana is one of America's best-known makers of appliances of all kinds. The home page is a refrigerator. Click on the refrigerator magnets for information on all Amana products, recipes, FAQs, and more.

Amish Handmade Quilts

 http://amishhandmadequilts.com/

These folks in northern Indiana specialize in making quilts which feature vivid colors and prints. They make log cabin designs, lone star designs, and other traditional patterns as well. The quilts are made by actual Amish people from northern Indiana and are purveyed here on the Web by friends of theirs, since the Amish are forbidden such tools of modernity as the computer.

American Express

 http://www.americanexpress.com

I've got an American Express card. You've got one. Heck, we've all got 'em. We wouldn't leave home without them. The company was founded by Major Daniel Butterfield, who is also noted as the composer of *Taps*. How is that for trivia?

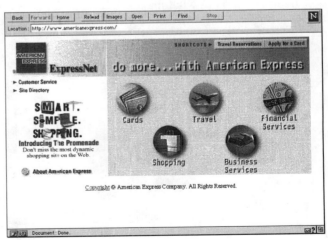

GREAT AMERICAN WEBSITES

Apple Computer

 http://www.apple.com

Apple Computer was the brainchild of the two Steves—Wozniak and Jobs—and has proven an unprecedented American success story through the years. Can the company hang on in the midst of its current troubles? The history of the firm goes back to 1977 when the Apple II was introduced at the first West Coast Computer Faire. With a rich 20 years to look back on, does Apple have another 20 to look forward to?

AT&T

 http://www.att.com/

Alexander Graham Bell started it all. Today it lies at the heart of our technological society and is a major building block in the infrastructure of—yes, you guessed it—the Internet. Find out what makes AT&T tick.

Barnwood Originals

 http://www.huntana.com/Barnwood/

What do the folks at Barnwood Originals do? They take aged wood reclaimed from old homesteads, barns, and fences in Southwestern Montana and recycle it for use in building custom furniture.

L.L. Bean

 http://www.llbean.com

Could there ever be a more uniquely American purveyor of goods than good old L.L. Bean? I think not.

The firm was founded in 1912 by Leon Leonwood Bean, a Maine outdoorsman who lived in Freeport. "L.L.," as he was called, grew tired of coming home with wet, sore feet from the heavy leather woodsman's boots of his day. He invented a new kind of boot that combined lightweight leather tops with waterproof rubber bottoms, incorporating the best features of both materials.

The practical advantages of his new L.L. Bean Boots were readily apparent, and he soon sold 100 pairs to fellow sportsmen through the mail. Unfortunately, 90 pairs were sent back when the stitching gave way. L.L. refunded his customers' money and started over with an improved boot. Today, Bean Boots and the legendary Guarantee of 100 percent satisfaction they helped create are famous around the world. The Guarantee, by the way, is uncompromising: "Our products are guaranteed to give 100 percent satisfaction in every way. Return anything purchased from us at any time if it proves otherwise. We will replace it, refund your purchase price or credit your credit card, as you wish. We do not want you to have anything from L.L. Bean that is not completely satisfactory."

The Guarantee extends beyond boots to the hundreds of other fine products sold by the current generation at L.L. Bean.

Ben & Jerry's Ice Cream

 http://www.benjerry.com/

What could be more American than apple pie? Apple pie à la mode! Visit with Vermont's most famous ice cream makers. And if you ever wondered what happened to flavors like "Miz Jelena's Sweet Potato Pie" and "Fred & Ginger," stroll through the flavor graveyard—the resting place of flavors long gone.

Bethlehem Steel

 http://www.bethsteel.com/

Bethlehem Steel was founded in 1857 as the Saucona Iron Company of South Bethlehem, Pennsylvania. In 1861 the name of the firm was changed to Bethlehem Iron Company and finally, in 1899, it became Bethlehem Steel. In the course of its long

history, the firm has supplied the steel for railroad ties and skyscrapers nationwide, and in so doing has changed the face of the country.

Bird Houses Handmade in North Carolina

 http://www.wildbirdz.com/nchouses.htm

Made from genuine North Carolina pine, these sturdy birdhouses are as beautiful as they are efficient. And they are all handmade in the mountains of North Carolina by a group of wood-carving retirees.

H.H. Brown

 http://www.hhbrown.com/

In 1883, H.H. Brown began hand making shoes in Natick, Massachusetts. He knew his customers well and understood they were searching for great looking, durable, and comfortable shoes. Originality and commitment to old-fashioned craftsmanship remain absolutes within the firm where, to this day, there is no room for cutting corners, gimmicks, hype, or compromise. Today the firm is a wholly-owned subsidiary of Berkshire Hathaway.

Canes and Walking Sticks Handmade in Wilderville, Oregon

 http://www.houseofcanes.com/

Survey a full line of canes and walking sticks lovingly handcrafted by Mark Fontaine of Wilderville, Oregon. Online tutorials tell you how to judge the proper height of a cane or walking stick to match your needs. You may browse a fully illustrated online catalog of readily available canes and walking sticks, or design your own custom-made cane, complete with initials and ornamental carving.

Caterpillar

 http://www.caterpillar.com

The story of Caterpillar dates back to the late 19th century when Daniel Best and Benjamin Holt each were experimenting with ways to fulfill the promise steam tractors held for farming. Prior to forming Caterpillar in 1925, the Best and Holt families collectively had pioneered track-type tractors and the gasoline powered tractor engine.

The Chubb Group

 http://www.chubb.com/

The Chubb Group is ranked by *Fortune Magazine* in the top half of its Fortune 500 listing. Based on market capitalization, the corporation is among the five largest publicly owned insurance organizations in the United States and the 15 largest insurance organizations worldwide.

Coca Cola

 http://www.cocacola.com

Coca Cola is the world's largest beverage company. Although U.S.-founded and U.S.-based, the business is global. Every day consumers enjoy more than 773 million servings of Coca Cola. And perhaps you were one of them today.

Country Brooms Handcrafted in the U.S.A.

 http://206.232.146.5/44broom/a01-02.htm

Here you have traditional hand-crafted brooms and sweeps for floors and fireplaces handmade in traditional colonial styles. Selections include a kitchen broom, cobweb sweep, whisk broom, and more.

Crosby Saddles

 http://www.horsemall.com/crosby/crosby.html

Crosby saddles have been proudly hand-made in a family-owned shop in the village of Copperas Cove, Texas for generations. The full line of fine Crosby saddles, for men, women, and children, is now to be found on the Web with a handy "800" number for ordering. When you call, you will likely be talking to one of the Crosbys themselves. Buffalo Bill used these saddles, and now the tradition continues.

Damn Fine Clocks

 http://205.226.96.50/dfc/page1.htm

That's the name of the company: Damn Fine Clocks. It is based in Missoula, Montana where Dick Baker, Don Swenson, Carol Baker, and Todd Swenson are dedicated to making, well, damn fine clocks. Todd, who is a teenager, named the company. Figures.

The clocks are crafted from windfall trees of all species, rough sawed dimension hardwood and softwood lumber. Of course, all the wood is stored and dried under cover until thoroughly cured to prevent cracking and checking.

John Deere

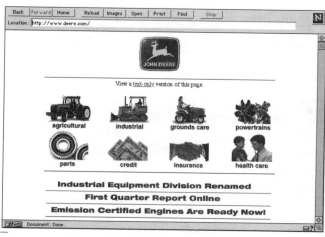

http://www.deere.com

As John Deere has grown, so has grown the country. I do not believe there is a farm on the continent that does not use a John Deere tractor, nor an industrial site that does not use some of their heavy equipment. John Deere is a fixture of the countryside.

Digital Equipment

http://www.digital.com/

Based in Massachusetts, Digital provides state-of-the-art solutions for data warehousing, electronic data interchange, high-performance computing, mail and messaging, and more. Their products include AlphaServers and AlphaStations as well as software solutions.

Disney

http://www.disney.com

It is the most downright American company on earth. Whether you are talking movies or theme parks or junky plastic toys, it is all-American born and bred. There are few more thoroughly American characters than Mickey, Minnie, Donald, and of course, Goofy.

Dow Chemical

http://www.dow.com/

Dow Chemical Corporation strives to be the very best in its field, using chemistry to create products that will enhance the lives of consumers. Based in the U.S.A., Dow is the fifth largest chemical company in the world, with annual sales of more than $20 billion. The firm provides chemicals, plastics, energy, agricultural products, consumer goods, and environmental services.

Duck Decoys

http://www.asionline.com/decoys.html

Proudly made by hand in the U.S.A., these wooden duck decoys are some of the finest in the world. Many are antiques carved by the skilled decoy makers of central Minnesota at the turn of the century. All are absolutely beautiful.

DuPont

 http://www.dupont.com

Come to Maryland! Innovate in a wonderful research lab! Manufacture and sell paints and abrasives! Work to make chemicals family-friendly! Check on DuPont career opportunities, stock prices, and more.

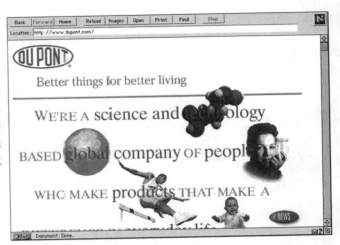

Electric Boat Corporation

 http://www.gdeb.com/

Electric Boat was founded in the late 1890s in order to build the *Holland*, a 54-foot submersible that was powered on the surface by a 50-horsepower gasoline engine and by electric batteries when submerged. The vessel was designed by John Phillip Holland, who is generally acknowledged as the father of the modern submarine. The Holland was accepted by the U.S. Navy on April 11, 1900, marking the beginning of the U.S. Submarine Force.

Subsequently, Electric Boat has held a reputation for nearly a hundred years as the free world's pioneer designer and builder of submarines. In 1913, Electric Boat built the first *Seawolf* and *Nautilus* subs. In the 1960s, they pioneered development of the Polaris class subs. Today, the company works to position itself for the 21st century while working on the new *Seawolf*, the next generation attack submarine.

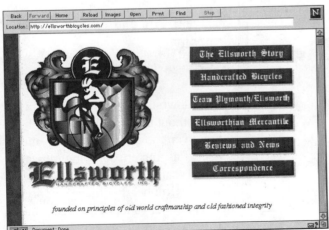

Ellsworth Handcrafted Bicycles from California

 http://ellsworthbicycles.com/

At the workshops of Ellsworth—in Ramona, California—they hand build only the finest bicycles. "We don't make entry level bikes," the Ellsworthians write. "We don't make 'price point' bikes. We meticulously compose a lightweight combination of strength, performance, and reliability on an uncompromising chassis."

Ford Motor Company

 http://www.ford.com

The Ford Motor Company is an American tradition. The company entered the business world without fanfare on June 16, 1903, when the late Henry Ford and 11 associates filed incorporation papers at Michigan's State Capitol in Lansing. With an abundance of faith, but only $28,000 in cash, the pioneering industrialists gave birth to what was to become one of the world's largest corporations. Few companies are as closely identified with the history and development of America throughout the 20th century as Ford. And perhaps no other

American firm is as well known across the globe.

At the time of its incorporation, Ford was a tiny operation in a converted Detroit wagon factory staffed with 10 people. Today, the company is the world's second largest industrial corporation, and is the second largest producer of cars and trucks, with active manufacturing, assembly, or sales operations in 31 countries on six continents.

General Motors

 http://www.gmc.com/

General Motors is another huge, whopping American success story—a success story which came to maturity along with so many other things American, in the 1960s. Find out what drives them at the GMC Web pages.

Goodyear Tire and Rubber Company

 http://www.goodyear.com/

What would American football be without the Goodyear blimp hovering over the field at all our major games, flashing encouraging messages to both teams? U.S.-based Goodyear Tire and Rubber has been supplying tires and other rubber goods to Americans for generations, and will for many decades to come, I'm sure.

Harley-Davidson Motorcycles

 http://www.harley-davidson.com/homea

Now here's a Website with an attitude. The home page greets you with "Welcome to the Harley-Davidson World Wide Web site. Now go away." Of course, they'd be happiest if you left on a Harley. Little did Milwaukee engineers William Harley and Arthur Davidson know when they started tinkering with engines in 1903 that their products would become the touchstone for an entire American subculture. These pages will tell you all about what the Harley-Davidson Company has become today.

HarperCollins Publishers

 http://www.harpercollins.com

HarperCollins is the publishing house of Mark Twain, Edna St. Vincent Millay, Laura Ingalls Wilder (of *Little House on the Prairie* fame), Thomas Wolfe, John F. Kennedy, Martin Luther King, Jr., and Maurice Sendak. The firm was founded in 1817 by the brothers James and John Harper. Today the firm continues strong. They will publish my book *The Lion's Pride*—the story of Theodore Roosevelt and his family during the First World War—in 1998.

Ted Hood Yachts, Rhode Island

 http://www.thco.com/Hood51.html

One thing we know how to make in Rhode Island is boats: specifically, sailboats. In fact, a large number of America's Cup vessels have been built right here in Bristol in the past, and will continue to be in the future. It is something of an America's Cup construction center. One of the leading yacht construction firms in Rhode Island is that of Ted Hood, whose vessels are known the world around for their clean lines and efficient handling.

IBM: International Business Machines

 http://www.ibm.com/

IBM needs no introduction. It is the quintessential American success story. We all know what they do, how long they've done it, and the industry the folks at IBM helped invent.

IBM is also a company that takes the environment seriously. The people at IBM recognized that more than most other industries; the information technology industry has the capacity to help shift environmental odds in the planet's favor.

A firm belief that computer technology has the capability to help solve a wide range of environmental problems is the imperative behind the IBM Environmental Research Program, which has contributed $16 million in technology grants for computer-based studies of problems.

Right now, as I write, a U.S. Department of Energy molecular sciences lab is installing what will be IBM's most powerful parallel computer for research on such critical environmental problems as cleaning up polluted sites and safety-treating and storing radioactive waste. Computational simulations and modeling will enable researchers

to perform environmental molecular science research essential to solving these problems.

IBM has also donated a data storage system to the University of California, Berkeley, for a digital library research project. The storage, exceeding six terabytes, will provide online access to a vast amount of ground and aerial photos, maps, and other visuals pertaining to the California environment.

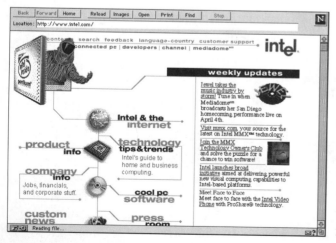

Intel

http://www.intel.com

Intel—they make the chips that have made America famous! One of the nicest features available at the Intel Web page is the Intel Museum, where they document the 25-year history of the microchip with vivid photographs, interviews, and historical essays.

Jack Daniel's Distillery

 http://www.jackdaniels.com/

Visit America's oldest registered distillery, located in Lynchburg, Tennessee. Have the bartender pour you a virtual drink, or muse on the relative merits of classic JD and Gentleman Jack, the distillery's first new recipe in over a century. And tour the place, at an appropriately leisurely, Tennessee pace.

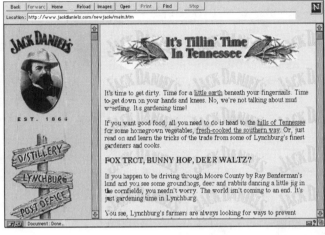

Johnson & Johnson

 http://www.jnj.com/

Just think Band-Aids. And diaper powder. 1997, as I'm sure you were already aware, marks the 75th anniversary of the Band-Aid. For this and other Johnson & Johnson trivia, access their Website.

Kayaks Handmade in the U.S.A.

 http://www.rockisland.com/ ~osprey/handcrafted.html

You have to go to a skilled artisan, a person such as the man from Washington state who maintains this Web page, if you want to get a genuinely good kayak. Some things simply cannot be mass produced, and kayaks are among these. Instead of aluminum, which the large commercial manufacturers use, you want a wood frame,

which provides more flexibility. Get more details from this informative Web page.

Kelloggs

 http://www.kelloggs.com

What's more American than apple pie? Why, Kelloggs Corn Flakes, of course, not to mention Tony the Tiger himself. Find

out about the two health-food-nut brothers who founded the firm at the turn of the century, the history of Tony as a marketing icon, and other interesting trivia.

about the wide array of Levi's products. Or, as the Levi Strauss folks so humbly put it—step into the most outrageous walk-in closet in cyberspace.

Lands' End Direct Merchants

 http://www.landsend.com/

Another American success story is that of the firm of Lands' End Direct Merchants, located in Dodgeville, Wisconsin. Their slogan: "Outfit everyone in comfort at comfortable Direct Merchant Prices."

Levi Strauss Jeans

 http://www.levi.com/menu

Next to Coca-Cola, Levi's may be the most universal products America has ever produced. Check out these pages for all

Eli Lilly

 http://www.lilly.com/

Eli Lilly and Company is, according to its Web page, "a global research-based pharmaceutical corporation headquartered in Indianapolis, Indiana that is dedicated to creating and delivering pharmaceutical-based health care solutions which enable people to live longer, healthier, and more active lives."

Lionel Trains

 http://www.lionel.com/

A Lionel O-guage electric train set has been a treasured plaything in millions of American homes for over 50 years. If you happen to be near Chesterfield, Michigan, just northeast of Detroit, you can drop in at the Visitor Center in Lionel's corporate headquarters for all the electric trains your little heart desires. If that's inconvenient, take a virtual tour through these pages instead, filled with graphics, history of electric trains, hints for hobbyists, how to join the Railroaders Club, where to find dealers, and more.

Lockheed Martin

 http://www.lockheed.com/

Lockheed is in the forefront of high technology flight instrumentation, rocketry, and passenger jet development. They are a critical supplier for NASA as they have been from the very start of the American manned space program.

Lotus

 http://www.lotus.com

Lotus is another American success story. It all began with the classic spreadsheet 1-2-3 and now the company provides such ground-shaking products as Lotus Notes, Domino, SmartSuite, and more, including Approach, FastCall, and LotusScript.

Martin Guitars

 http://www.mguitar.com/

A family-owned American enterprise for over 160 years, the Martin Guitar Company sets a standard for quality in American acoustic musical instruments. These attractive pages feature a catalog of Martin instruments, strings, and related products, complete with color photos, history, and more.

Mauna Loa Macadamia Nuts

 http://www.maunaloa.com/

If you thought a macadamia nut was the most sinful snack not involving chocolate, you'll be happy to learn that these yummy nuts are high in monounsaturated fats and help lower cholesterol. Well, maybe...if you can restrain yourself from eating them by the handful. Mauna Loa is Hawaii's largest source for macadamia nuts. Their product line includes plenty of goodies featuring macadamia nuts. Check out these pages for recipes, news, and even investment opportunities in a macadamia nut orchard.

Merrill Lynch

 http://www.ml.com/

For more than 50 years Merrill Lynch has been a leader in the American brokerage industry, offering a variety of financial products in addition to standard stock sales and purchases. Today, they can even do it for you right there online.

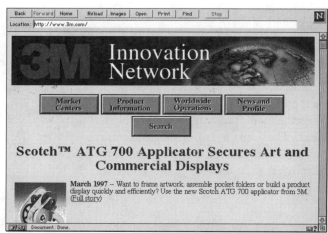

Microsoft Company

 http://microsoft.com

This is a good little American company you might want to keep an eye on. They have a broad selection of software products that show signs of catching on, especially one in particular...I think it is called *Doorknobs* or *Porches* or *Windows* or something like that. Rumor has it the stock is a good one and keeps going up, up, up. The chairman's name is *Fences* or *Walls* or *Gates* or something like that.

Minnesota Mining and Manufacturing (3M)

 http://www.3m.com/

3M was founded in 1902 at the Lake Superior town of Two Harbors, Minnesota, when five businessmen agreed to mine a mineral deposit for grinding wheel abrasives. But the deposits proved to be of little value, and the new Minnesota Mining and Manufacturing Company quickly moved to nearby Duluth to focus on sandpaper products.

The firm produced the world's first waterproof sandpaper in the early 1920s. In 1925 Richard Drew, a young lab assistant, invented masking tape which was soon issued to the public under 3M's new "Scotch" brand label. In the 1950s, 3M introduced the Thermo-Fax copying process, Scotchguard fabric protection, and videotape. In the 1960s, they invented dry-silver microfilm, carbonless papers, and overhead projection systems.

The innovation continues. In the 1990s 3M has net sales of over $15 billion annually, with 30 percent of those revenues coming from products created within the past four years.

Mobil

 http://www.mobil.com

Mobil Oil is, quite simply, a giant. It is into gas stations, gas exploration, refining, and dozens of other related ventures. The history of the firm goes back to the 1870s and is amply discussed within the scope of these Web pages, along with all other aspects of Mobil's corporate profile.

Morgan Stanley

 http://www.ms.com/

Dave Renehan, who is a Managing Director of Morgan Stanley & Co. Incorporated, wouldn't forgive me if I didn't include the Morgan Stanley Web page in this book. Morgan Stanley was incorporated in 1935 and established to continue the investment banking business of J.P. Morgan & Co. following the enactment of the Banking Act of 1933 (the Glass-Steagall Act) which barred commercial banks from engaging in investment banking transactions. In 1941, the firm qualified for membership in the New York Stock Exchange.

Northrop Grumman

 http://www.northgrum.com/

Headquartered in Los Angeles, Northrop Grumman is a leading designer, systems integrator, and manufacturer of military surveillance and combat aircraft, defense electronics and systems, airspace management systems, information systems, marine systems, precision weapons, space systems, and more. Northrop Grumman is the prime contractor for the U.S. Air Force's B-2 Stealth

bomber, a long-range heavy bomber with low-observable characteristics and all-altitude capability to penetrate the most sophisticated air defenses.

Northstar Hand-Carved Wooden Pens from Texas

 http://www.tditx.com/northstar/index.html

Lovingly carved in the Lone Star State by Marv North, these fine sculpted hardwood writing instruments are ideal gifts for friends, family, or your favorite author. Cartridges, carriers, and other accoutrements are also available.

Ogilvy & Mather Advertising

 http://www.ogilvy.com

Modern advertising was invented in America, on Madison Avenue in New

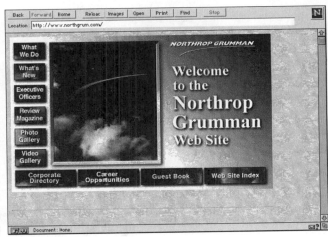

York. In fact, David Ogilvy was the first ad man to identify and promote brand-building advertising. His classic 1955 speech on the topic is surprisingly current. Ogilvy remains one of the most famous names in advertising along with a handful of titans (Raymond Rubicam, Leo Burnett, William Bernebach, and Ted Bates) who formed the business in the years after World War II.

In 1949, Ogilvy founded the agency which is now known as Ogilvy & Mather. Starting with no clients and a staff of two, he built the company into a worldwide enterprise that nevertheless is still based on Madison Avenue.

Perhaps more than any other advertising agency in the country, Ogilvy & Mather has been built on a set of clearly defined principles reflecting the views of its founder. Ogilvy defined these principles early in his career and has never wavered from them. He has always believed that the function of advertising is to *sell*, and that it is possible to precisely determine those techniques by which sales are most likely to be produced.

In 1936, at the age of 25, he declared "Every advertisement must tell the whole sales story...every word in the copy must count," adding that "permanent success has rarely been built by frivolity and people do not buy from clowns." In a speech to the Association of National Advertisers in 1992, he was still sounding the same theme: "If you focus your advertising budget on entertaining the consumer, you may not sell as much of your product as you like. People don't buy a new detergent because the manufacturer told a joke on television last night. They buy it because it promises a benefit."

Despite the austerity of his doctrine, Ogilvy as a copywriter is personally responsible for many of advertising's most famously sophisticated campaigns. These include: The Man in the Hathaway Shirt, and perhaps the best known headline ever written for an automobile ad: "At 60 miles an hour the loudest noise in this Rolls Royce comes from the electric clock."

Owens Corning

http://www.owens-corning.com/

You've got Owens Corning products all over your house. The firm, which invented glass fiber, boasts a fascinating history of innovation and entrepreneurship. This legacy has continued as the company has grown into the world leader in advanced glass and building material systems.

Pepsi

 http://www.pepsi.com

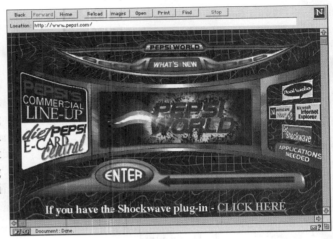

Any soda that is O.K. with Ray Charles is O.K. by me. Uh huh. Check out all the latest news concerning one of America's two favorite cola drinks. Find out who will be the next celebrity to show up in those annoying ads. And get a complete history of Pepsi from "day one."

Piper Aircraft

 http://www.newpiper.com/

Generations of American flying enthusiasts have been piloting and riding happily in Piper Cubs and Cherokees for many years. There's a good chance you've been in one yourself. But if aircraft names like Archer, Arrow, Saratoga, Seminole, Seneca, or Warrior are new to you, check out these pages to learn what else this thriving Vero Beach, Florida enterprise is manufacturing for the next generation of American pilots.

Pixar

 http://www.pixar.com

Steve Jobs' latest fascination, Pixar creates computer graphics animations and state-of-the-art tools for computer graphics animation and does so with elegance and efficiency. The company is one of the fastest growing and most promising in the country and has already produced at least one classic film: *Toy Story*.

Pixar's objective is to combine proprietary technology and world-class creative talent to develop computer-animated feature films with a new three-dimensional appearance, memorable characters, and heartwarming stories that appeal to audiences of all ages.

Toy Story was released in November of 1995 and reflects the creative and technical achievements of Pixar. It received tremendous critical acclaim and has become an enormous box office success, generating over $184 million in domestic box office revenues. This makes *Toy Story* the third most successful animated feature film ever, surpassed only by Disney's *The Lion King* and *Aladdin*.

Porcelain Dolls Handcrafted in Pennsylvania

 http://janellen.ptd.net/katnpat.htm

Check out this online catalog of hand-crafted porcelain dolls individually poured, cleaned, painted, fired, and assembled by two women in southern York County, Pennsylvania. This is a great example of the type of small American business that can maximize the potential of the Web for marketing just as easily as can Pepsi and Apple.

Procter & Gamble

 http://www.pg.com/info/library/

In 1837, Cincinnatti candle maker William Procter and soap maker James Gamble met through marrying sisters. Their new father-in-law convinced the pair to become business partners, and Procter & Gamble was born. The company now spends more on advertising than all but a handful of companies and markets a vast number of household and personal products. Visit the history pages for the story of Ivory Soap.

Random House Publishing Group

 http://www.randomhouse.com

Random House is an American publishing institution and has been ever since its founding, decades ago, by Bennet Cerf. Random House continues strong, as do its many imprints including Crown, Knopf, and Vintage.

Raytheon

 http://www.raytheon.com/

The chairman emeritus of defense contractor Raytheon—based in Lexington, Massachusetts—is Charles Francis Adams, direct descendant of John Adams and John Quincy Adams. In fact, the family of old patriots has now, and has always had, a large financial stake in the venture.

Samuel Adams Brewery

 http://www.samadams.com/

Though the beer has been on store shelves for scarcely more than a decade, the Samuel Adams brewery takes pains to link itself to two centuries of American history. These attractive pages will introduce you to a classic American entrepreneurial success story, with history, a brewery tour, product information, links to other sites, and more.

Schlage Locks

 http://www.schlagelock.com/schlage/

Boy, what these guys know about locks! At these nicely arranged pages, you can find out about Schlage's 70-year history, beginning with San Francisco inventor Walter Schlage and the world's first push-button cylindrical lock. You can also learn about locks from the beginning of time. Find out about other companies now associated with Schlage. Even find out the correct way to pronounce "Schlage."

Sears

 http://www.sears.com/

For generations, Sears, Roebuck and Company brought store-quality merchandise to the wilderness prairies through mail order. Launched in the late 19th century, Sears provided one-stop shopping for yarns, linens, and other household items. The tradition continues today in Sears stores nationwide, even though the mail order business has gone south.

Singer Sewing Machine Company

 http://www.singerco.com

I.M. Singer's company has been producing high-quality sewing machines for more than 144 years. Today, the Singer Company is the largest sewing machine manufacturer in the world. Its sewing-related products are available in more than 140 countries, and it also produces other consumer durables for the home.

Sun Microsystems

 http://www.sun.com/

Sun is in the forefront of the latest in computer technology and is certainly the mar-

ket leader as regards to Java computing and all that spins off from this. Sun was born and raised in the U.S.A.—homemade and home-grown.

Tabasco Sauce

 http://www.tabasco.com/html/ product_hotsauce.html

Tabasco sauce is good for you! Find out how in these hot pages set up by the McIlhenny Company of Avery Island, Louisiana. And these guys know about more than pepper sauce—they know how to have a good time. Check out links to music events, arts and games, recipes, and plenty more.

United Parcel Service

 http://www.ups.com

What would American Christmases be like without United Parcel Service? What would we do without those brown-uniformed men and women who hike across our lawns schlepping presents from cousins and uncles and aunts in Phoenix and South Bend and Sioux City?

U.S.A. Made

 http://www.usamade.com

This extensive set of Web pages provides a database of links to the home pages of firms offering products that are made 100 percent in the United States of America. Here you'll find clothing manufacturers, publishers, computer makers, software developers, and much more.

Vermont Maple Syrup

 http://www.gmsh.com/ gmsh/welcome.htm

Though it's only one of countless purveyors of Vermont's sweetest product, Green Mountain Sugar House in Ludlow, Vermont has erected a Website offering a variety of maple products, including syrup, candy, fudge, and spreads. And since the smart shopper will want to compare prices, you can also stop at the Putnam Family Farm (**http://www.sover. net/~bputnam/**) where they sell syrup by the gallon and have done so since 1854.

Wells Fargo

 http://www.wellsfargo.com/

Since 1852, the Wells Fargo stagecoach has been a symbol of reliable service across the American West. Over 100 years ago, the Wells Fargo stages traveled across thousands of miles of desert, prairie, and mountain roads to deliver mail and cash. During the Gold Rush, Wells Fargo provided regular communications (including the first electronic transaction, by telegraph, in 1864), delivered vital goods, converted unprocessed gold into U.S. gold coins, and provided checks and bank drafts. Today, Wells Fargo continues to provide personal, responsive, service by connecting their customers with essential financial services 24 hours a day.

Westinghouse

 http://www.westinghouse.com/

Westinghouse is not just refrigerators and coffee makers. It is also CBS. And both outfits were born and bred in the good old U.S. of A. I am happy to say that Westinghouse is a firm which takes its environmental responsibilities seriously. Recently the EPA honored Westinghouse as one of only two 1996 "Green Lights Partners" of the Year in the large corporation category.

Whirlpool

 http://www.whirlpool.com

Whirlpool, of course, supplies the largest percentage of America's washers, dryers, refrigerators, and other large appliances. All the stuff is made right here in the U.S.A., by Americans for Americans.

Zippo Lighters

 http://www.zippomfg.com/

Whatever your opinion of smoking, you can't argue with the fact that Zippo lighters—plain and fancy—have been part of our cultural identity since before World War II. Now you can visit the Zippo home page, devoted largely to establishing Zippo's place in our history. Find out about the Zippo museum in Bradford, Pennsylvania, which displays items of interest like a 14-foot U.S. flag made entirely of Zippo lighters.

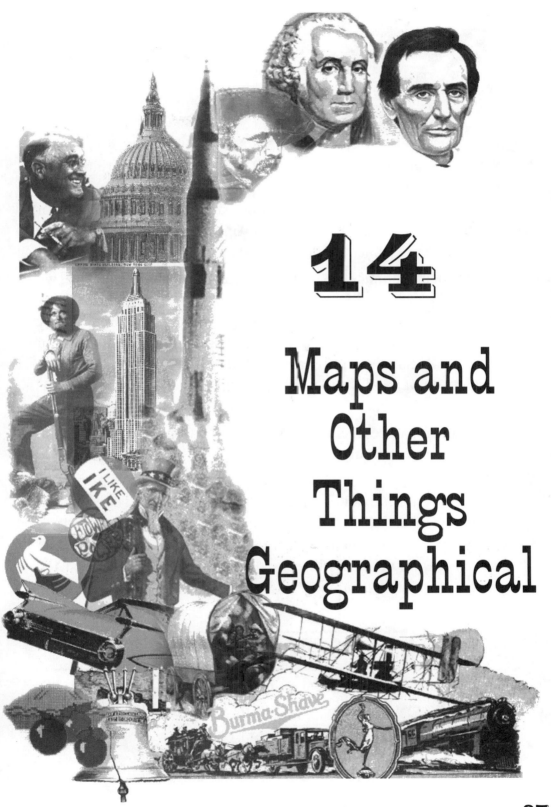

14

Maps and Other Things Geographical

American geography, eh? Well, let's start with some key statistics. We are talking about a total of 9,372,610 square km (3,618,765 square miles). For comparison, it is useful to know that this is about four-tenths the size of the former USSR, about one-third the size of Africa, about one-half the size of South America, slightly smaller than China, and about two and one-half times the size of Western Europe.

Our terrain and climate are, to say the least, varied. Climatewise, we range from tropical (Hawaii) to arctic conditions (Alaska). We also have vast forests and vast deserts. The bulk of our landscape is comprised by the large central plain of our middle West, rising into the mountains of the Far West. But then we also have the hills and low mountains of the East, the broad river valleys of Alaska, and the rugged volcanic topography of Hawaii. You see, we have it all.

Our natural resources include coal, copper, lead, phosphates, uranium, bauxite, gold, iron, mercury, nickel, potash, silver, tungsten, zinc, crude oil, natural gas, and timber.

Ecologically we are not doing great but we are doing better than at any moment in the last 40 years. Pollution control measures are slowly—too slowly—improving air and water quality, and bringing down the rate of acid rain. Agricultural fertilizer and pesticide pollution are on the decline. Let's pray this continues.

The United States Geological Survey (USGS)

As part of the U.S Department of the Interior, the mission of the U.S. Geological Survey (**http://www.usgs.gov/**) is to scientifically examine and classify the public land of the U.S. with respect to geological structure, mineral resources, and products of what they formally called "the national domain."

The areas of science the USGS concerns itself with are geology, topography, and hydrology. The scientific data the department collects and processes assists them in the wise management of the nation's natural resources and in promoting the health, safety, and well-being of U.S citizens. This data consists of maps, databases, descriptions and analyses of water, energy, mineral resources, land surface, underlying geologic structure, natural hazards, and dynamic processes of the earth.

The country faces some serious issues with regard to the environment: ensuring an adequate supply of water, energy, and mineral resources for the current population and future generations, determining if the use of resources alters the natural environment, and assessing how the global environment is changing in terms of geologic time. The Survey is also charged with predicting and mitigating the danger and effects of natural hazards such as earthquakes and volcanoes.

The USGS publishes the results of its work in many forms including reports, maps, databases, and, of course, online via the USGS Website. For specific information on USGS mapping go to **http://mapping. usgs.gov/**.

Maps of All Kinds

There are, of course, all kinds of maps. We've got topographical maps, road maps, railroad maps (**http://pavel.physics.sunysb.edu/RR/ maps.html**), trail maps, and so forth. But there are also other thematic maps containing data that goes beyond delineation of terrain, roads, railroads, and trails. There are maps which convey a great deal of quantitative data related to our society as represented across the geographic land mass of the United States.

Consider this sobering map (Figure 14-1) which demonstrates the percentages nationwide for children living in poverty in 1992.

We can use maps to convey vast quantities of good and bad news about ourselves, our values, and our priorities. It would be interesting to triangulate the data from the map with data from another map meant to delineate government dollars dedicated to child welfare per state.

The Office of Social and Economic Data Analysis at the University of Missouri (**http://www.oseda.missouri.edu/index.html**) makes a broad range of thematic maps available online that are all quite interesting. Here you'll find online interactive state maps (each 8,000 to 10,000 bytes in size) delineating agricultural, educational, household, income, population, and youth statistics. Here you'll also find county maps and school district maps providing snapshot glimpses of the same statistics within those unique geographic windows.

FIGURE 14-1

*Percentage of children living in poverty. The solid dark states have the highest percentages (**http:// www.oseda.missouri. edu/graphics/us/youth/ uskidpov.gif**)*

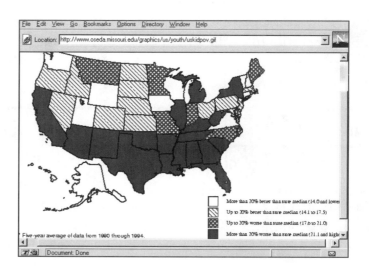

Additional maps show which counties nationwide are "commuting dependent" (with 40% or more of their inhabitants working outside the county), farming dependent (with 20% or more of all income coming from in-county farming), government dependent (with 25% or more labor working for the government), manufacturing dependent, mining dependent, welfare dependent (yes! welfare dependent), and retirement dependent.

So far as the individual states are concerned, different maps show population percent change (1990-96 and 1990-93), population per square mile, African Americans as a percent of total population, Asian and Pacific Islanders as a percent of total population, Native Americans as a percent of total population, Hispanics as a percent of total population, and population age demographics.

Maps and Geography on the Web

The Web is loaded with resources related to the various terrains and climates of the United States, maps of the United States, and geological and hydrological data. What follows is a concise cyberguide to some of the best of these.

Boston Online Map

 http://www.trucking.org/
how_to_drive/boston_map.html

Here is a detailed clickable map of Boston highways and roads. Click on a portion of the map to zoom in for more details on local roads, and so forth. I personally find Boston a very easy town to navigate in and around.

California Geographical Survey

 http://130.166.124.2/

Hosted by the Department of Geography at California State University, Northridge, this excellent set of Web pages provides a variety of useful geographical resources related to the study of

California. The site includes an Electronic Map Archive, cartographic resources that include digital map bases, California census data, and much more.

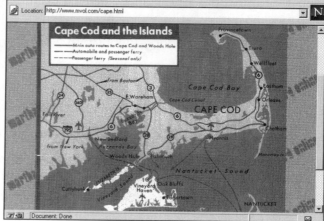

Cape Cod Map

 http://www.mvol.com/ cape.html

This map not only shows Cape Cod and its approaches from Boston and New York, but also the adjacent islands including Martha's Vineyard and Nantucket, the Elizabeth Islands, and Cuttyhunk.

The Census Bureau

 http://www.census.gov

This is the government agency that counts the population of the U.S. every ten years. But in addition to merely counting the populace, the Census Bureau classifies us in more ways than you can shake a database at. Come to this Web page for all sorts of useful facts and figures about the United States population. These include state and county income and poverty estimates, percentage of population broken out by age, and annual statistics related to housing vacancies and home ownership.

Chalk Butte Digital Maps

 http://www.chalkbutte.com/index.html

Chalk Butte Inc. of Boulder, Wyoming produces color-shaded relief maps from digital elevation data. Chalk Butte's current products include some unusual items—the Colorado Plateau and its drainage, and a map of the Michigan Peninsula highlighting features left over after the last glacial recession. You can get these unique maps as paper wall maps or electronically on CD-ROM.

Charleston, South Carolina Map: 1869

 http://www.lib.utexas.edu/Libs/ PCL/Map_collection/historical/ Charleston_1869.jpg

Part of the historical archives kept by the University of Texas at Austin, this map is a marvelously detailed street plan of the carefully laid out southern seaport city of Charleston just after the Civil War. Wander the squares, waterfront, and cemeteries. Sadly, the location of Rhett Butler's house is not indicated.

Chicago Map: Free

 http://www.kemper.com/lite/about/chicagomap.html

Care for a free printed map of one of the greatest cities in the world? You can have it. Just go to this Website and fill in your name and address and the good folks at Kemper Investments will send you the map.

Classification of Wetlands and Deep Water Habitats of the United States

 http://www.nwi.fws.gov/classman.html

This detailed paper by Lewis Cowardin, Virginia Carter, Edward T. LaRoe, and Francis Golet details the classification of various types of wetlands and deepwater habitats throughout the United States. The report is profusely illustrated with all sorts of interesting maps.

Clearview U.S. Relief Maps

 http://ssnet.com/~dale/us.html

From coast to coast, and border to border, these Clearview relief maps provide a realistically-tinted view of the United States normally reserved for astronauts. The maps are available in a variety of sizes. Clearview, the company marketing these maps, is located in Newark, Delaware.

Dallas Map

 http://tgimaps.com/DALLAS/dallas.html

Here is an easy, intuitive map of the Dallas metropolitan area. The map clearly shows all the major roads and highways, delineates key landmarks and attractions, and highlights major destinations such as the Dallas/Fort Worth airport.

Detroit Map

 http://www.hdo.com/ccity.html

Here is quite a beautiful roadmap of greater Detroit showing not only the ma-

jor roads of the city but also the Detroit River, the Rouge River, and other geographical highlights. It is really very nicely rendered.

Fredericksburg and Spotsylvania (Virginia) National Military Park Map

 http://www.nps.gov/frsp/tour.htm

The Fredericksburg and Spotsylvania National Military Park preserves the sites of four important battles of the Civil War. The battlefields encompassed by the park include the Battle of Fredericksburg, the Chancellorsville Campaign, the Battle of the Wilderness, and the Battle of Spotsylvania Court House. Using the clickable map at this site, you can choose any of several absorbing walking tours, get detailed trail maps, and learn fascinating historical facts about what you're seeing. If you go, don't miss the "Stonewall" Jackson shrine.

Geography Departments in the United States

 http://www.dartmouth.edu/pages/geog/usgeog.html

Here is an alphabetical, hyperlinked directory to Web pages of departments of Geography throughout the United States,

from Hawaii to Maine and from Florida to Alaska. This is a very useful resource.

Geologic Mapping and Regional Geologic Studies in the Eastern United States

 http://geology.er.usgs.gov/gmapeast/eastgmap.html

The Eastern Geologic Mapping Team of the United States Geological Survey (USGS) conducts research in the Eastern United States. Here you'll find a large collection of online maps related to their ongoing research in the East.

Studies include the Vermont-USGS Cooperative Geologic Mapping Project, the Mid-Atlantic Corridor Project, the Southeastern Regional Geology Project, the Florida Geology and Ecosystems Project, and the National Park Service/USGS Cooperative Project.

Hammond Maps

 http://www.hammondmap.com

The best maps and cartographic products in the world are homegrown in the United States and come from Hammond, Inc. While visiting this site be sure to investigate the Hammond Digital Cartographic Database.

Historical Las Vegas Strip Casino Map

 http://www.prairienet.org/~scruffy/e.htm

I'll bet you never dreamed there were this many casinos in Las Vegas, past or present! Now you can find the exact location of the place where you lost your shirt (or hit your jackpot). You also get links to home pages of many thriving Las Vegas gaming enterprises and even a link to an entertaining video clip of the implosion of the Dunes in 1993.

Kickapoo Maps

 http://www.kickapoo.com

The late Perry Van Arsdale spent 20 years compiling the historical maps now available at the Kickapoo Maps Website. Origi-

nally, his goal was to present a history of America before 1900 that would be appealing to children, including his granddaughter. Clearly, Van Arsdale's work will appeal to all ages of history enthusiasts. Locate old roads, famous trails, emigrant routes from the Atlantic and Pacific, stage lines, army forts, mining towns, and more with accompanying historical notes.

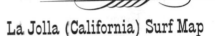

La Jolla (California) Surf Map

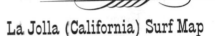 http://204.216.57.25/~surfman/

This site offers every little nugget of information you'll need to find your ideal surfing spot on the La Jolla coast. The map at the site is a thumbnail version of a 24 x 36-inch printed map (which the folks at Mellow Kat Publications of Del Mar, California hope you'll want to buy). But much of the information on the map is explained for free on these beautiful, well-illustrated pages. It's worth a visit even if you can't swim.

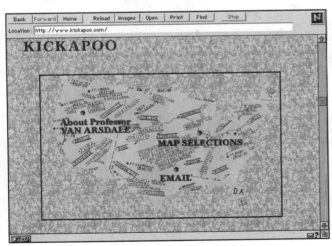

Las Vegas Map

http://www.intermind.net/im/lvmaps/bigmaplv.html

This splendid clickable map of Las Vegas shows you every street in the gridlike desert city and designates major points of interest such as UNLV, the Convention

Center, and, of course, the various gambling strips.

Long Island Sound Map

 http://www.savethesound.org/lismap.htm

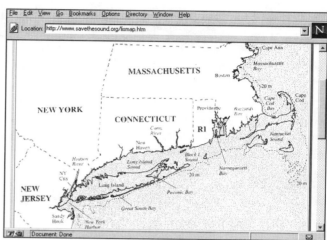

This is an excellent map showing not only Long Island Sound but also the Peconic Bay, the Great South Bay, Block Island Sound, Narragansett Bay, Nantucket Sound, Cape Cod Bay, and Massachusetts Bay.

Los Angeles Map

 http://log04.nswses.navy.mil/la_area.htm

Here is a great online map of downtown Los Angeles and its approaches. Print it out and take it with you when you next endeavor to navigate one of the most beautiful, and most confusing, cities in the world.

Los Angeles Rock and Roll Road Map

 http://www.net101.com/rocknroll/

At last! An exhaustive set of area and detail maps highlighting every cool and sacred spot associated with the L.A. rock scene.

Here is where you'll find all the clubs, the locations that inspired rock songs, record stores and companies, historic concert sites, places where the stars bit the dust, hangouts, and more goodies that celebrate the famous, infamous, and just plain fabulous.

Manhattan Subway Map (Interactive)

 http://www.transarc.com/afs/transarc.com/public/brail/html/transit/manhattan.html

Here's an interactive map of the New York City subway system. Working with this map is a Java applet that has to be running for this to work. Click a subway station on the map; you'll see a red dot placed on it. Then click another station and the Java program will calculate your more direct route and display it in very descriptive and verbose text in a program window.

Massachusetts Map from the 18th Century

 http://www.philaprintshop.com/
images/morsema.jpg

Access this Web page to discover a beautiful old map from the 18th century depicting eastern Massachusetts including Cape Cod and the borders of New Hampshire and Rhode Island.

Mississippi River Basin Headwaters Map

 http://www.mhbriverwatch.dst.mn.us/
ctymap/ctymap.html

This excellent map of the headwaters of the Mississippi River is quite detailed and shows the Turtle River, Lake Itasca, Leech Lake River, Cass Lake, Prairie River, Swan River, Splithand River, and Willow River, along with other tributaries.

National Cooperative Geologic Mapping Program

 http://ncgmp.usgs.gov/

The United States Geologic Survey and the U.S. Department of the Interior are hosts to the National Cooperative Geological Mapping Program, a cooperative effort to marry geologic maps and electronic databases. The USGS and DOI hope to use this system for purposes you might expect, such as evaluating the risk of environmental hazards like earthquakes and volcanoes. But the departments also state their intention to use this system for purposes you might not expect, including natural resource allocation, land use, and "to guide public policy."

New Orleans Maps

 http://www.neworleans.com/maps.html

New Orleans is a walking town. And just about anywhere you walk, you're likely to find a party. This site offers up street maps of the French Quarter, the whole city of New Orleans, plus Mardi Gras route maps and schedules so you can follow your favorite Krewe through the wild and wonderful festivities in New Orleans and surrounding communities.

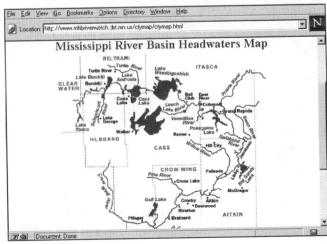

New York City Vertical Subterranean Map

 http://www.nationalgeographic.com/ modules/nyunderground/index.html

The National Geographic people took a virtual core sample of 800 feet under New York City and offer an amazing interactive tour of everything you'll find on this vertical geographic map. Also provided are links to audio tours and a fine photo gallery in addition to detailed explanations of everything you find lurking down there.

New York State Map

 http://www.nuwebny.com/nyarea.htm

Click on the different portions of the map to zoom in on more detailed maps of specific areas, and to access tourist and road information for specific regions such as the Hudson Valley, Catskills, Adirondacks, Thousand Islands, and Finger Lakes.

Philadelphia Map

 http://www.disc.dla.mil/cbu/n/ map.html

This map delineates all the key access roads for the city of Philadelphia, showing the relationships and junctions of high-

ways 76, 85, 95, and 295 as these enter and circle the city proper.

Potomac Watershed Network

 http://web.gmu.edu/bios/Potomac/ pwn/pwnlinks.html

It has been called the nation's river. The Potomac Watershed Network provides detailed geological and ecological information on the river and the watershed which feeds it. Come here for maps, data files, and details.

Providence (Rhode Island) Map

 http://www.providenceri.com/ providencemap.html

Here is a very nice map of Providence, Rhode Island, showing all the major roads, College Hill (home of Brown Univer-

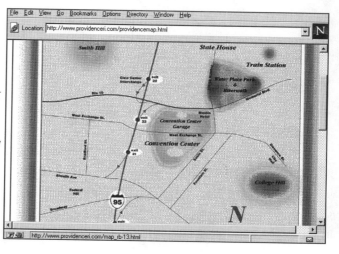

sity), the Convention Center, the State House and Train Station, and other points of interest.

Railroad, Subway and Tram Maps

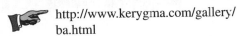 http://pavel.physics.sunysb.edu/ RR/maps.html

Maintained by a physics professor at the State University of New York, this is the world's largest online collection of railroad, subway, and tram maps. The collection features 255 maps, 95 showing railroads, 29 showing trams, 129 showing subways, and 2 showing other types of transportation systems.

San Francisco Bay Area Relief Map

 http://www.kerygma.com/gallery/ ba.html

This is more than a map. It is art created from a combination of cartographic information and satellite images of San Francisco Bay and the region around it. The image is truly beautiful.

Seattle Map

http://www.kcts.org/gifs/ninemap.htm

Here is an attractive map of downtown Seattle, Washington. All major streets are delineated, as are pier numbers and parks

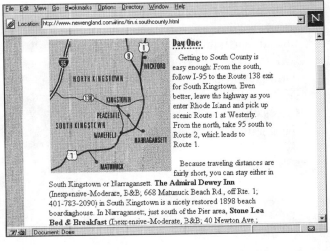

Day One:

Getting to South County is easy enough: From the south, follow I-95 to the Route 138 exit for South Kingstown. Even better, leave the highway as you enter Rhode Island and pick up scenic Route 1 at Westerly. From the north, take 95 south to Route 2, which leads to Route 1.

Because traveling distances are fairly short, you can stay either in South Kingstown or Narragansett. **The Admiral Dewey Inn** (Inexpensive-Moderate, B&B; 668 Matunuck Beach Rd., off Rte. 1; 401-783-2090) in South Kingstown is a nicely restored 1898 beach boardinghouse. In Narragansett, just south of the Pier area, **Stone Lea Bed & Breakfast** (Inexpensive-Moderate, B&B; 40 Newton Ave.;

and other structures and thoroughfares of interest.

South County, Rhode Island

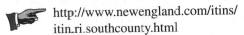 http://www.newengland.com/itins/ itin.ri.southcounty.html

South County, Rhode Island embraces the villages of Wickford (where I live, a village in the township of North Kingstown), Peacedale, Wakefield, Matunuck, Narragansett, and several other townships. This Web page provides a map and details on the region.

Southern California Earthquake Maps

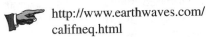 http://www.earthwaves.com/ califneq.html

At this site, maintained by the Southern California Earthquake Center, Cal Tech, you can locate major active faults and epicenters of significant historical earthquakes in Southern California. Nervous about an earthquake hitting where you are standing between now and 2004? Check these fascinating maps for the scientists' best guess.

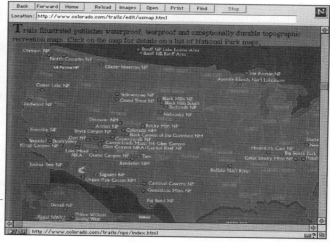

Thomas Bros. Maps

 http://www.thomas.com

For most of a century, Thomas Bros. Maps have been the favorites of delivery drivers and locals alike. Thomas Bros. has excellent street guides, wall maps, and road atlases for most every urban area in the western United States. On their Web pages, find out about their map products, as well as their other products including software (maps on CD and mapping software for the PC).

T.I. Maps, Moab, Utah

 http://moab-utah.com/ti/maps.html

T.I. Maps stocks nothing but maps. They're located in Moab, Utah, near some of the most beautiful scenery on earth. So, naturally, T.I. Maps specializes in maps and guides for exploring southeastern Utah on foot or otherwise. Moab maps, bike and hiking trail maps, global positioning system,

topos, off-road maps, U.S.G.S. maps, and more—everything you need before heading off to Arches and beyond.

Trails Illustrated Topographic Maps

 http://www.colorado.com/trails

Trails Illustrated is publisher of over 160 tearproof, waterproof topographical maps of U.S. national parks and other recreation areas. Explore these lovely illustrated pages for information on maps of Colorado, Utah, Alaska, New Mexico, North Carolina, and Puerto Rico, plus a series of mountain biking maps.

Virginia in the 18th Century

 http://www.philaprintshop.com/ images/morseva.jpg

This page provides a beautiful reproduction of an 18th century map of Virginia showing mountains, waterways, and the Pennsylvania border. The map is hand-drawn and absolutely gorgeous.

Washington, D.C. Metro Map

☛ http://www.fedworld.gov/ntis/map.htm

This useful map of the major arteries in and around the Washington, D.C. metropolitan area shows you, among other things, the fabled "Beltway" comprised as it is of Route 95 on the East, South, and Southwest, and Route 495 on the North and Northeast.

Washington State Map

☛ http://www.televar.com/chambers/wenatchee/map.html

This is an excellent general map of the state of Washington showing all the major arteries and key townships such as Bellingham, Everett, Seattle, Tacoma, Vancouver, Yakima, Spokane, and the Tri-Cities Area.

Washington State Parks Maps

☛ http://www.parks.wa.gov/MapInfo.htm

The Washington State Parks and Recreation Department has set up this site to offer regional maps locating every state park from the eastern high desert to the wilds of the Olympic Peninsula and the islands of Puget Sound. You can then link to comprehensive information on each park.

Wetlands Division of the EPA

☛ http://www.epa.gov/OWOW/sec7/page1.html

This is the home page for the Wetlands Division of the EPA's office of Wetlands, Oceans, and Watersheds. The resources you'll find here are extensive and include transcripts of Wetlands testimony before the U.S. Senate, great maps, and much more.

Wolf Recovery Map

☛ http://www.defenders.org/ynpmap.html

Dedicated to the protection of wild animals and plants in their natural habitats, Defenders of Wildlife is an organization that pursues this goal through litigation and lobbying. One of their projects is the restoration of wolves into the ecosystem of Yellowstone Park and the wilds of Idaho. This map shows the geographic area of the wolf restoration program. You can also link to plenty of related sites on subjects of wildlife protection.

15

Music,
American
Style

John Hammond (**http://www.rockhall.com/induct/hammjohn. html**)—the legendary record producer who started his career at Columbia Records by signing Bessie Smith and ended it by signing Bruce Springsteen—once said the greatest contribution of the United States to world culture were the Declaration of Independence and the musics of blues and jazz. To that I would add both our native, traditional folk music and the composed citified folk music of our urban players, such as Woody Guthrie, and of course the offerings of the likes of Cole Porter (**http://www.shubert.com/cole.html**), Gershwin, Irving Berlin, Aaron Copland, and Leonard Bernstein (**http://www.music.indiana.edu/ ~l631/mustheater.html**). Is American musical theater and American symphonic music any less a contribution than jazz? Of course not.

Me and Gary

Like many kids of the New York Metropolitan area, my first glance at real music was when I attended one of Leonard Bernstein's great "Young People's Concerts" with the New York Philharmonic. Perhaps I was six or seven. It was an experience I shall always remember.

It was not until about ten years later that I encountered a different— and perhaps more subtly real—American music.

It all involved getting on the bus. Lugging my guitar, I'd jump the Merrick Road bus out of my affluent Long Island community after my high school let out and head toward the city line. There, in a run-down house, I'd have my lessons with Reverend Gary Davis. I was in fact one of several white boys whom Gary did his best to teach the blues.

Gary Davis was without question one of the greatest guitar players to ever perform African-American music. His distinctive, highly personalized style has influenced generations of musicians. From bluesman like

Blind Boy Fuller to rockers like Bob Weir and Jorma Kaukonen, any player who has heard him has been influenced by his mastery.

Of all the truly marvelous guitarists to come out of the Carolinas—guitarists such as Willie Walker, Blind Blake, and Blind Boy Fuller—Gary Davis (Figure 15-1) was the best. And this is not to take anything away from Walker, Blake, or Fuller. Davis was simply miraculous. Not only was his guitar playing magnificent, but his voice could chill to the bone.

He was born in 1896 in South Carolina; he died in 1972 in Jamaica, Queens, New York. He went partially blind as a child, suffering from ulcerated eyes, and became totally blind by 1926. He played harp by five, banjo by six, and guitar by seven, and worked with Willie Walker as a street musician in tobacco-rich towns like Greenville and Durham. In 1933 he was ordained a minister of the Free Baptist Connection Church, and was considered to sing his own brand of holy blues until the day he died in 1972.

His first recordings were made for the ARC label in New York in 1935 at sessions which included Blind Boy Fuller and Bull City Red. Davis was paid a meager $40 by J.B. Long to record his first 14 sides and,

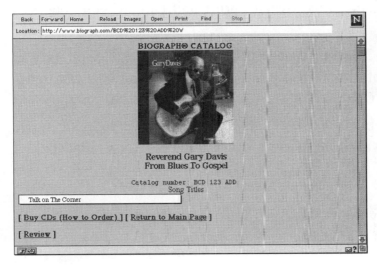

FIGURE 15-1
Gary Davis
(http://www.biograph.
com/BCD%20123%20
ADD%20W)

embittered by his treatment, he did not record again until the mid-1940s. Later, in the 1950s and 1960s, he became a standard presence at folk festivals nationwide.

Davis often shied away from performing bawdy blues songs after becoming a minister—but not always. I noticed that his reluctance was usually linked to the proximity of his wife. If she was not around then he could be coaxed into such songs as "Sally, Where'd You Get Your Whiskey From?" and "Cocaine Blues." More often, however, he performed a sort of blues-gospel combination: songs such as "Lord, I Wish I Could See" and "You Better Get Right."

His guitar work was amazingly complex. People who hear him on record today, and who did not have the opportunity to see him play, are astonished to learn that he only used two picking fingers whether playing six-string or his 12-string "bozo" guitar.

Me and Moe

Somewhat like his friend Gary Davis, Moses Asch was a study in contrasts. He was mean and lovable, gruff and patient, generous and demanding.

Moe (Figure 15-2) as I first met him was an elderly man. Well, he was 71 in the summer of 1976 when I, at age twenty, found my way to his office near Lincoln Center.

The episode had begun a few months earlier when I was playing music at a waterfront festival on the Hudson River with Pete Seeger. Pete pulled me aside after the gig.

"Moe Asch at Folkways is bugging me to make another record for him," he said. "Why don't you come into the studio with me and we'll see what we can put together."

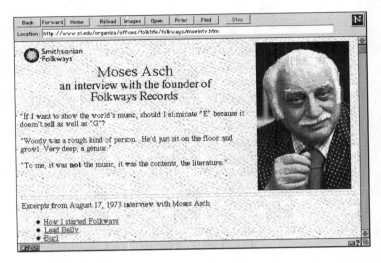

FIGURE 15-2

Meet Moses Asch
(http://www.si.edu/
organiza/offices/folklife/
folkways/moeintv.htm/)

A few weeks later, after some rehearsals at Pete's house overlooking the Hudson near Beacon, New York, we were in the studio. The sessions went quickly. There was a minimum of overdubbing and few retakes. We shot through the songs in two or three days at the most, always leaving time at the end of each day to go sailing. On the fourth day, we did the mix. And on the fifth day I went to see Moe, whom I'd not met before, carrying the tapes.

"You the kid?" Moe said as I placed the tapes on his desk.

I didn't understand what he meant. "Excuse me?" I said.

"You the kid Pete told me about?" he demanded impatiently. "You the kid with the..." He pantomimed playing a guitar.

"Yes."

"Sign this," he said, pushing a contract—actually two copies of a contract—toward me without any further explanation. Pete had told me there would be some paperwork. I signed and then Moe signed and then he gave one back to me and said "Tell your Daddy to put that in some place safe."

He seemed gnarled and old and mean. Later, when I got to know him better, he just seemed gnarled and old, and the meanness, I came to realize, was just an extremely wry sense of humor meant good-naturedly for all those who were hip enough to get it. The others could just go to Hell. Moe did not suffer fools gladly.

The son of Hemingway's favorite novelist—Sholem Asch—Moe was born in Warsaw, grew up in Brooklyn and was educated in Koblenz, Germany.

He issued his first recordings in 1939 on Asch Records. During World War II, when many major labels discontinued their recordings of blues and folk music in response to a shortage of shellac used for making the old 78-rpm records, Moe began recording folk and blues artists who otherwise would have gone unnoticed: Woody Guthrie, Leadbelly, Burl Ives, Josh White, and Pete Seeger among them. At the same time, while a Musicians Union ban prevented many major labels from recording jazz, Moe recorded such performers as Coleman Hawkins (**http://www. beatthief.com/greatday/people/hawkins.html**) and Mary Lou Williams (**http://www.beatthief.com/greatday/people/williams.html**).

Moe started the Folkways label (**http://www.si.edu/folkways**) in 1947. His ambition was anything but humble. He meant to document "all the music of the world." The result was the Folkways Records catalogue which eventually contained more than 2,000 recordings. Moe never allowed any of them to go out of print, no matter how small the demand for such titles as "Shepherd Flute Music from the Andes." As folklorist Alan Lomax remembers, "No one ever came to Moe with any interesting material that he didn't arrange to publish."

The Folkways collection of recordings helped spur the folk music revival of the 1950s and early 1960s. The members of the Kingston Trio first heard the songs "Tom Dooley" and "Where Have All the Flowers Gone?" on Folkways LPs. Woody Guthrie's Folkways albums were Bob Dylan's first introduction to folk music, and Dylan's very first commercial recording was a cut on a Folkways record. Later, when Dylan did his debut studio album for Columbia, most of the cuts were songs he'd learned from the Folkways "Anthology of American Folk Music."

When Moe died in 1986, Dylan played a key role in making sure the marvelous archive that was Folkways did not disappear into oblivion but rather wound up administered by the Smithsonian Institution. Dylan helped raise money to support the transfer of the collection. He arranged for Columbia Records to issue an album entitled "Folkways: A Vision Shared." Then he arranged for a host of musicians—among them Pete Seeger, U2, Arlo Guthrie, Bruce Springsteen, Doc Watson, John Mellencamp, Sweet Honey in the Rock, Emmy Lou Harris, Brian Wilson, and Little Richard—to perform the songs of Woody Guthrie and Leadbelly. Dylan himself performed Woody's "Pretty Boy Floyd." The album was a fabulous success and all royalties went to support Folkways at the Smithsonian.

American Music in Cyberspace

There is a great deal of information related to American music on the World Wide Web. From Delta blues to the great symphony orchestras, it is all here. Let's take the information superhighway's turnoff for Tin Pan Alley, and see what we can find.

Louis Armstrong

 http://www.rockhall.com/induct/
armslou.html

That's right. We're talking about "Satchmo"—Louis Armstrong. Since his death, he has been marginalized and trivialized and made into a pop figure. In fact, he was a virtuoso trumpet player and a great jazz innovator.

P.D.Q. Bach

 http://pages.wooster.edu/sillarsd/pdq/

P.D.Q. Bach, J.S. Bach's last and least-talented child, produced a frightening musical body of work. This work was recently "discovered" by Professor Peter Schickele, one of America's great musical deconstructionists, who has made it his life's work to

293

popularize this odd and usually hilarious "repertoire." Visit this unofficial site for information on P.D.Q. Bach's works, Professor Shickele's recordings of same, and even a libretto for P.D.Q.'s opera "The Abduction of Figaro."

Joan Baez

 http://baez.woz.org/

Server space for Joan Baez's official home page has been donated by her pal Steve Wozniak. Here you'll find a biography and discography, tour information, a Joan photo gallery, and lots more.

The Band

 http://www-ia.hiof.no/~janh/
TheBand.html

The Band is distinctly American, even though it was formed in Toronto and comprised of four Canadians and just one American. Originally formed as Ronnie Hawkins' backup band, they of course gained fame recording in that ugly pink house in Woodstock where they created "Music from Big Pink" and, with Bob Dylan, "The Basement Tapes." Either The Band or the Grateful Dead is my favorite band on the planet—I'm not sure which. I keep bouncing back and forth. I love these guys, though. What can be better than Levon Helm, Robbie Robertson, Rick Danko, Richard Manuel, and Garth Hudson cooking with juice? Nothing.

Irving Berlin

 http://www.theatlantic.com/atlantic/
issues/96mar/everyman/everyman.htm

According to Jerome Kern, Irving Berlin wasn't a part of American music, he *was* American music. In a sense, at least, Kern was correct. Berlin certainly personified one precise era of American music with such classics as "White Christmas." This authoritative Web biography provides an exhaustive, insightful consideration of Berlin and his contribution.

Leonard Bernstein

 http://www.classicalmus.com/artists/
bernstei.html

One of my abiding memories from growing up in New York is of the great Young People's Concerts hosted by Leonard Bernstein and the New York Philharmonic. Of course, Bernstein was more than just a conductor. He was also one of the greatest composers ever produced by the United States. Find out more about him via this detailed Web biography.

The Blue Highway

 http://www.vivanet.com/~blues/

The Blue Highway is the number one source for information on the blues—and the people who make the blues—on the World Wide Web.

Here you'll find an extensive collection of links giving information on Robert Johnson, Mississippi John Hurt, Bessie Smith, Muddy Waters, B.B. King, Buddy Guy, W.C. Handy, Charley Patton, Blind Lemon Jefferson, Leadbelly, Son House, Bukka White, T-Bone Walker, Willie Dixon, Howlin' Wolf, Sonny Boy Williamson II, Lightnin' Hopkins, Albert King, Elmore James, John Lee Hooker, and many others.

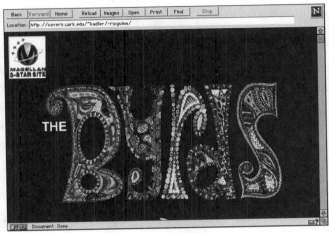

The site includes great sound files including Robert Johnson performing "Cross Road Blues," Mississippi John Hurt performing "Ain't No Tellin'," Bessie Smith performing "St. Louis Blues," Muddy Waters performing "Hoochie Coochie Man," B.B. King performing "The Thrill is Gone," and Buddy Guy performing "Damn Right, I've Got the Blues."

For additional great blues-related resources on the Web check out Blues-Link (**http://transport.com/~firm/links.html**).

The Byrds

 http://cavern.uark.edu/~kadler/rmcguinn/

Here is a great set of Web pages dedicated to one of my favorite '60s bands, the Byrds. The site includes individual band member biographies, discographies, and much more. There is also a link to Roger McGuinn's personal home page (**http://pw2.netcom.com/~mcguinn/index.html**). In addition to being an excellent musician, Roger is also one of the nicest, most down-to-earth people in the galaxy.

Boston Symphony Orchestra

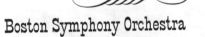 http://www.bso.org/

The Boston Symphony Orchestra not only holds a regular season in Boston, but also presents summer concerts at Tanglewood and provides an institutional base for the Boston Pops orchestra. Find out more at the official Boston Symphony Orchestra Website.

John Cage

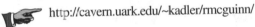 http://www.emf.net/~mal/cage.html

John Cage (1912-1992) ranks among America's most influential 20th century composers and musical pioneers. He's best remembered for his collaborative work with modern dancer Merce Cunningham. He's most notorious for his performance piece consisting entirely of silence. But there's much more to the man and the composer than that. If you want to know more about Cage, Malcolm Humes has trolled the Net on your behalf, collating many interesting sites and providing musical, scholarly, and even discussion group links. In addition, a good biography article can be found at **http://www.lovely.com/bios/cage.html**.

Carnegie Hall

 http://www.carnegiehall.org

It is one of the premier recital halls in the world. People from all over the planet come to Carnegie Hall to debut their talents, build their careers, or simply hear the world's finest musicians. Now you can visit as well, via the Web.

John Coltrane

 http://sd.znet.com/~bydesign/
coltrane.john/

John Coltrane (1926-1967) was a great composer and saxophonist. He is often described as mystic, prophetic, angelic, and saintly. This site provides a biography, critical analysis, and links to discographies and other sites devoted to a man who redefined jazz in the transition from bop to free jazz.

The title "saint" is not used lightly in reference to Coltrane. Visit **http://sd.znet. com/~bydesign/coltrane.john/saint-john. html** to look in on San Francisco's Saint John's African Orthodox Church, more commonly known as the Church of John Coltrane. Here jazz and spirituality meet in their purest forms.

Aaron Copland

 http://kennedy-center.org/explore/
honors/html/1979/copland.html

Perhaps no other composer is associated with American themes than Aaron Copland. Some have called him the Andrew Wyeth of American symphonic music, others the Norman Rockwell. He might be either, depending on the moods of his various pieces. Copland was born in 1900. He died in 1990, having written over 100 separate pieces (among them "Appalachian Spring"), having won a Pulitzer Prize and an

Academy Award, and having been honored with a Congressional Medal for patriotism. In addition to the Web page elucidated here, also check out the great online bio to be found at **http://www.incwell.com/Biographies/Copland.html/**.

Dallas Symphony Orchestra

 http://www.dallassymphony.com

Under the direction of Andrew Litton, the Dallas Symphony Orchestra maintains an extensive performance and touring schedule which includes world tours interspersed with busy home seasons in Dallas. This is generally acknowledged to be one of the great orchestras of the world.

Miles Davis

 http://www.slip.net/~mrlane/Miles.html

Cool, iconoclastic, adventurous, sometimes scary, widely imitated, and often misunderstood, Miles stands at the rarefied pinnacle of the jazz pantheon. Understanding and appreciating all his moods and styles is the work of a lifetime. To visit with a fan who has made his life work just that, check out these well-linked pages.

Dirty Linen Magazine

 http://kiwi.futuris.net/linen/

Dirty Linen Magazine provides great insights on contemporary American folk music. The magazine includes interviews, concert and record reviews, song sheets, and much more. If you are interested in folk music, you won't want to be without *Dirty Linen*. One particularly nice aspect of *Dirty Linen* is the magazine's extensive online

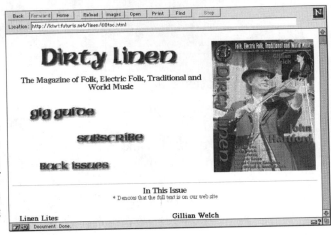

tour schedules for many folk and acoustic music acts. Some of this information is impossible to find elsewhere.

Bob Dylan

 http://www.2020tech.com/dylan/ index.html

Of course, Dylan needs no introduction. Here you'll find great pictures of Bob, mostly in concert. Another very good site is the Bob Dylan Who's Who—**http://bob. nbr.no/dok/who/**.

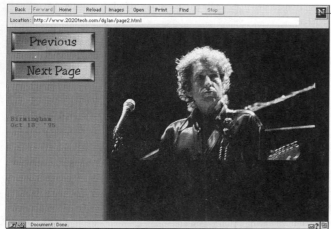

The Everly Brothers

 http://www.rockhall.com/ induct/everly.html

From 1957 to 1960, Don and Phil Everly averaged a Top 10 hit every four months, including "Bye, Bye Love," "When Will I Be Loved," "Wake Up Little Susie," "All I Have To Do," and "Bird Dog." Their vocal harmony

style provided inspiration for, among others, John Lennon and Paul McCartney.

Folk Book

 http://www.cgrg.ohio-state.edu/ folkbook/

This is your number one stop on the World Wide Web for information about folk artists, folk venues, and more. Here you will also find concert and recording reviews, folk music-oriented radio and television shows, and folk festival details.

Folk-Legacy Records

 http://www.folklegacy.com

For several decades now Folk-Legacy Records has been run by Sandy and Caroline Paton out of their home in northern Connecticut. Folk-Legacy is home to such artists as Gordon Bok, Anne Mayo Muir, Ed Trickett, and Bill Staines, among others.

Aretha Franklin

 http://www.aristarec.com/aretha/ home.html

There is perhaps no one who defines the Motown Sound more than Aretha Franklin. The daughter of a minister, she began singing in her father's church as a child and hasn't stopped since. The list of her hits is a long one. Come to the Arista Records pages dedicated to Aretha for images and details from her wonderful career.

George and Ira Gershwin Archive

 http://www.sju.edu/~bs065903/ gershwin

Before his premature death in 1937, George Gershwin composed hundreds of beautiful musical pieces, for many of which his brother Ira supplied lyrics. Ira lived on until 1983. Come to these Web pages for detailed information on the complete works and careers of George and Ira Gershwin. The site is the brainchild of Brian Sweeney. Thanks, Brian.

The Grateful Dead

 http://grateful.dead.net/

Ah, The Grateful Dead. You've gotta love 'em. It is simply a question of attitude. Cool people love the Dead and that is all there is to it. Consider the man whom I consider both the hippest and smartest politician in the country—William Weld of Massachusetts. He wore a mourning band for a week after Jerry Garcia died.

Nanci Griffith

 http://www.sover.net/~rschrull/ ngriffith/gchpage.html

My wife and I first encountered Nanci Griffith about ten years ago when she was opening for the Everly Brothers. We have loved her music ever since: a subtle blend of folk and country, with a dash of Celtic influence. Absolutely beautiful.

Arlo Guthrie: Arlonet

 http://www.clark.net/pub/downin/ cgi-bin/arlonet.html

The son of legendary folksinger Woody Guthrie (see next), Arlo Guthrie first came to national attention in 1967 with the release of *Alice's Restaurant*.

Today, thirty years later, my friend Arlo continues to be ever-popular with folkies around the country and around the planet.

I owe him a special debt of thanks, because he is titular head of the only Church I can stand the idea of belonging to, and which I and my wife Christa help support.

About three years ago Arlo purchased the desanctified Episcopal Church in Stockbridge, Massachusetts, which played such a large role in both the story-song and the film named *Alice's Restaurant*. He uses part of the building as his office, while the rest of the building has been given over to his non-profit Guthrie Center, which serves as headquarters for local volunteers who help out in the community. The Center is also a place for retreats and silent prayer. Arlo calls it his "home church."

"The second day that I was in this old church," Arlo writes, "the local preacher came by. I was mopping up the floor. It was in the evening and the lights were on. There was a glass door, so I couldn't run away and pretend I wasn't there. So, I let him in. He introduced himself and said, 'Arlo, I just came by to find out what you're doing here.' I said, 'I'm not doing much. I'm just mop-ping up the floor.' He said, 'No, Arlo, I mean what are you doing here? What kind of church is this?' And I didn't know what to say. So, I just said, 'Well, it's a Bring Your Own God church.' And he didn't really want to smile, but he couldn't stop it from spreading across his face. He said, 'I've never heard of a church like that.' I said, 'Well, you know, when you think about it, every church is like that.' He said, 'Well, I guess you're right.' And we left it like that."

Arlo's home church is an attempt to express religious feelings or beliefs as service, and Arlo emphasizes the idea of service as a practical form of prayer. Thus the Guthrie Center has programs for abused children, the elderly, people with AIDS, people with cancer, and so on. As Arlo puts it, "You have to live your life as a prayer. And how you deal with every moment is how you pray."

At the Arlonet Web pages you'll find lots of information about both Arlo and the Guthrie Center. The Web pages are the brainchild of, and are maintained by, Dave Downin.

Woody Guthrie

 http://www.artsci.wustl.edu/ ~davida/woody.html

Who was this Woody (Woodrow Wilson) Guthrie who was born in Oklahoma in 1912 and died in Brooklyn in 1967? Those who know only a little bit about him usually think of him simply as Arlo's Dad. Or they think of him as the guy David Carradine portrayed in the Oscar-winning film *Bound for Glory*, based on Woody's autobiography of the same name. Or they think of him as Bob Dylan's great influence—the man whom Dylan emulated in his early years and whom he first came to New York to see.

Woody was dying of Huntington's Disease by the time Dylan met him. He resided full-time at the Brooklyn State Hospital. "Where do you look for this hope that you're seeking?" Dylan told an interviewer in the mid-'60s. "You can go to the church of your choice, or you can go to the Brooklyn State Hospital. You'll find God in the church of your choice. You'll find Woody Guthrie in the Brooklyn State Hospital."

Guthrie wrote over one thousand songs (among them the classics "This Land is Your Land," "Oklahoma Hills," and "So Long, It's Been Good to Know Ya"). He also wrote an autobiography (*Bound for Glory*) and a splendid novel, *Seeds of Man*. He was, quite simply, a genius. And his genius is ably depicted here at this Website with words, images, and sound files.

It is worth noting that Arlo Guthrie says his father would have "absolutely, without question, loved without a doubt the whole Internet scene. He would have been on all the time. He was a fabulous typist. He could type faster than most secretaries, and he would have loved the idea of people all over the world being able to freely communicate with each other."

Merle Haggard

 http://www.TheHag.com/

Country music stars come and they go. But few have the longevity and are as talented and creative as Merle Haggard. Haggard is a consummate professional—having mastered the country music idiom at many different levels. These delightful, exhaustive pages tell all about the man, the legend, and the music.

John Hammond, Jr.

 http://www.vivanet.com/~catbauer/
bio/hammond.html

His father was the famous Columbia A&R man to whom I've alluded to earlier in this chapter. And his paternal grandmother was a Vanderbilt. Benny Goodman was an uncle by marriage. Still, despite these rarified connections, John Hammond, Jr. is an outstanding bluesman to whom I've been listening for years. He plays small venues. He is probably at a pub near your town sometime soon. Do not miss the show.

Yip Harburg

 http://now-voyager.com/chapters/ friends/yip_harburg.htm

Yip Harbug was a friend of mine. We were introduced by Pete Seeger in New York City in the 1970s. He was a genius. He was not a musician. So why am I including him here? He was one of the best lyricists America ever produced. He wrote the lyrics for all the songs in "The Wizard of Oz," including "Somewhere Over the Rainbow." He also wrote "Hey, It's Only a Paper Moon" and countless songs for the Marx Brothers, including "Hello, I Must Be Going" and "Lydia the Tattooed Lady." Then there is also another minor effort, the Depression-era classic "Brother Can You Spare a Dime?"

Billie Holiday: Lady Day

 http://www.enmu.edu/~daym/ mus103/billie.htm

From her early classic 1930s recordings with Benny Goodman (produced by Goodman's brother-in-law, John Hammond) to her terrible death as a heroin addict in 1959, Billie Holiday always remained one of the great voices of American jazz. Movie-goers will remember Billie as portrayed by Diana Ross in the film *Lady Sings the Blues*. These Web pages detail Billie's troubled yet somehow triumphant life, providing vivid facts, images, and links to sound files which form a unique portrait of a true jazz genius.

Jazz Central Station

 http://www.jazzcentralstation.com/

Here is all the information you will ever need on one of the most original of American contributions to music: jazz. The site includes artist biographies, discographies, critical essays, record company links, and more.

Blind Lemon Jefferson

 http://bioc09.uthscsa.edu/~seale/ bljeff.html

Blind Lemon Jefferson was one of the most popular male blues recording artists of the 1920s. Born in Couchman,

Texas, he was blind from early childhood, but nevertheless went on to record 43 record albums. Jefferson was a mentor of Leadbelly. And Eric Clapton has included him with Robert Johnson as one of his heroes.

One of Blind Lemon's greatest songs was "See That My Grave is Kept Clean." Now, the good folks who have mounted this Web page are trying to raise money to make sure Blind Lemon's grave in Wortham, Texas is at least marked.

WELCOME, MUSIC LOVERS!

It's very obvious to me that Spike Jones doesn't get enough coverage on the Web or anywhere else. This page is a tribute to

THE MAN WHO MURDERED MUSIC

Jefferson Airplane

 http://grove.ufl.edu/~number6/
Jefferson.Airplane/airplane.html

As I have mentioned previously, I've long loved acoustic blues. One of my favorite contemporary practitioners of this art form—along with John Hammond, Jr.—is Jorma Kaukonen, known in another life as the lead guitarist for the Jefferson Airplane. At this Website you'll find complete information on one of the best bands of the '60s, along with up-to-date information on the latest incarnation of Jefferson Starship and such great spin-off operations as Hot Tuna.

Spike Jones

 http://www.geocities.com/SunsetStrip/
4020/spike.html

This site is dedicated to "The Man Who Murdered Music"—bandleader Spike

Jones. Fronting a combo that included, in addition to the normal jazz instruments, a starter's pistol, car horns, countless noise makers, and the deranged vocalist Doodles Weaver, Jones amazed a war-weary America in 1943 with the impossibly frantic "Cocktails For Two." Now, more than 30 years after his death, he's still a weekly mainstay on Dr. Demento's cult radio program. Get a biography, sound files, lyrics from Spike's hits, pictures, information on the Spike Jones International Fan Club, plus links to other sites for Spike-heads at this site.

Kronos Quartet

 http://www.lochnet.com/client/gs/
kq.html

String quartets will never be the same after Kronos. This group brought hipness and style to the world of classical music. They're astonishing musicians. They're exciting to watch. They dress in Laurie Anderson's hand-me-downs. In their concerts of 20th century music they're just as likely to play Jimi Hendrix as Bartok. Modern composers are lining up to write new commissioned works for them. Check out these well-designed pages for all about Kronos, including chat groups, tour schedules, sound clips from Kronos recordings, and more.

after more than 60 albums linking jazz, blues, swing, and rock styles, her star has not diminished. Visit this site for a loving biography, links to discographies, and more.

More biographic and career infornation can be found at **http://www.wic.org/bio/plee.htm**.

Leadbelly

 http://cycad.com/cgi-bin/Leadbelly/index.html

Huddie Ledbetter—Leadbelly—was born in 1885 and died in late 1949. He was known as the "King of the Twelve-String Guitar" and he was a one-time protégé of the great Blind Lemon Jefferson. Leadbelly was a long-time inmate of several southern penitentiaries. He was a murderer and he was a genius.

Miss Peggy Lee

 http://www.chaoskitty.com/b_kitty/plee.html

Miss Peggy Lee (born Norma Egstrom in North Dakota in 1922) has contributed far more to American music than "Fever"—as a singer, lyricist, composer, and musical innovator, she exemplifies popular music at its best. Her first hit was "Why Don't You Do Right?," recorded with Benny Goodman in 1942. Duke Ellington nicknamed her "The Queen." And

Tom Lehrer

 http://www.keaveny.demon.co.uk/lehrer/lehrer.htm

Tom Lehrer is one of America's most gifted social and political gadflies. Since his start at Harvard in the early '50s, Lehrer has produced more biting musical commentaries on American life, politics, and social mythology than just about anybody. Visit this site for lyrics to all his recorded works (including "The Old Dope Peddler" and "The Masochism Tango"), a suitably cynical biography, information on his recordings, and much more.

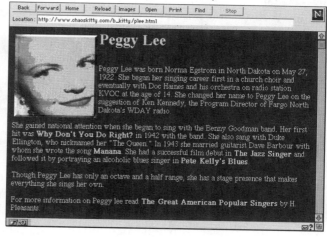

Jerry Lee Lewis

 http://www.rockhall.com/induct/lewijerr.html

Jerry Lee Lewis rocks on, still pounding away after all these years on such classics as "Whole Lotta' Shakin' Going On," "Great Balls of Fire," and "Breathless." He is no less fiery and wild today than he was forty years ago.

Lincoln Center

 http://www.lincolncenter.org/

Lincoln Center in New York City includes the Metropolitan Opera (**http://www.metopera.org**), Alice Tully Hall, Avery Fisher Hall, the New York City Ballet, and more. It is, of course, home to the New York Philharmonic (**http://www.nyphilharmon.org**), among other ensembles and performance companies. It is also home to the Juilliard School of Music.

Little Richard

 http://www.srv.net/~roxtar/lrichard.html

Little Richard is nothing short of an American classic. Many of his recordings are absolute classics, too, among them "Tutti Frutti," "Long Tall Sally," "Ready Teddy," "Good Golly Miss Molly," and "Lucille." Come to this site for a brief biography, song lyrics, and more. You may also want to check out Little Richard's page at the Rock & Roll Hall of Fame (**http://www.rockhall.com/induct/richlitt.html**).

Los Angeles Philharmonic

 http://www.laphil.org/

Under the direction of Esa-Pekka Salonen, the Los Angeles Philharmonic is truly one of the great orchestras of the world. Not only do they perform worldwide, they also have an extensive outreach and education program for children.

Bobby McFerrin

 http://www.bobbymcferrin.com/home.html

Two generations ago, Ella Fitzgerald's scat singing forever changed and enriched the scope of human vocal expression. Today, a similar honor goes to Bobby

McFerrin, whose imagination, huge range, and sheer joy have brought jazz, classical, and world musics together in unforeseen, new ways. Whether interpreting Vivaldi or Chick Corea, or flying off on one of a thousand improv tangents, McFerrin is truly and uniquely American. These beautiful pages trace his entire career, including performances, recordings, films, and video.

The Mills Brothers

 http://www.cumberlink.com/mills/

Like Elvis, the Mills Brothers had "early" and "late" incarnations. But whether you're a fan of the high-energy "Hold That Tiger" quartet of the '30s or the syrupy harmonies of their "Paper Doll" heyday in the '50s, this site has something for you. This is the official Website of The Society for the Preservation and Promotion of The Mills Brothers Musical History (The Mills

Brothers Society). Join the Society. Get the newsletter. And hold that tiger.

Joni Mitchell

 http://www.well.com/user/wallyb/ jonihome.html

How could we ever be without Joni Mitchell—that wonderful, engaging songwriter, singer, musician, poet, and painter? She has given us 19 great albums over the course of 25 years, every one of them a little something different.

Bill Monroe & the Bluegrass Boys

 http://www.banjo.com/BG/Profiles/ BillMonroe.html

When Bill Monroe died in September of 1996, an era ended. Widely hailed as the "father" of bluegrass music, Bill Monroe made countless recordings and toured the world, defining a new style as he did so.

Phil Ochs

http://www.cs.pdx.edu/~trent/ ochs/

I knew Phil Ochs in the early '70s: a gifted, tragic figure and an outstanding human being. He was a great songwriter somewhat overshadowed by an even greater songwriter: Bob Dylan. But some of Phil's songs remain classics, among them "Outside of a Small Circle of Friends," "Draft Dodger Rag," and "I Ain't a'Marchin' Any More."

Peter, Paul & Mary

 http://www.magick.net/~ppm/nppm.html

It seems they have been around forever. I listened to them when I was a kid. Now my kids listen to them. Remember back in the '70s when Spiro Agnew condemned "Puff, the Magic Dragon" as a drug song? What a moron.

This is the home page for Peter, Paul & Mary. You will find pictures, sounds, and a schedule of concerts for 1996. PP&M has been playing folk music for over 35 years, and their latest album, PP M& (LifeLines), was released on April 11.

U. Utah Phillips

 http://www.hidwater.com/utah/

There are two types of people in the United States: the types who know U. Utah Phillips and the types who don't. Poet, hobo, songwriter, singer, guitarist, union organizer, and philosopher, he is sometimes called (by himself) "the golden voice of the great Southwest." I used to bump into him every year at the (now-defunct) Fox Hollow Folk Festival in New York State. Utah is an American original.

Buddy Rich

 http://sun.goddard.edu/~buddyrich/index.html

Buddy Rich, who died in 1987, was one of the great jazz drummers of the post-war period. He started out with Artie Shaw and then went on to perform with other leading jazz bands around the country and around the world.

Paul Robeson

 http://www.cs.uchicago.edu/discussions/cpsr/robeson/

April 9, 1998 will be the centennial of the birth of singer, musicologist, actor, activist, and writer Paul Robeson. At this set of Web pages you will find complete information on the life and career of Robeson, who died in 1976.

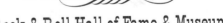

Rock & Roll Hall of Fame & Museum

 http://www.rockhall.com/

Take a stroll through a virtual museum of rock and roll, one that mimics the fantastic museum in Cleveland. Here you'll find

307

great information exhibits about rockers and their influences, including such Hall of Famers as Bill Haley, Buddy Holly, Woody Guthrie, and, of course, Pete Seeger!

The memorabilia is awesome and includes Grace Slick's dress from Woodstock, Jimi Hendrix's handwritten lyrics for "Purple Haze," two of Roger McGuinn's trademark 12-string Rickenbacker guitars from the Byrds, and more.

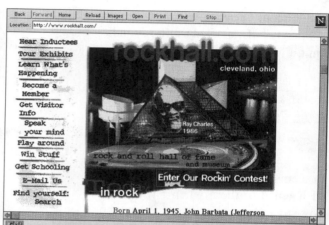

Run D.M.C.

 http://www.duke.edu/~jk2/dmc.html

This growing site is dedicated to Run D.M.C., pioneers of rap from Queens, New York City, and now among the "elders" of rap culture. If you're into the genre, you can link with many related sites from here. If it's all new to you, drop in to check out some fine lyric examples presented as poetry (without the boom-box bass line) and learn to appreciate this American-born art form a little better.

Gil Scott-Heron

 http://www.tvtrecords.com/bands/gil.html

It's pretty rare for an entire American musical form or movement to be able to trace its genesis to a single artist or piece of music. But Gil Scott-Heron's 1970 political bombshell "The Revolution Will Not Be Televised" is widely credited as the first rap song. Visit this site to find out more about this performer who acted as a bridge between the beat poets and the rappers of today. You can also find a good interview with Scott-Heron at **http://www.widemedia.com/fix/gil.html**.

John Sebastian

 http://hal9000.tky.hut.fi/JBS/index.html

One of my favorite moments from the film *Woodstock* is John Sebastian in his tie-dyed shirt singing "I'll Paint Rainbows All Over Your Blues." The former lead man for The Lovin' Spoonful is still going strong. Get the details at this, his home page.

Pete Seeger Appreciation Page

 http://ourworld.compuserve.com/
homepages/JimCapaldi

I've spoken elsewhere in this book about my dear friends Toshi and Pete Seeger, and have in fact dedicated this book to both of them. Peter is the composer of such classic songs as "Where Have All the Flowers Gone?" which was a hit for the Kingston Trio in the United States and then a hit again in Europe, when Marlene Dietrich recorded it in German. Another of his is "Turn, Turn, Turn" which was a hit for the Byrds. But these classic songs are just bellwethers of Pete's enormous contribution and influence. As I mentioned earlier in this chapter, during my relatively brief musical career it was my honor to record with Pete for Folkways Records in 1976.

"The artist of ancient times inspired, entertained, educated his fellow citizens," Pete has written recently. "Modern artists have an additional responsibility—to encourage others to be artists. Why? Because technology is going to destroy the human soul unless we realize that each of us must in some way be a creator as well as a spectator or consumer... Make your own music, write your own books, if you would keep your soul." Right on.

Many thanks to Jim Capaldi for this Website, which is packed with great information about Pete. For information on Pete's latest studio recording, which has just won a Grammy, go to the Website addressed as **http://www.livingmusic.com/ pete/**.

BOOKS WRITTEN BY PETE SEEGER, ALONE OR WITH OTHERS

Abiyoyo. New York: Macmillan, 1985.
American Favorite Ballads, Tunes And Folksongs As Sung By Pete Seeger

Frank Sinatra

 http://www.sinatralist.com/

Quite different from Pete Seeger: Frank Sinatra. This is the home page for the Internet mailing list devoted to discussions of Frank and his music. The folks at the Sinatra organization are in the process of mounting their own Web page, which is not quite there yet. When it is, the address will be **http://sinatra.org/**.

Sing Out! Magazine

 http://www.libertynet.org:80/~singout/

Sing Out! Magazine is a print magazine focused on American folk music. Since its founding in May of 1950 by Pete Seeger and others, *Sing Out!* has been printing lead sheets for traditional and contemporary folk songs along with feature articles, interviews, recording and book reviews, and much more.

Bessie Smith

 http://www.surfin.com/
TheBlueFlameCafe/Bessie_Smith.html

Bessie Smith earned the title "Empress of the Blues" for her forceful delivery of classic blues as well as her outspokenly emancipated lifestyle. "Tain't Nobody's Bisnezz If I Do," "Back Water Blues," and "Poor Man's Blues" are all classics, as is "Nobody Knows You When You're Down and Out." She died at age 43 of injuries received in an auto accident in 1937. At this Website you'll not only find a full bio and pics, but also sound files of such classic songs as "St. Louis Blues."

Smithsonian/Folkways Records

 http://www.si.edu/folkways

As I've mentioned earlier in this chapter, it was back in 1976 that Pete Seeger and I recorded *Fifty Sail on Newburgh Bay* for Folkways Records. That is just one of the

thousands of recordings you'll find here at the Website for Smithsonian/Folkways.

John Philip Sousa

 http://plato.digiweb.com/~dlovrien/
sousa/music.htm

Is there any more American music than the stirring marches of John Philip Sousa? Here you'll find an extensive archive of sound files containing virtually everything Sousa ever wrote performed by such great ensembles as the Boston Pops.

Bruce Springsteen

 http://taurus.cira.colostate.edu/mocko/
springsteen.html

This is your number one stepping-off place on the Web for links to information on Bruce and his music. Here you have dozens of links to Sony's official Bruce page, Matt Orell's Web discography for Bruce, Atsushi Shionozaki's Springsteen bootlegs Web page, and so on. Whatever you want in the way of information about "the Boss," you can find it here.

Sweet Honey in the Rock

 http://www.singers.com/
sweethoney.html

As their Web page explains, Sweet Honey in the Rock is not just a singing group, "It is a traveling and

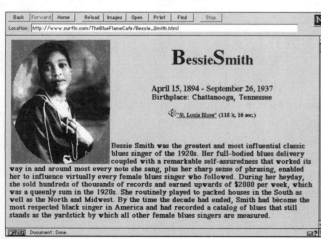

community-based cultural institution dedicated to the preservation and celebration of African-American culture through performances." And the performances are full of some of the most beautiful music on the planet.

Livingston Taylor

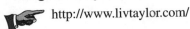 http://www.livtaylor.com/

His brother James may be a notch more famous, but Livingston Taylor remains my favorite of the two. For just as James is a notch more famous, so is Liv just a notch less commercial and a notch more relaxed.

Sonny Terry and Brownie McGhee

 http://www.island.net/~blues/
sonnyter.html

Sonny Terry, the great old blues harmonica player, lived in Queens not far from Gary Davis. For years he'd been teamed up with guitarist and singer Brownie McGhee, and the two were an institution at folk festivals

throughout the '60s and '70s. Sonny outlived Brownie by a few years and died in 1986.

Jay Ungar and Molly Mason

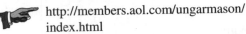 http://members.aol.com/ungarmason/
index.html

Jay Ungar and Molly Mason are traditional musicians of the very first rank. They are perhaps best known for Jay's beautiful composition "Ashokan Farewell" which formed the backbone of the soundtrack to Ken Burns' documentary epic "The Civil War."

Susanne Vega

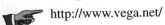 http://www.vega.net/

She is, quite simply, captivating. And she is one of the best contemporary singer-songwriters in the United States. Her compositions are as unique as they are engaging, and her voice a powerful artistic tool.

Loudon Wainwright III

 http://world.std.com/~rmura/loudon/

His most famous recording was "Dead Skunk" which was a #1 hit in Little Rock, Arkansas for six weeks in 1972. He made three appearances on *MASH* in 1975 as Captain Calvin Spaulding, the singing surgeon. And he is one of the best singer-songwriters on the planet. His latest underground hit was "Jesse Don't Like It," which helped slow down, if not completely forestall, Jesse Helms' efforts to gut federal support for the arts. So get into Loudon Wainwright III!

Fats Waller

 http://www.pastperfect.com/
noteshtml/fatsnotes.html

Thomas "Fats" Waller (1904-1943) was one of the most inventive and entertaining pianists America ever produced. He started writing for Broadway at 22 and then blazed across the American jazz landscape with countless concerts and recordings until his untimely death at 39. He will always be remembered for penning "Ain't Misbehavin'," still one of the best pop songs of the century. Visit this site for a good biography.

A commodious list of available band and solo recordings can be found at **http://www.biograph.com/Waller,%20Thomas%20%22Fats%22**. And for a nice candid shot of Fats on his way to play at Harlem's Apollo Theatre, check out **http://pastperfect.com/gallery/fats.htm**l.

Orson Welk

 http://www.users.interport.net/
~borgia1/index.html

One of the finest bands on the planet is also one of the most obscure. It is always so. Founded and directed by Carmen Borgia and Deb Hiett Borgia, Orson Welk puts out a fantastic and original sound. Visit the home page for sound files and judge for yourself.

Robin & Linda Williams

 http://www.dn.net/williams/

No, not that Robin Williams. I am talking about Robin and Linda Williams, the folk musicians. They recently passed the twenty-year mark in their collaboration as musical and marital partners, and the relationship seems to be going strong on all fronts.

Windham Hill Records

 http://www.windham.com/
main.html

Will Ackerman's Windham Hill Records was really in the right place at the right time. When he released his first moody, gentle solo guitar album and followed it up with an equally introspective album from pianist George Winston, the label's success heralded New Age music's explosion into the marketplace. Windham Hill has grown and changed dramatically over the years and now boasts sublabels featuring vocal and instrumental music aimed at the New Age generation, if not exclusively New Age ears. These attractive pages introduce you to the music and the musicians, past and present, including Tuck & Patti, Michael Hedges, Liz Story, and the latest addition to the WH family: Yanni.

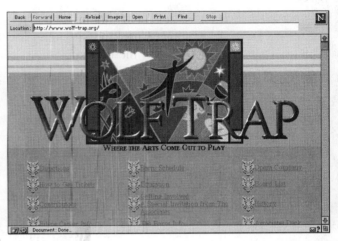

Wolf Trap Foundation for the Performing Arts

 http://www.wolf-trap.org/

The mission of Wolf Trap, located at Vienna, Virginia, is to enrich, educate, and provide enjoyment to large, diverse audiences through a broad spectrum of accessi-ble, high-qaulity activities in the performing arts. The place is one of the premier performance venues in the country. Symphonies, opera companies, banjo players, and rockers—they all come here to share their talents. Find out more on the Web.

Neil Young

 http://www.cs.uit.no/Music/View/
young,+neil

He's been through it all, from Buffalo Springfield to Crosby, Stills, Nash & Young to Neil Young and Crazy Horse and back again. And he remains a classic to this day. Ladies and gentlemen, I give you Neil Young.

16

Extavaganzas,
Parades &
Festivals

Americans love spectacles. We love them just as much as did the old Romans. But instead of feeding Christians to the lions, we have awards shows, festivals, and fireworks on the fourth of July.

The Spectacle of Oscar

One of our great American rituals is the annual Oscar awards ceremonies (**http://www.oscars.org/ampas/1awards.html**). The entertainment is routinely bad. The script is routinely dumb. And we, the audience out there in TV-land, are routinely glued to our seats, watching the culmination of the great annual competition between our cultural heroes—the famous movie stars and directors we relate to and idolize. It is spectacle of the highest order.

It was not always so.

The first Academy Awards ceremony was held in May of 1929 in Hollywood's Roosevelt Hotel. The price of admission was $10, and sound was the newest movie technology. The event was attended by a whopping 250 (Figure 16-1).

At the first Oscar Awards banquets, the results were known in advance. The award committee routinely gave the results to the newspapers so they could publish them as early as possible following the ceremony. But this practice resulted in information leaks, which took the suspense out of the event. In the early '40s, the practice was changed to the sealed envelope system in use now.

The first Awards ceremony that was something like what we know today was held in 1943. This ceremony—which for the first time did not include a banquet—was held at Grauman's Chinese Theater and was broadcast overseas by network radio. Later, they were moved to the Los

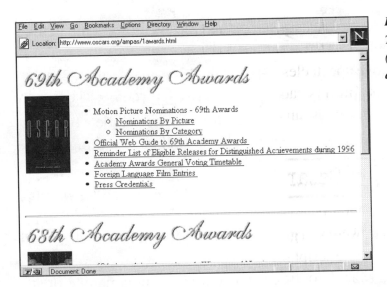

FIGURE 16-1

The Academy Awards
(***http://www.oscars.org/***
ampas/1awards.html)

Angeles Shrine Auditorium, and finally in 1949, to the Academy's own theater. From there, things progressed. In 1953 the Academy Award ceremony, hosted by Bob Hope, was televised for the first time.

There have only been three instances when the schedule of the Awards ceremony has been interrupted or disrupted. In 1938, floods in Los Angeles delayed the event. In 1968, the ceremony was delayed several days out of respect for Dr. Martin Luther King, Jr., who was assassinated a few days before the originally scheduled Awards presentation and whose funeral was to be held on the originally scheduled Awards date. In 1981, the Awards were again postponed because of the assassination attempt on President Ronald Reagan.

The Spectacle of the Macy's Thanksgiving Parade

That most American of holidays—Thanksgiving—simply would not be the same without the spectacle of the Macy's Thanksgiving Parade. I grew up in New York, so perhaps the parade means more to me than to others—but I doubt it.

Nationally televised, it is the nation's kickoff to the holiday season, and it's watched by millions of Americans every year. 1997 marks its 71st year. Viewership last year (1996) was 45 million. The parade's two-and-a-half-mile route is packed with excited kids of all ages waiting for the extravaganza to begin.

Featuring more than 3,000 Macy's employees who participate on a volunteer basis, the parade (Figure 16-2) begins at New York's Museum of Natural History (**http://www.amnh.org**) on the upper-west side of Manhattan.

For decades, the Macy's Parade has featured stunning parade floats, some of the best marching bands in the country, and the giant character balloons for which the parade is so well-known. The '96 parade featured no fewer than 118 entrants including floats, marching bands, clowns, and giant balloon characters.

FIGURE 16-2

*Macy's Thanksgiving Parade (**http://www. festivals.com/macy/**)*

What would the Puritans who began the tradition of Thanksgiving think of such ostentation? I don't think they'd like it much. But my kids sure have some fun with it.

Parades have been around for thousands of years, beginning simply as processions of military units. Two thousand years ago the Roman Empire held parades to celebrate army victories and pagan holidays. Even the pyramids of Egypt and ancient sites in Mexico and Asia have wall paintings showing parades and processions.

The modern tradition of parades originated in the Middle Ages, in celebration of religious festivals, seasonal events, or the entry of a king into a city. The word "parade" comes from the French "to prepare" or "show off"—which is exactly what people did, with armies demonstrating their marching ability and acrobats performing incredible feats.

In the United States there were parades even before the Revolutionary War, but the oldest Thanksgiving Day parade tradition in the nation exists in Philadelphia, where the first such parade was held in 1920. The New York Macy's parade did not start until 1924.

The Spectacle of the Circus

There are few things quite so uniquely American as the circus—and there is nothing like it in the world. Originally started in England, the art and showmanship of the circus was perfected, refined, and popularized in the United States. In the early days of this century, some thought the silent film would kill the circus. Didn't happen. Then sound films and professional sports were thought likely to kill the circus. Didn't happen. Then TV came along, and dire predictions for the circus' inevitable doom were made once again.

Still, the circus as an institution is not dead. And those skeptics, those non-believers, who went to the trouble of making funeral arrangements for the circus only a few short years ago have had to withdraw the death notice. Send the circus no flowers. Send no condolences to the survivors of this rich tradition. The Big Top is alive and well.

The traveling circus has been a part of the American landscape since the early 19th century, and there are still many today with long traditions. One such circus is the Carson & Barnes 5-Ring Circus (**http://www. circusweb.com/CB**), which travels America and performs under the largest "Big Top" on earth. This circus has been owned and operated by the same family for four generations (Figure 16-3).

The Carson & Barnes "Big Top" tent is truly enormous. It is 397 feet long and 145 feet wide; and it is covered with 60,000 square feet of specially fabricated fire- and waterproof polyvinyl material suspended with over two miles of rope and steel cables. Just watching the circus set up and "tear down" is a show in itself.

FIGURE 16-3
The Carson & Barnes
5-Ring Circus
*(**http://www.circusweb.**
com/CB)*

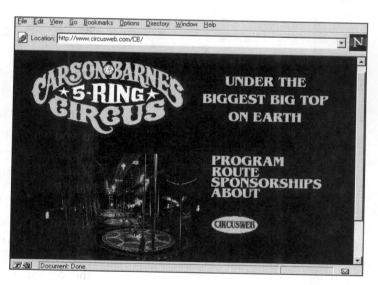

On days when I don't feel like writing, I often fantasize about what it would be like to work for a circus: a little circus, a modest circus of the type that covers 20 miles in a day and does shows in seven little towns a week. It wouldn't be easy, I know, but it would always be interesting.

Spectacles and Ceremonies on the Web

Our "meatspace" spectacles find their equivalent in cyberspace. (By the way, "meatspace" is the antithesis of cyberspace. This is the term coined by John Perry Barlow and meant to describe the real world where we live and breathe as opposed to the cyberworld where we don't actually live or breathe.)

Almost every occasion and event of contemporary America has its correlative Website. I speak not only of sports extravaganzas, circuses, and award ceremonies, but also of the pageantry associated with American holidays. There are many things to discover along this line on the Web, so let's begin.

All American Music Festival

 http://www.bandfest.com/

This annual festival features the best marching bands from high schools all across the United States and is ongoing every spring from mid-March through mid-June. The site is Orlando's Disneyworld. The festival is competitive. The best bands in the country get flown in by Disney and provided free room and board. Get more details at the Web page, and may the best band win.

Bluegrass Festivals Nationwide

 http://www.banjo.com/BG/ BG-Festival.html

Here you will find links for dozens of annual Bluegrass festivals including the Old Settler's Bluegrass & Acoustic Music Festivals (Round Rock, Texas), the Howlin' Coyote Bluegrass Festival (Twentynine Palms, California), the Festival of the Bluegrass (Lexington, Kentucky), the Huck Finn Bluegrass Festival (Victorville, California), and the Noppet Hill Bluegrass Festival (Lanesboro, Massachusetts).

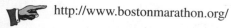
Boston Marathon

 http://www.bostonmarathon.org/

Runners have gathered in Boston to run the intense Marathon more than 100 times. Here's a virtual gathering place for runners and spectators alike, who are thrilled by this living spectacle of American sports history. Come to the official Boston Marathon Website to learn how to register for the next run, or how to volunteer to be on the support staff. Then visit **http://marathon.townonline.com/main.html** for more exciting stuff including stride-by-stride coverage of the '97 race, video clips, and a digital photo gallery.

Britt Festivals, Jacksonville, Oregon

 http://www.mind.net/britt/

Where can you go to lounge on a lovely wooded hillside while world-class classical, jazz, folk, and country musicians perform on an airy stage? For nearly 35 years, people have been flocking to the Britt Festivals near Jacksonville, Oregon for just that magic mix. From June through August each year, a series of wide-ranging concerts and dance programs are presented in this spectacular setting, located on the estate of 19th century photographer Peter Britt. These lovely pages will acquaint you with the festival, the artists, and the program schedule.

Cable Ace Awards

 http://www.cableace.org/

Like the Oscars and the Grammies, the Cable Ace Awards Ceremony is an enormous spectacle of wealth, celebrity, and talent. The Awards recognize the very best in Cable programming nationwide.

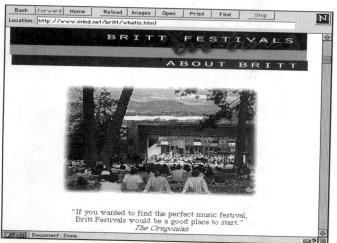

"If you wanted to find the perfect music festival, Britt Festivals would be a good place to start."
The Oregonian

Chicago Blues Festival

 http://www.ci.chi.il.us/Tourism/Festivals/Blues/Blues.html

Over 600,000 blues lovers attend this annual event, held in early June on the Chicago lakefront in Grant Park. Chicago is rightly proud of her blues heritage. Nowhere else will you enjoy a better lineup of performers or feel more strongly how the blues has helped shape the culture of America.

It's even free! Check out these pages for festival lineup schedules, with links to hotels, transportation, and other events.

Thursday, June 5 through Sunday, June 8, 1997
Noon - 10:00 p.m.

Chicago Fringe & Buskers Festival

 http://home.earthlink.net/
~jellis1111/

The Chicago Fringe & Buskers Festival is still quite small compared to the large street arts festival of Edinburgh which it attempts to emulate, but it is growing fast. The Festival is always held in the first two weeks of June.

Chicago Underground Film Festival

 http://www.deafear.com/~cuff/

The Chicago Underground Film Festival is an annual event featuring the wildest and most unexpected American films— films that run so far counter to the culture, they are, in fact, *underground*. Check it out.

Chinese New Year as Celebrated in the United States

 http://www.tat-usa.com/festival/
fhistory.htm

This insightful set of Web pages provides detailed information on festivities meant to celebrate the Chinese New Year in Boston, Houston, New York, Los Angeles, and other towns with large Chinese populations. What we are talking about, of course, is the coolest of street parades featuring brilliant costumes, huge dragons, acrobats, and fireworks. In the Chinese community it is a time for cleaning house, repaying debts, wrapping up old business, enjoying incredible feats, giving "red envelopes" of lucky money to friends and relatives and, most importantly, renewing family ties and remembering ancestors.

Christmas Tree Lighting Festivals

 http://festivals.com/xmas/treefest.htm

The tradition of the decorated Christmas tree is an ancient one that goes back thousands of years. But community Christmas trees and lighted lawn trees are uniquely American, and Christmas tree lighting festivals are common in many

American communities, including my little town of Wickford, Rhode Island.

President Calvin Coolidge inaugurated the annual tradition of lighting the "National Christmas Tree" in 1923. This, the largest of all Christmas tree lighting festivals, takes place each winter on the south lawn of the White House.

Updated annually—usually in the early Autumn—this Web page provides all the details, nationwide. (By the way, the home page for the National Christmas Tree Association is **http://www.christree.org** and Santa's domain on the Web is **http://www.christmas.com**. He's a jolly old geek.)

Circus Art at the John and Mable Ringling Museum

 http://www.ringling.org/ring9.html

Here is a fascinating collection of circus artifacts including posters, prints, drawings, and classic photographs. Here you'll also find classic costumes and accoutrements, props used by famous circus performers, and rare carved circus wagons.

Circus World Museum

 http://www.next-wave.net/nextwave/cwmpix.htm

The Circus World Museum of Baraboo, Wisconsin is owned by the State Historical Society of Wisconsin. At the museum, both in Baraboo and online, you will find many fascinating details of circus history along with artifacts of P.T. Barnum and other circus greats. The museum also has an "unofficial" Web page located at the URL **http://www.next-wave. net/nextwave/cwmpix.htm**.

Civil War Reenactments

 http://ncwa.org/

All across the country, dedicated groups of history buffs reenact Civil War battles, striving for meticulous historical accuracy, right down to hand-sewn uniforms. These are amazing events, and well worth taking your kids to. The home page of the National Civil War Association, **http://ncwa.org/**, is a good place to start for general information about the reenactment scene.

The site at **http://marin.org/npo/cwar/**, set up by a California reenactment group, links you to every local reenactment brigade or group and every reenactment open to the public around the country. Pop over to **http://marin.org/npo/cwar/racw/** for details on this particular group's reenactment schedule in Northern California and how individuals and school groups can get involved and get a taste of American history not available through books or movies.

Clowns of America International

 http://www.clown.org/

Clowns of America International has created this Web page in the hopes of spreading joy and happiness through clowning around. If you are interested in becoming a clown, or just love clowns, this is a mandatory stop on the information superhighway.

Coney Island

 http://www.brooklynonline.com/coneyisland/

Coney Island is America's quintessential amusement park. It's a never-ending state fair and as American as apple pie. These pages are full of great photos of the park and rides, designed to give you an idea of what kind of fun kids and adults alike can have here.

DucKon

 http://www.mcs.net/~tallison/duckon/PR1.html

If you're into science fiction conventions, you probably have heard of DucKon, an annual get-together held in Chicago. If you aren't, this site is worth a visit to acquaint yourself with a festive event of, by, and for the science fiction and fantasy literature fan. This is a peculiarly American subcultural phenomenon, where "furry folk" can meet Klingon wannabes, self-identified "sci-fi nerds" can share "filk" songs, books and collectible paraphernalia can be bought and traded, and sci-fi and fantasy imaginations can run rampant and have fun.

Florida Folk Festival

 http://www.dos.state.fl.us/dhr/folklife/index.html

As one of the oldest folk festivals in the United States, the Florida Folk Festival features folk songs, dances, legends, crafts, foods, and other forms of traditional expression. Held every Memorial Day weekend on the banks of the Suwannee River in White Springs, this festival draws thousands of locals and national recording artists alike.

The Flying High Circus

 http://mailer.fsu.edu/~mpeters/fsucircus.html

The Flying High Circus is comprised of students at Florida State University, Tallahassee. Just look for the tent, located right across the street from the campus baseball field. Or visit them on the Web! They have ground acts (such as juggling and hand bal-

ancing) and aerial acts (such as the flying trapeze). No clowning, however. And no animal acts.

Fourth of July in Washington, D.C.

 http://www.nps.gov/nacc/4th/

Fourth of July celebrations in Washington, D.C. are always extensive and include not only fireworks but also concerts and other extra special events, such as a parade. This page is updated annually to tell you exactly what is happening, and when.

The Grammy Awards

 http://www.grammy.com/

The Grammy Awards are, of course, the music industry's equivalent of the Oscars. And the awards evening, usually held in late winter, is just as much a spectacle as is the Oscar ceremonies. Find out all about the Grammy Awards at Grammy's official website. My friend Pete Seeger has just won a Grammy for the best Traditional Folk Album of 1996: *Pete!* (**http://www.livingmusic.com**).

The Great Circus Parade

 http://circus.compuware.com/

The great circus parades winding their way from town to town with their bright-colored wagons, raucous circus animals, and cacophonous music have marked the arrival of fun and games to communities for generations.

Commemorating these great parades of yore, the Great Circus Parade is held every year in Milwaukee. Get details at this Website. While you are visiting the site, you can also get details on the fantastic Circus World Museum—another Wisconsin institution. You should also check out images of the "Great Circus Train"—**http://www.baraboo.com/cwm/cwm.htm**.

1997 Parade – Sunday, July 13th in Milwaukee, WI

Looking Back on a Wondrous Week of Fun and Excitement – 1996

All aboard the Great Circus Parade Train. (Click to open Train Controller.)

The Great Hudson River Revival

 http://www.clearwater.org/festival.html

The Hudson River Sloop *Clearwater's* Great Hudson River Revival, the nation's oldest environmental and arts festivals, is held every year in late June in Westchester County, New York. Performers have included Tom Paxton, Holly Near, Ronnie Gilbert, Pete Seeger, Ani DeFranco, John Gorka, Dar Williams, and many others.

The Iditarod: The Last Great Race on Earth

 http://www.iditarod.com

On March 1, 1997, 56 mushers and almost 900 dogs lined up for the start of the 25th annual running of the world's longest sled dog race, the Iditarod—a 1,200-mile endurance test of the harshest, coldest terrain between Anchorage and Nome, Alaska. The race is a spectacle of both bravery and endurance.

The Kennedy Center Honors

 http://kennedy-center.org/explore/honors/html/maindoc.html

Each year, the Kennedy Center hands out lifetime achievement medals in the arts to five distinguished Americans. In 1996 the awardees included playwright Edward Albee, country musician Johnny Cash, and actor Jack Lemmon. In 1995 they included opera singer Marilyn Horne, blues musician B.B. King, actor Sidney Poitier, and play-

wright Neil Simon. 1994 was a big year in our household for, honored along with actor Kirk Douglas, soul singer Aretha Franklin and several others, was Pete Seeger (a.k.a. "Uncle Pete" to my kids) sitting right there in the presidential box at the ceremonies, on national television, with the other celebrities and, of course, Bill and Hillary Clinton.

Kentucky Derby

 http://festivals.com/kenderby/index.htm

It's more than a horse race! It's bourbon and bluegrass! It's two weeks of sports and cultural celebration leading up to the Big Race. Get yourself a mint julep, stroll through these friendly Kentucky pages, and join in the fun.

The Kerrville Folk Festival

http://www.fmp.com/kerrvill.html

Beginning every Memorial Day, in a sleepy little place called Quiet Valley Ranch—eight miles south of quiet Kerrville, Texas—the peace and quiet is shattered. The Kerrville Folk Festival, famous for its good music and great food, goes on for an entire 21 days. Past performers have included Peter Yarrow, Bob Gibson, and Butch Hancock.

Maine Arts Festival

http://www.mainearts.org/festhome.html

Held annually during the first week of August in Brunswick, Maine, the Maine Festival has grown to become Maine's biggest and most diverse annual cultural event. The festival addresses all the arts, both traditional and contemporary, including music, dance, theater, visual arts, fine handicrafts, prose, poetry, and more. There were a thousand artists present in 1996, and an audience of more than 20,000.

Often, though not always, present at the Maine Arts Festival is my friend Michael Cooney, known to many as the "one-man folk festival."

Michael has been helping others to experience the beauty, power, and humor of old and new songs for over 35 years, in countless halls, clubs, and coffeehouses in the U.S., Canada, Mexico, Great Britain, and Europe. He has performed, lectured, or done residencies at hundreds of U.S. and Canadian colleges and schools of all levels. He has performed at most of the major North American folk festivals, including the National Folk Festival, the Newport Folk Festival (**http://www.newportfolk.com**), the Mariposa Folk Festival, and the Philadelphia Folk Festival (**http://www. pfs.org**). He served six years on the board of the National Folk Festival in Washington, D.C. In 1986 he was Artistic Director of Philadelphia's "Maritime America Festival" (part of "We the People 200—the National Celebration of the 200th Anniversary of the United States Constitution." And for more than twenty years Michael was a director of, contributor to, and columnist for the U.S.'s oldest folk music magazine, *Sing Out!* (**http://www.libertynet.org~singout/**).

All those credentials, and still Michael doesn't have a Web page. There is another Michael Cooney, a musician, on the Web—a world-champion whistler (that's right, whistler) of classical and sacred music (**http://www.easylisteninwhistlin.com**). But he is not the fellow I've been talking about. Although the Michael Cooney of folk fame has no Web page, he does have an e-mail address: *mcooney@midcoast.com*. His recordings are available from Folk-Legacy Records (**http://www.folklegacy.com**).

Mardi Gras

http://www.fattuesday.com

Mardi Gras is an ancient Christian festival routinely celebrated to mark the last day before the start of Lent—Fat Tuesday. The day French-Canadian explorer Sieur d'Iberville and his men camped 60 miles south of New Orleans in 1699 happened to be Mardi Gras, March 3 of that year, so he named that place Pointe du Mardi Gras. It didn't take long for the French of New Orleans to start celebrating this holiday in the New World.

Historians say that Mardi Gras was observed by masked balls and bawdy street processions in New Orleans as early as the 1700s. By 1806, the festivities had gotten so rowdy that Mardi Gras celebrations were forbidden, but by all accounts this law was summarily ignored. In 1817, masks were declared illegal. But by 1823, the celebration that had been going on all along became legal again, and by 1826 even masking was legalized.

"Bals masqués" (masked balls), also known as "tableau balls," were so fashionable in the 19th century that by law the season was limited to January 1 through Mardi Gras Day in order to keep the population from celebrating all year long. The first formal Mardi Gras parade was held in either 1835 or 1838.

Mystery Dinner Theatre

 http://www.murdermysteryinc.com/ dinnertheater.htm

How would you like to attend a lavish banquet during which one of the guests gets mysteriously (and usually hilariously) murdered and then everyone has to figure out "who dunnit?" Murder Mystery, Inc. presents evenings like this at restaurants, hotels, on boats, in trains, and prob-

ably anywhere you hire them to show up. The producers have been writing and presenting audience participation mystery plays for years. Check out these pages for photos and plenty of amusing information. Join them for dinner. It'll slay you.

New Orleans Jazz and Heritage

 http://nojazzfest.com/97f/97frames.html

It started in 1970 and was big fun. Now, 27 years later, it's colossal fun: the Jazz and Heritage Festival. Imagine 60,000 people a day for two weekends in April and May jammed into a race track oval, eating the tastiest food on the planet and strolling among a dozen stages featuring the hottest jazz, blues, rock, folk, and gospel musicians alive. Now you can tweak your imagination on these Web pages. Get illustrated recipes, page through great posters, find out who's playing and how to get there. Laissez les bons temps roulez!

New York Jazz Festival

http://www.nyjazzfest.com/

Usually held the last two weeks of June, the New York Jazz Festival is one of the premier Jazz events on the planet. It includes club performances as well as performances on piers, at parks, and on rooftops. Visit the Web page for details.

New York Lesbian and Gay Film Festival

 http://www.newfestival.com/

Held annually at the Joseph Papp Public Theater in New York, the New York Lesbian and Gay Film Festival features films by and about gay individuals, lives, and culture. These are not only dramatic works but also documentaries. The festival is usually held during the first two weeks of June.

New York Underground Film Festival

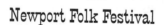 http://www.nyuff.com/

The New York Underground Film Festival is held annually in late March. It is held at the New York Film Academy in Greenwich Village and features low-budget (actually, very low-budget) student and avant-garde films.

Newport Folk Festival

 http://www.newportfolk.com/

Since 1958, the annual Newport Folk Festival has been a tradition every summer here in Rhode Island. Through the years, the festival has featured such performers as Bob Dylan, Joni Mitchell, and Van Morrison. Today the tradition continues through the generosity of Ben & Jerry's Ice Cream Company and is officially called *Ben & Jerry's Folk Festival - Newport*. Go to the Web page to find out who is playing this year.

Northwest Folklife Festival, Seattle

 http://www.nwfolklife.org/folklife/

Now in its 25th year, the Seattle Northwest Folklife Festival is one of the largest free multi-cultural events in the country. It's held on Memorial Day weekend every year and draws so many eager people that the population of Seattle doubles. Food, crafts, music performances and workshops, theatre, children's hands-on workshops, ethnic and traditional arts exhibitions, and more! This site will inspire you to be part of the happy throng next year.

Oregon Shakespeare Festival, Ashland

http://www.mind.net/osf/

The Ashland Shakespeare extravaganza began in 1935 and has annually presented Shakespeare in several venues in this picturesque Southern Oregon town. The 1997 program presents lots more than Shakespeare (including "Death of a Salesman" and "Turn of the Screw"). The calendar runs through the whole year, so you're sure to be able to find a free weekend. Check out this site for short descriptions of each play, and full information on the ongoing festivities.

Renaissance Faires

 http://renaissance-faire.com/

Since the late 60s, Renaissance Faires have popped up all over the country to the continuing delight of young and old. Whether you want to dress up in period finery and participate or just go in your civvies and gawk, these dramatic and crafts extravaganzas are great fun. Come to this clearinghouse home page for information on Faires nationwide, with descriptions, directions, links, and even a gallery of photos to get you in the mood.

San Francisco Carnaval Parade

 http://www.carnaval.com/sf/index.htm

Not to be confused with Mardi Gras, the Carnaval celebration grew into full flower in the ultimate party town: Rio de Janiero. But every Memorial Day weekend, San Francisco gives Rio a run for its money with their own wild parade through the Mission District. This is as colorful a party as you'll find anywhere in the country. Come

to these pages for jumping photos and encouragement to add this Carnaval to your itinerary next year.

San Francisco Mime Troupe

 http://www2.sfmt.org/sfmt/home.html

A unique theatre group, the Mime Troupe has presented political and social commentary in their musical comedy theatre productions for 35 years. What's unique about them? Well, for one thing, the shows are free. They are usually presented in the open, like in Golden Gate Park. But this is serious theatre, for all the comedy. The Troupe was honored in 1987 with a Tony Award for "excellence in regional theatre." The site at **http://arts.ucsc.edu/a+l/ sfmt bio.html** provides a good history of this remarkable group. The Troupe's home page, **http://www2.sfmt.org/sfmt/home.html**, will direct you to future performances.

Society For Creative Anachronism: Pennsic War

 http://www.sca.org/

History buffs who really want to go all out with their enthusiasms can't go any farther than do the dedicated members of the S.C.A. For over 26 years, the S.C.A. has held regional, national, and international revels and events, in which everyone involved is fully in the character of a pre-15th century person, relating to one another in a complex society with lords and ladies, knights in shining armor, the works. The annual Pennsic War, in which armies in full period regalia duke it out in mock combat, takes place every August near Slippery Rock, Pennsylvania. If you want to join the fun, no casual visitors are invited. You'll have to join the Society, get into costume, and work on your persona. Sound like fun? Check out these multi-linked pages to find out more.

Sundance Film Festival

 http://www.sundancechannel.com/
festival/

Founded in 1981 by Robert Redford, the Sundance Film Festival strives to develop new talent and preserve and celebrate independent film. Each year, Sundance highlights the very best independent films being made.

The Superbowl

 http://www.superbowl.com

There is nothing quite so spectacular as the Superbowl. At this official Website you'll find an extensive illustrated history of the Superbowl, game statistics, half-time

show histories, and much more. By the way, here is some Superbowl trivia for you. The first two Superbowls were simply called the AFL-NFL Championship Games. It wasn't until Superbowl III that the term Superbowl was officially adopted. Legend has it that the Superbowl got its name from a toy called the Super Ball, which was a favorite of Kansas City Chiefs owner Lamar Hunt's children.

Telluride Wine Festival

 http://www.telluridemm.com/trideinfo/
winefest.html

As if you didn't already have enough reasons to want to go to Telluride, Colorado—site of some of the finest skiing and most beautiful countryside in the world—now they've even got a wine festival every June.

Tournament of Roses

http://www.heraldtribune.com/roses/

The Tournament of Roses parade and football game are both great American traditions. Both events—the parade and the game—are enormous spectacles attracting thousands upon thousands of participants (and millions upon millions of television viewers) annually.

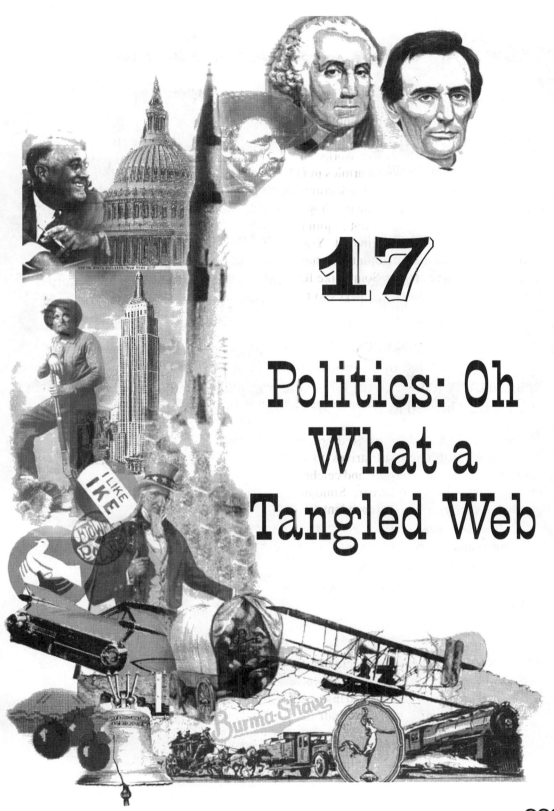

17

Politics: Oh What a Tangled Web

O*h, what a tangled web we weave when first we practice to deceive."* We all remember the old rhyme by Sir Walter Scott. We all had grandmothers who told us about George Washington and the cherry tree, and how important it was never to tell a lie.

Well, wake up and smell the coffee. That story itself is a lie. It was made up by the Reverend Mason Locke Weems (Figure 17-1) for inclusion in his early 19th century book entitled *Life of Washington*. Weems first published the biography as an 80-page pamphlet in 1800, and kept revising and expanding it thereafter. He added the anecdote about the cherry tree, which he said he'd gotten from an "old lady," to his 228-page ninth edition issued in 1809. Later in life, Weems admitted the tale was spurious. (By the way, you'll find the original text of Weems' account at the URL addressed as **http://mbti.gmu.edu/~cgrymes/dumfries/ctree.html**.)

And so it goes.

FIGURE 17-1

Mason Locke Weems (http://mbti.gmu.edu/~cgrymes/dumfries/parson.html)

Still, Washington and his compatriots were a great deal more honest than the average politician in our own day. For starters, Washington and the other Founders thought political office would be something one would volunteer to do for a short time before anxiously returning to one's own affairs. All the early presidents, senators, and representatives routinely made it clear they'd prefer to be doing other things, but were willing to serve—for a time—for the good of the country. They viewed public service as an obligation and an interruption of their real careers.

They—and in *they* I include George Washington, Thomas Jefferson, John Adams, Benjamin Franklin, and my forbear Charles Carroll (Figure 17-2)—would be horrified to know there is now a large constituency of people who consider themselves professional career politicians, and that an enormous business of fund-raising, political strategizing and lobbying has grown up around this core group.

This was not what the Founders had in mind.

Today, confronting a political environment that is rife with influence peddling and shady dealings, the old phrase about the tangled Web has a

FIGURE 17-2
Charles Carroll of Carrollton—a.k.a., great, great, great, great, great-grandpa (**http://www.mdarchives. state.md.us/msa/speccol/ 2221/04/06/html/ 0000.html**)

strange and sad resonance as we watch our contemporary political institutions move into cyberspace, taking their often malignant cynicism with them.

But be that as it may, the Web resources relating to politics—and the industry of politics—are extensive. Not only do the major federal government bodies and agencies have their own Websites, but so do virtually every state government agency, not to mention lobbyists, fund-raisers, and think tanks. Perhaps, armed with enough information from these various resources, we'll finally be able to sort out what all those politicos are up to. At least it might be easier to keep an eye on them.

Profile in Pragmatism

Nothing is as it seems in contemporary politics. For example, in politics sincerity is the most real form of cynicism. Consider the case of John F. Kennedy and his book *Profiles in Courage*.

It is, of course, useless to go yet again into the debate over the authorship of *Profiles*, the book for which Kennedy was awarded the 1957 Pulitzer Prize (**http://www.pulitzer.org**) for biography. All evidence indicates that *Profiles* was chiefly the creation of several advisors led by Kennedy's (Figure 17-3) friend and speechwriter Theodore Sorenson. The loyal Sorenson has provided only the softest refutation of this charge, saying vaguely that the true author of a work is he or she who "stands behind" the words, whatever that means.

Allowing Sorenson's loose construction for the term "author," we can join him in allowing Kennedy the byline for *Profiles*. Undoubtedly, Kennedy was the source for the key notions expressed in the book. At the very least, he approved the exemplars of political courage presented.

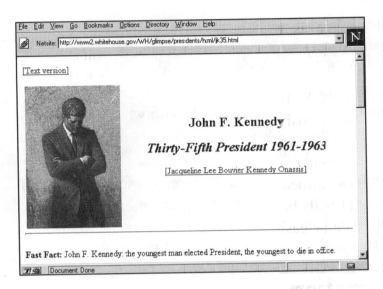

FIGURE 17-3
John F. Kennedy, a ghost with a ghostwriter (http://www2.whitehouse. gov/WH/glimpse/presidents/ html/jk35.html)

Thus we—just like the electorate of 1960—are meant to believe that Kennedy revered and emulated the altruistic political courage depicted in *Profiles*.

This courage is one that calls for the abandonment of popularity in order to take stands that, while not enjoying the favor of colleagues or constituents, hold the greatest moral value by promising the greatest national good. It is a courage defined by principle overriding pragmatism. It is a courage that indicates the absence of cynicism.

And it is a courage that, whenever it appears, is almost always a mirage.

No one knew this better than John Kennedy. An interested student of history, Kennedy surely realized that many of the acts narrated in *Profiles* were not feats of altruism. They were instead adventures in opportunism.

Profiles opens by depicting young John Quincy Adams, who renounced the Federalist party of his father and supported the Jefferson

Embargo of 1807 as a first-term senator from Massachusetts. The book paints this moment in Adams' career as a signal example of right over-riding pragmatism. But in fact, Adams' action was not a principled, semi-suicidal defection from a sturdy political power-base. It was instead the shrewd abandonment of a diminished party with which the country at large had already lost sympathy and from which an ambitious young man, hurrying toward his future, was wise to flee.

The book then applauds Senator Daniel Webster's vote for passage of the Fugitive Slave Law, which helped preserve the Union as part of the Compromise of 1850. According to *Profiles*, when Webster cast his vote in favor of the Fugitive Slave measure he courted the hatred of a Bay State electorate characterized by radical abolitionist sentiment.

But the radical abolitionists were in fact a minority. With his endorse-ment of the Compromise, Webster was pragmatically bowing to the wishes of the majority of the national electorate. Webster was also at the same time securing the indebtedness of a friend in the White House, Millard Fillmore (Figure 17-4), who would shortly reward him with a Cabinet appointment.

FIGURE 17-4
Millard Fillmore
(http://elections.eb.com/
elec/micro/208/99.html)

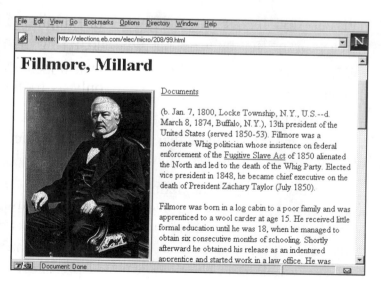

File Edit View Go Bookmarks Options Directory Window Help

Netsite: http://elections.eb.com/elec/micro/208/99.html

Fillmore, Millard

Documents

(b. Jan. 7, 1800, Locke Township, N.Y., U.S.--d. March 8, 1874, Buffalo, N.Y.), 13th president of the United States (served 1850-53). Fillmore was a moderate Whig politician whose insistence on federal enforcement of the Fugitive Slave Act of 1850 alienated the North and led to the death of the Whig Party. Elected vice president in 1848, he became chief executive on the death of President Zachary Taylor (July 1850).

Fillmore was born in a log cabin to a poor family and was apprenticed to a wool carder at age 15. He received little formal education until he was 18, when he managed to obtain six consecutive months of schooling. Shortly afterward he obtained his release as an indentured apprentice and started work in a law office. He was

Document: Done

One of the more accurate chapters in *Profiles* applauds Edmund G. Ross, the obscure, one-term senator from Kansas who defied his home-state radical Republican majority, as well as his radical Republican Senate colleagues, by voting against conviction in the 1868 impeachment of President Andrew Johnson.

President Johnson had enraged Ross and other radicals by refusing to support retributive "reconstruction" in the former Confederacy, preferring instead to push for the more benign reconciliation recommended by conservative "Lincoln" Republicans. Despite his lack of regard for Johnson, Ross found abhorrent the idea that a President might be impeached and removed from office for purely political reasons. Unlike others in his wing of the Republican party, Ross recognized the drama in which he acted as a Constitutional crisis. Thus his vote which, in addition to saving Johnson's presidency, probably also saved the federal system of government.

As payment for his high-mindedness, Ross was never again elected to office. When he returned to Kansas in 1871, he and his family were threatened, rebuked, and reduced to poverty. Then he was promptly forgotten.

There is a deep moral in the story of Edmund Ross. Politicians who act uncompromisingly on pure principle, flying in the face of both party and constituents, generally do not remain in politics long. And they die in obscurity. They remain in history only as footnotes and curiosities: freaks of political nature.

This fact was well-known to John Kennedy, who chose to have his mention in the history books be something more than just a footnote.

And so it was that the shrewd Kennedy put his name to a book of dubious historical veracity but great political usefulness. By paying homage to the presumed political courage of Webster and Adams, Kennedy implied that he could be counted upon to emulate the same unique brand of selfless political courage that he presented as having been theirs.

In fact, what he could be counted upon to emulate was the calculating pragmatism and knack for self-preservation that Webster and Adams bequeathed to all—such as Kennedy—with the wit to read their stories and understand their lessons.

Evening the Score

Having taken a stab at the Democrats via Kennedy I must, of course, provide balance by taking a shot at a Republican. Let's see? Who's a good target? I know! Newt Gingrich!

As we all know, 51-year-old Newt Gingrich was elected Speaker of the House after a long congressional career during which he never held a committee chairmanship and likewise never succeeded in authoring even a single piece of successful legislation.

Evidently an egoist of the first-rank, the newly-ascended Newt immediately mustered the gumption (or was it the *audacity*?) to compare himself with one of his most distinguished predecessors in the Speakership: venerable Henry Clay (Figure 17-5) of Kentucky.

FIGURE 17-5
Henry Clay
(http://elections.eb.com/
elec/micro/131/12.html)

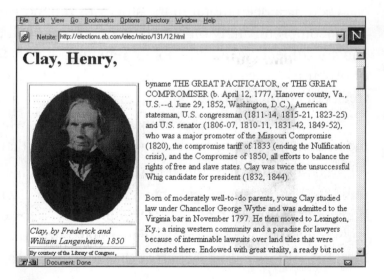

Clay was the most important Congressional leader of the early 19th century and quite possibly the most formidable politician ever known to the House of Representatives, the Senate, or indeed, the city of Washington. By the time he reached the age of 51, Clay had served more than a decade as Speaker, had played a critical role in negotiating an end to the War of 1812, and had put in four years as John Quincy Adams' (Figure 17-6) Secretary of State (during which time he enunciated the "Good Neighborhood" policy of U.S.-Latin American relations and was offered but refused appointment to the Supreme Court).

One would have expected at least a few chuckles from the gallery in response to Gingrich's prematurely optimistic measure of himself against the accomplished Clay. The absence of such hilarity was not, I suspect, the result of informed public consensus with Gingrich's self-important estimate. It was, rather, a consequence of that general historical illiteracy which Robert Penn Warren recognized as "the damnation of the modern world."

One would think that as an historian himself Speaker Gingrich would understand the very, very high bar that he or anyone else must jump over

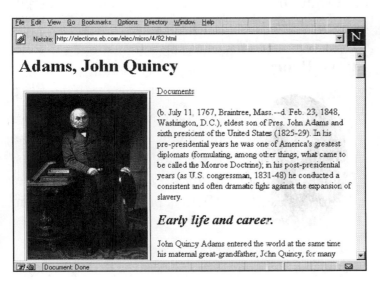

FIGURE 17-6
*John Quincy Adams,
under whom Clay served
as Secretary of State
(**http://elections.eb.com/
elec/micro/4/82.html**)*

before getting anywhere near the historical importance of Henry Clay. For as Lincoln and FDR are to the Presidency, so is Clay to the Speakership, to congressional (including senatorial) careers in general, and indeed to the essence of American statesmanship. Few have been greater than he, or have had more profound an impact on their era.

So great were the greatest of Clay's achievements as Speaker of the House (to which post he was elected at age 34), diplomat, and senator, that they have become fundamental benchmarks in the timeline of U.S. history—benchmarks that no student can (or, at least, *should*) escape secondary school without learning.

A few highlights:

As Speaker in 1820, Clay was instrumental in devising the Missouri Compromise, which temporarily resolved the bitter sectional dispute over the extension of slavery into the West and accomplished what was to Clay the most vital of imperatives: preservation of the Union.

In 1831, Clay won election as Senator from Kentucky and became leader of the opposition to Andrew Jackson. He ran unsuccessfully against Jackson for the Presidency in 1832, and in the process became the philosophical father of that movement which eventually coalesced into first the Whig and then the Republican Party.

In 1849, after seven years of self-prescribed absence from Congress and yet another unsuccessful run for the Presidency, Clay returned to the Senate. And now his skill at political compromise—already demonstrated in the Missouri debate—proved crucial once again. Victory in the Mexican War had brought bitter division over whether slavery would be allowed in the conquered Southwest. Clay, working in tandem with his friend and colleague Daniel Webster (Figure 17-7), helped persuade Congress to accept the Compromise of 1850, thus preserving the Union yet again.

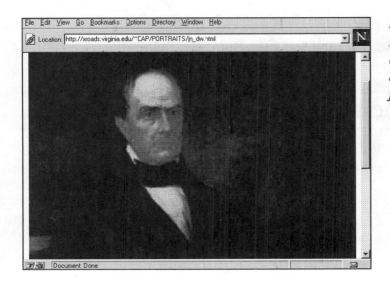

FIGURE 17-7
Daniel Webster
(***http://xroads.virginia.
edu/~CAP/PORTRAITS/
jn_dw.html***)

Along with Webster and Adams, Clay's closest colleagues in public life were no less than Thomas Hart Benton and John C. Calhoun. Abraham Lincoln met the man he called "the great compromiser" and "defender of the union" but once and wound up idolizing him forever. Clay was Lincoln's "beau ideal of a statesman" and "the man for whom I fought all my life."

In other words: this was no small man, Henry Clay. This was no shooting star rocketing briefly through the heavens. Clay served as a robust, enduring light in the American political firmament for more than four critical decades. And when he died, at age 75 in 1852, he was mourned not just by the small constituency of a district or state, but rather by a nation.

It was not so long ago that Dan Quayle had to be reminded he is no John Kennedy. Likewise we must point out to Newt Gingrich that he is no Henry Clay—at least not yet. Of course, I suppose it may be possible that he will demonstrate, over the long years, the wit and fortitude and historical significance that would put him in the same stratum as Clay.

But when and if Gingrich ever reaches that divine apex, it will not be necessary for him to point out to us the luminous fact of his ascension.

Politics on the Web

There are extensive political resources on the Web: resources relating to our political past, our political present, and our political future. Let's go browse a few.

All Politics

 http://allpolitics.com/

This fantastic Website maintained by CNN and *Time Magazine* gives you free, daily updates on all the latest political news. The site includes engaging political analysis by Stuart Rothenberg and much, much more.

All Things Political

 http://www.federal.com/political.html

All Things Political bills itself as "a look at Washington from the citizen's perspective." It includes the full texts of recent speeches by Newt Gingrich and Bill Clinton, as well as links to political discussion groups.

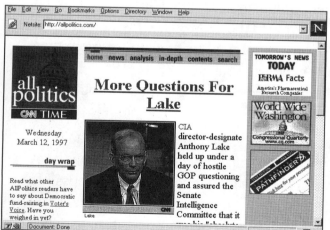

American Conservative Union

 http://www.townhall.com/ conservative/

As the oldest conservative lobbying organization in the country, the American Conservative Union conveys and promotes the fundamental values of conservatism. The ACU's focus is on the doctrine of original intent of the framers of the Constitution.

American Legislative Exchange Council

 http://www.alec.org/

The American Legislative Exchange Council is, as the great hyphenator Jack Kemp describes it, "bringing to America a chance to recapture the soul of America...to allow every single American man or woman—irrespective of their ethnic background—irrespective of their color—a chance to be part of the greatest democracy—the greatest freedom—the greatest system on the face of the earth." Fine, Jack, but can't we punctuate this a bit better?

The American Prospect

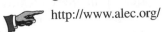 http://epn.org/prospect.html

The American Prospect is a magazine dedicated to debating the issues important to America from a liberal perspective, providing a forum for chewing over hard subjects. It was first published on paper in 1990, the brainchild of Paul Starr, Robert Kuttner, and Robert B. Reich, former Clinton Secretary of Labor. Now you can read current and back issues online at these easy-to-read pages, with provocative articles on subjects including the dangers of bipartisanship, fallout from welfare reform, and the questionable logic underlying the move to privatize Social Security.

California Public Interest Research Group (CALPIRG)

 http://www.pirg.org/pirg/calpirg/

CALPIRG is a citizen's lobbying organization, representing the collective clout of thousands of small individual supporters in California. The organization uses support funds to hire environmental attorneys, scientists, consumer advocates, and other public interest professionals. CALPIRG then investigates pollution, exposes consumer scams, documents special interest influence, crafts and shepherds legislative and initiative remedies, and fights legislation and initiatives it believes are against the intersts of California citizens. Peruse this site for full information on CALPIRG's many ongoing campaigns, as well as links which can help anyone be a more informed and involved voter.

Capital Research Center

 http://www.townhall.com/crc/

Established in 1984, the Capital Research Center studies non-profit "public interest" and advocacy groups. The CRC hopes to illuminate their agendas, identify their funding sources, and measure their impact on public opinion and policy.

The Cato Institute

 http://www.libertarian.org/cato/

The Cato Institute is fast becoming Washington's premier conservative think-tank. Founded in 1977, the Institute is a non-partisan, public policy research foundation. The Institute is named for *Cato's Letters*, libertarian pamphlets that helped lay the philosophical foundation for the American Revolution.

The Cato Institute hopes to broaden political debate to include more consideration of traditional American principles such as limited central government, individual liberty, and peace.

When you visit this site, be sure to read the text of P.J. O'Rourke's brilliant speech entitled "The Liberty Manifesto."

Center for Individual Rights

 http://www.townhall.com/cir/

Committed to protecting individual rights, the Center for Individual Rights (or CIR) focuses primarily on civil liberties, economic freedom of speech, and civil rights—key areas where individual rights are particularly at risk. Visit the Web pages of CIR for more information.

Central Intelligence Agency

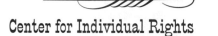 http://www.odci.gov/cia/

Not everything about the C.I.A. is secret. Come to their Website for links to C.I.A. periodicals and maps, suggested reading lists, some history, and useful updates on who's running every other country in the world. As you might expect, to get past the C.I.A. home page, you must agree to let them investigate you while you investigate them.

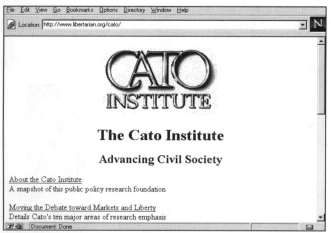

The Claremont Institute for the Study of Statesmanship and Political Philosophy

 http://www.townhall.com/claremont/

The mission of the Claremont Institute is to "restore the principles of the American Founding to their rightful, preeminent authority in the American national life." In other words, this is a conservative think tank, *à la* the Heritage Foundation.

Congressional Quarterly

 http://www.cq.com

As the name implies, *Congressional Quarterly* is a quarterly publication of a private, commercial publishing company in Washington, D.C. named CQ Inc. CQ prides itself on providing non-partisan news and information on the goings on of government and politics. On these Web pages you'll find breaking news from Washington and interesting articles and information.

Conservative Site of the Day

 http://www.netrunner.net/~covers/csite/

Every day the Webmaster at this site picks a set of Internet pages he chooses to label the "Conservative Site of the Day." These vary in their tone and con-

tert, and are often worth checking out. There is also a database of previous Conservative Sites of the Day, complete with hyperlinks.

Democratic Party

 http://www.democrats.org

Here is the official Website for the Democratic Party. I particularly enjoyed the FAQs. How much does it cost to sleep in the

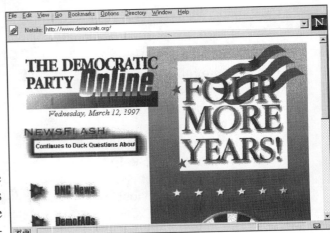

Lincoln Bedroom? (Answer: $100,000.) How much does it cost to sleep *with Barbara Streisand* in the Lincoln Bedroom? (Answer: $5.00). And so on. Here you also have links to the Democratic Governors Association, the College Democrats, and the Democratic Legislative Campaign Committee.

The Discovery Institute

 http://www.townhall.com/discovery/

The Discovery Institute is dedicated to developing and promoting policies that the organization believes support representative government, free markets, and individual liberties. Read here about the Institute's current projects, and about their printed reports and products.

Electronic Frontier Foundation

 http://www.eff.org

The Electronic Frontier Foundation is a non-profit organization that develops and assumes positions on topical political issues relating to privacy, free expression, public access to the Internet, and responsibility in media. The EFF takes stands on a variety of issues, publishes its opinions, and lobbies governments to adopt its positions.

Environmental Protection Agency

 http://www.epa.gov/

Monitoring and protecting the environment is an immense task. For its part, the U.S. Federal E.P.A. is engaged in hundreds of national, regional, and local projects in an attempt to balance the issues of safe water, air, and soil with the pressures of population and American commerce. Come to these pages for details on what is going on in each of the ten E.P.A. regions and many links to other resources.

FECInfo: The Non-Partisan Federal Candidate Campaign Money Page

 http://www.tray.com/FECInfo/
index.html-ssi

This is the place on the Web where you can find out exactly *who* gave *what* to *which* federal candidates, and *when*. This exten-

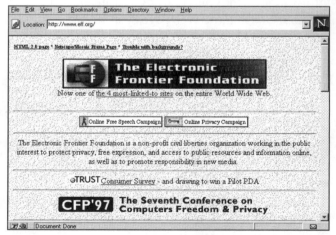

sive database not only tracks both "hard" and "soft" money, but also money associated with the most potent exception to the current campaign finance rules: Issue Advocacy. Are we ready to have foreign nationals, foreign corporations, or even *foreign governments* influence the outcome of American elections with their dollars? Think about it. Since "Issue Advocacy" money is not regulated at all—and hence, not disclosed—*any* entity can spend gigantic amounts of money in specifically targeted races and influence outcomes.

Federal Communications Commission

 http://www.fcc.gov/

The job of the F.C.C. is to encourage competition in all communications markets (wire, radio, television, satellite, and whatever comes next) and protect the public interest. If you're having trouble with phone access to the Internet or are unhappy with what the market says you must bear, you may find helpful information in one of the many wide-ranging essays on these pages. You can even find out how to contact the agency to give them a piece of your mind.

The Federal Reserve

 http://www.bog.frb.fed.us/aboutfrs.htm

The value of the U.S. dollar isn't tied to the amount of gold we hoard in Ft. Knox

anymore. Instead, the Federal Reserve System. the central bank of the United States, manipulates how much money is in circulation and decides how much interest banks can charge for loans, thus maintaining a stable economy. Find out about how the system works, about each of the twelve regional Federal Reserve Banks, and about the people in charge of the delicate and largely incomprehensible monetary dance.

The Federalist Society

 http://www.fed-soc.org/

The Federalist Society is an organization dedicated to affirming several founding principles of the Constitution. Among these are that the federal government exists to protect individual freedoms, that the checks and balances inherent in the structural separation of governmental powers is vitally important, and that the judicial branch must be limited to upholding the law—not creating it. On these Web pages, and in real life, the Federalist Society promotes an awareness of the importance of these fundamental principles.

Green Party

http://www.greens.org/usa/

The Green political movement, already well-entrenched in Europe, is beginning to take shape in America today. It's sometimes difficult to get a handle on the movement's progress since it is, by design, a grass-roots construct, without the kind of strong leadership that most easily attracts the media. But at this site you can learn about the Greens and the Green Party U.S.A. Read the Program, which amounts to the Greens' ever-evolving, consensus-driven party platform. Plus, get links to informative publications, related sites, and even online chat groups.

The Heartland Institute

 http://www.heartland.org/

The Heartland Institute is a nonprofit, nonpartisan think-tank headquartered outside Chicago, Illinois. Heartland applies cutting-edge research to state and local public policy issues, with an emphasis on initiatives meant to cut taxes and reduce government spending.

The Heritage Foundation

 http://www.townhall.com/heritage/

The Heritage Foundation is probably the premier conservative think-tank of this modern era. Since 1973, this non-profit, non-partisan research and educational institute has been synthesizing and promoting conservative poli-

cies based on the fundamental principles of free enterprise, limited government, individual freedoms, traditional American values, and a strong national defense.

Heritage performs accurate research aimed at current policy issues and offers these findings to members of Congress, congressional staff members, the executive branch, the news media, and academia.

Lyndon B. Johnson Presidential Library and Museum

 http://www.lbjlib.utexas.edu/

The Lyndon B. Johnson Presidential Library and Museum archives and displays the papers and memorabilia of this late President. The Website offers a searchable database of the artifacts and exhibits of the library and museum. Also offered here are information on educational programs and links to sites related to Johnson.

League of Women Voters

 http://www.lwv.org/~lwvus/

The League of Women Voters is one of the oldest nonpartisan voters organizations in the country. It works to encourage voter education, voter registration, and active, useful public debate of major issues.

Libertarian.org

 http://www.libertarian.org

Come here for dozens of links to libertarian organizations across the country. These include the Action Institute for the Study of Religion and Liberty, Gays and Lesbians for Individual Liberty, the Separation of School and State Alliance, the Cascade Policy Institute, and many others. You should also investigate the Web pages of the Libertarian Party (**http://www.lp.org**).

The Nation—Digital Edition

 http://www.TheNation.com/

Since the death of I.F. Stone, *The Nation* is perhaps America's last surviving weekly newsmagazine expressing a solidly left-leaning, progressive view of national and international politics. Like the paper version of the magazine, *The Nation Digital Edition* features punchy, well-written, well-researched articles with information and opinions that often fall through the cracks of the mainstream media.

National Conference of State Legislatures

 http://www.ncsl.org/

It would seem an impossible task to keep track of all 50 state legislatures, all the various members, all the different issues being handled in so many different ways. But that job is precisely the one the National Conference of State Legislatures has tackled. This site is a rich mine of information about who to contact about what issue in any state. You can download entire databases including names of state legislators, committee assignments, leadership positions, and your best avenues of access. Find out about environmental toxics, childhood care and education, the Intergovernmental Health Policy Project, state-federal issues, and more.

National Review Magazine

 http://www.townhall.com/
nationalreview/

Founded decades ago by the inimitable William F. Buckley, Jr., *National Review* remains the foremost—and by far the most literate—journal of conservative political thought in the country. The Website is just as elegant and eloquent as the print publication, featuring late-breaking Washington news, William F. Buckley's "Word of the Day" and, entertaining as always, the "Outrage du Jour." Here you'll also find Buckley's always-fascinating column "On the Right," along with the regularly updated, always hilarious "Letter from Al (Gore)." Check it out.

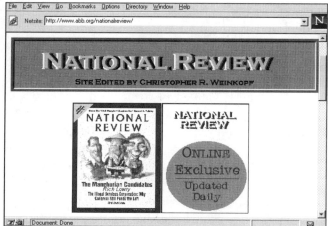

The Netizen

 http://www.netizen.com/netizen/

Affiliated with *HotWired*, The Netizen is trying to be the "town hall" of the online community—a place where every Net surf-er can visit, hear more informed and eloquent political and social opinion than is usual in your average chat room, and participate in daily polls and interactive threads. The subject matter usually has an Internet focus. Read lively "Media Rants" on Internet censorship. Check out past articles about kids' online rights, internet tracking of criminals, wiring up our schools, and even the opinion that the Net threatens democracy!

Richard Nixon Library and Birthplace

 http://www.chapman.edu/nixon/
index.html

Yup, this is the little house in Yorba Linda where it all started—the Nixon years! There is hardly a whisper of Watergate at the museum, nor is there a hint of it on the museum's Web pages. Of course, after all, there was nothing to that anyway...

P.J. O'Rourke Unofficial Home Page

http://www.web-presence.
com/mac/pjhome.shtml

Who said this? "No time left for pamphleting and leafleting, picketing and petitioning, talking and walking around. Time to TRASH THE STATE!" Abbie Hoffman? Huey Newton? Nope. It's P.J. O'Rourke, circa 1970. Like so many '60s and '70s lefties, P.J. is now a provocative (and usually satirical) libertarian. He is also, of course, the author of such national best-sellers as *Parliament of Whores*, *Give War a Chance*, and *All the Trouble in the World*.

Like so many other contemporary conservatives, O'Rourke was once a raving pinko with, as he says, a scab on his once-bleeding heart to prove it. How did the O'Rourke of 1970, who summarized the world of "grown-ups" as "materialism, sexual hang-ups, the Republican party, uncomfortable clothes, engagement rings, car accidents, Pat Boone, competition, patriotism, cheating, lying, ranch houses, TV, and suicide," become the O'Rourke of the 1990s who threatens to aim his shotgun at any revival of the '60s? How did the self-described "nightmare of the bourgeoisie," whose greatest desire was to destroy "individualistic property, selfish values, hateful concepts," end up in a suit and tie, behind a lectern, insisting that "Communists worship Satan, Socialists think perdition is a good system run by bad men, and liberals want us to go to Hell because it's warm there in the winter?"

Access this page and find out how.

Panama Canal Commission

 http://www.pananet.com/pancanal/

In 1903, Panama deeded a slice of itself from Caribbean to Pacific in perpetuity to the United States. The U.S. proceeded to carve the Panama Canal through that slice of Panama and has been running it ever since as a profitable enterprise. The Canal Commission is the agency that behaves like a corporation, overseeing the canal traffic, upkeep, toll collection, and the considerable work of managing the thousands of people needed for support of this monumental undertaking. We're giving the canal back to Panama in 1999. Until then, you can check these pages for more on the canal, its history, a gallery of photos, and maybe even how much it would cost to sail your yacht from one side to the other.

Progress and Freedom Foundation

 http://www.townhall.com/pff/

The Progress and Freedom Foundation pursues civil liberties in the broadest sense—a civil libertarian sense by and for American citizens dwelling in cyberspace. It provides information about free speech and related issues of concern to the digitally wired.

Republican National Committee

 http://www.rnc.org

Here is one-stop shopping for dozens of links related to national and regional Republican Party politics. Here you get the lastest Republican Party news, campaign information, party-leader profiles, and more. Be sure to check out the *Clinton Calendar*—"Day by day, scandal by scandal, flip-flop by flip-flop, it's all here."

The Right Side of the Web

 http://www.townhall.com/rtside/

The Right Side of the Web features a variety of conservative pundits and links. The site includes editorials, book reviews,

links to conservative organizations nationwide, and much more including weekly editorials and congressional voting reports.

Savers and Investors League

 http://www.townhall.com/savers/

The Savers and Investors League has a fundamental belief: that all of your savings and investments should be tax deductible and tax deferred until you, or your beneficiary, spend those moneys. The organization was founded in 1988 by Tom Kelly.

Socialist Party USA Cybercenter

http://152.2.22.81/spc/spc.html

Once the party of labor leader Eugene V. Debs, the Socialist Party has been around since the turn of the 20th century. Now the party seems clearly determined to continue on the American political scene well into the 21st century. Come here for political and historical essays, an explanation of party principles, and instructions on how to be a socialist during these difficult times.

dation, the National Review, the Frontiers of Freedom Institute, the Family Research Council, the Conservative Political Action Conference '97, the Progress and Freedom Foundation, Americans for a Balanced Budget, the American Conservative Union, the Bradly Foundation, and much more.

Thomas: Legislative Information on the Internet

 http://thomas.loc.gov/

The name comes from the fact that this legislative information service of the Library of Congress is in the spirit of Thomas Jefferson. Here you get summaries for all active and past House bills and resolutions, along with their status. Here you also get the complete Congressional Record, committee information, and historical documents such as the Declaration of Independence, the Federalist Papers, early Congressional documents (Constitutional Convention and Continental Congress broadsides), and more resources.

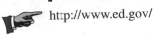

U.S. Department of Education

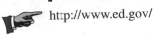 http://www.ed.gov/

Despite the widely expressed political view that this department is not needed, countless Americans are happy to benefit from their shares of the $13 billion in local and state school aid and individual student financial assistance distributed annually. Learn more about how the monetary pie is sliced up, as well as detailed accounts of all current projects, with links to other sites and agencies.

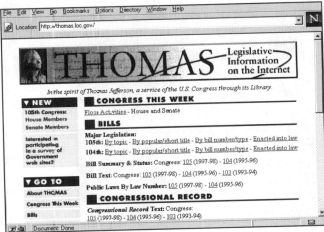

Town Hall

 http://www.townhall.com/townhall

Town Hall offers links to a wide range of conservative organizations and pundits, including the Heritage Foun-

The U.S. House of Representatives

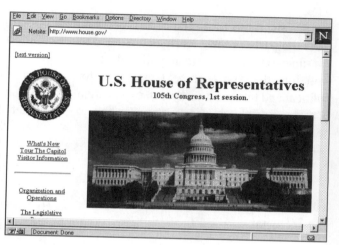

http://www.house.gov/

In addition to details on membership, committees, and agendas, this informative collection of Web pages offers detailed schedules for legislative activity in the House of Representaives and a Who's Who database complete with contact information which is searchable by member name, region or district. (By the way, I've sent the Webmaster an e-mail suggesting that this database also be searchable by IQ and provide a ranking of House members by IQ. Wouldn't that be interesting?) The Website also includes a fine tutorial on the internal operation and organization of the House and copious links to other government servers.

U.S. Office of Government Ethics

http://www.access.gpo.gov/usoge/

Did you even know there was such a federal agency as the Office of Government Ethics? It started out in 1978 as part of the Office of Personnel Management, then became its own agency in 1989. The Office is charged with preventing unethical conflicts of interest and with monitoring all the other related agencies' efforts to do similar prevention. Read more about this surprising little agency—what it can do and (as it takes

pains to clarify) what sorts of unethical behavior it has no jurisdiction over.

The United States Senate

http://www.senate.gov

Here is your online guide to Senator home pages, legislative activities, Senate committees, and much more. Track bills as they move through Senate committees by accessing select committee pages. The entire site is keyword searchable, but I came up with nothing when I searched using the term "criminal." Strange.

Vera Institute of Justice

http://broadway.vera.org/

Founded in 1961 by New York philanthropist Louis Schweitzer, the Vera Institute is a private, nonprofit organization dedicated to making our legal system more just. The Institute's first success was a profound reform of the American bail system, the first such reform since 1789. Institute members theorize an advance or reform, then try to demonstrate its success on a small or local scale, usually near their home base in New York City. Once they can demonstrate a good idea works, they hand it over to the government, which either lets an agency handle it or creates a new agency for the job. Currently, the Institute is at work on a number of projects dealing with juvenile justice and adolescent violence. Learn more about Vera's work at these comprehensive pages.

are there. The site includes not only a cyber-tour of the Executive Mansion, but also biographies and images of Bill Clinton and Al Gore, a useful "Interactive Citizens' Handbook" which is, in fact, an extensive guide to information about the federal government on the Internet, details on the history of the White House, an exhaustive virtual library of White House documents (though nothing incriminating), the latest presidential press releases, and special online activities for kids (courtesy of Socks, the Cat, who claims no knowledge of inappropriate campaign finance activities). You are also invited to sign the electronic guestbook and/or send e-mail to either President Clinton or Vice President Gore.

The White House

 http://www.whitehouse.gov

You don't have to stand in line to visit the White House. You don't have to make a big campaign contribution either. (Well, actually you do if you want to meet the President and press his flesh and get your pet project or pet agenda approved.) But if you want a less formal visit, just click on the URL **http://www.whitehouse.gov** and you

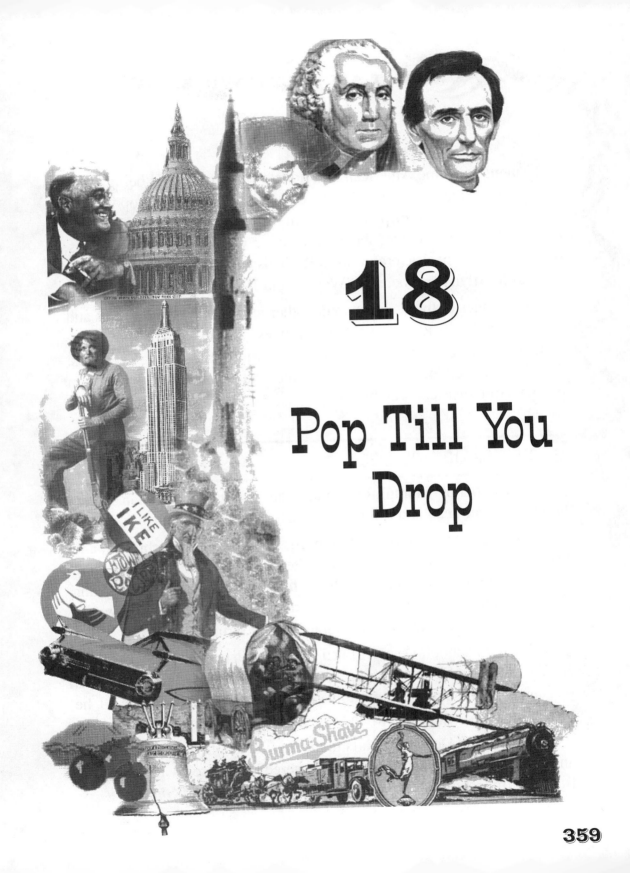

18

Pop Till You Drop

There are some American individuals who go beyond being great, go beyond being famous, and enter into the realm of pop iconography. I am speaking of people who, in their lives, became emblematic of something fundamental about our country, our culture, and ourselves, or at least of a specific era or attitude. (This can certainly be said of the likes of Marilyn Monroe, John Wayne, and Jackie Kennedy.)

The images of these and so many other icons will never leave us and will never die. They have taken on lives of their own. They have conquered death by becoming something more than a bag of bones. They've transcended a hard-to-define line, and become ideas rather than people. And ideas can't be buried.

Immortal James Dean

No one better exemplifies what I am talking about than James Dean—forever dead and forever young.

Born February 8, 1931 in Marion, Indiana to a dental technician and his wife, was James Byron Dean. At the tender age of five, Jimmy (Figure 18-1) moved to Los Angeles with his family only to return to Indiana three years later upon his mother's death. From that point, Dean would be raised by his aunt and uncle on their family farm.

After high school, Dean returned to California to attend Santa Monica Junior College and UCLA. During and after college, Dean managed bit parts on stage and in movies, and even in a few TV commercials. At age 20, he moved to New York where he landed dramatic roles in several TV shows.

In New York, Dean won parts in the Broadway plays *See the Jaguar*, and *The Immortalist*, and eventually garnered leading roles in the Warner Brothers films *East of Eden*, *Rebel Without a Cause*, and *Giant*.

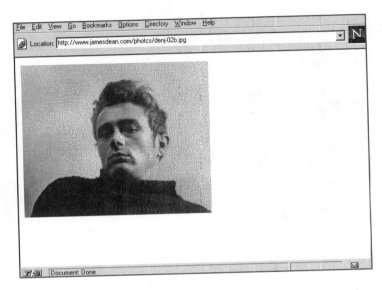

FIGURE 18-1
James Dean
(http://www.jamesdean.
com/photos/denj-02b.jpg)

Dean's life ended with a tragic automobile accident in September of 1955 at the age of 24. Despite having made only three films, his career had such momentum at the time of his death that his following after his death was almost cult-like.

It was perhaps appropriate that he told a friend, not long before his death, "If a man can bridge the gap between life and death—I mean, if he can live on after he's died—then maybe he was a great man."

Read more about this mysterious man and his legend at **http://www.jamesdean.com**.

Immortal Marilyn

Of course, another forever dead and forever young star is Marilyn Monroe. A thoroughly American sex kitten, Marilyn Monroe wasn't the first platinum blonde to find stardom in the movies. But Marilyn was special. True, she had a body to die for, but she had more. She had a personality that oozed sensuality. So powerful was her image that she made the *sound* of high-heel pumps famous. And her sexy squint and seductive pout made her irresistible (Figure 18-2).

FIGURE 18-2
Marilyn (http://www.
cmgww.com/marilyn/
images/photo2.jpg)

Her underlying tragedy added to her appeal. She loved the camera, but at the same time, she feared it. She also feared the public. And she was, as we now know, chronically unhappy in her romantic life while at the same time being prone to addictive behavior—behavior which wound up killing her at age 36. Her public, however, has not allowed her to die.

"Sometimes," she wrote, "I think it would be easier to avoid old age, to die young, but then you'd never complete your life, would you? You'd never wholly know yourself." I'm afraid not, Marilyn.

And Of Course We Can't Forget Bogie...

Humphrey DeForest Bogart was born to a prominent New York family in 1899. His father was a surgeon. His mother was a noted magazine illustrator.

Bogart served in the U.S. Navy during World War I on the troop carrier U.S.S. Leviathon as a boatswain's mate. During a brig detail, a prisoner asked Bogart for a light for his cigarette. As Bogart fumbled for a match, the prisoner smashed him across the mouth with his handcuffs giving Bogart his signature scar and lisp.

After the war, Bogart took up acting. He had a rather unremarkable theatrical career in the 1920s, but made it big in Hollywood with his appearances in *The Maltese Falcon* (1941), *Casablanca* (1942), and his Oscar-winning performance in *The African Queen* (1951).

Though somewhat typecast into playing tough guys, criminals, and characters with a slightly dark side or past, Bogart (Figure 18-3) made the best of his roles developing his rich and complex screen image for which he's known to this day.

By the way, if you are looking for an absolutely fabulous book on Bogart, check out the engaging, thoughtful memoir penned by his son, Stephen Humphrey Bogart, entitled *In Search of My Father*. In an era when we are deluged with mediocre autobiographies by the illiterate children of stars large and small, Stephen Bogart's book is an erudite exception to the rule of mediocrity characterized, as it is, by intelligence, wit, sympathy, and love.

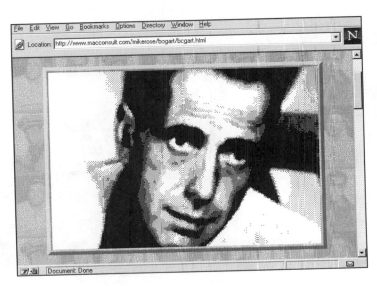

FIGURE 18-3
Bogart
(http://www.macconsult.
com/mikerose/bogart/
bogart.html)

...Or Those Who Are Not Quite Dead Yet

If you think about it, it is amazing some of the iconographic figures of the last fifty years are still hanging around the planet, not just breathing but sometimes even walking and talking. Not only that, they are located on the Web at the outer edge of the new digital frontier. Some are more useful than others.

Consider, if you will, the official (extensive, and incredibly slow-to-load) home page of Roy Rogers and Dale Evans (**http://www.royrogers. com**) (Figure 18-4). "Let's tell the Academy of Motion Picture Arts and Sciences that we want recognition given to Roy and Dale," insists the headline on the Web page.

Recognition for what? Mediocrity?

If you visit the Roy Rogers and Dale Evans Website, be sure to check out the page dedicated to their latest project: *RogersDale, USA*. It is more than just a theme park. It is "shopping, lodging, restaurants, shows, music, and memories *all wrapped up in fun*!" Picture a place, says Roy, "where

FIGURE 18-4
*The Official Roy Rogers and Dale Evans Website (**http://www.royrogers. com/**)*

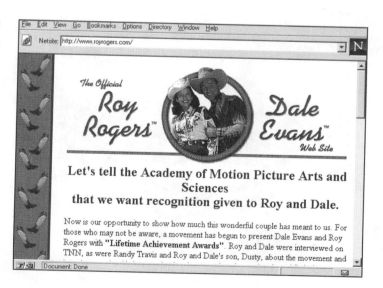

time moves slowly—a special time spanning a century and traveling through the '50s; a time of heroes and adventure, hard work, honesty, and fair play; a time of self-reliance and sharing; a time of family values and good neighbors. A quieter time, a simpler time, a time when our nation's basic ethics and values were shaped and tested—these times we celebrate."

Ah yes, the good old days. A time of lynchings and segregation. A time of annihilation of the Native Americans. A time of child labor. A time during most of which the women of America were politically disenfranchised, as were virtually all blacks. These times we celebrate. Everything was so great back then. Everything is so lousy now.

...Or Those Who Never Lived

Some of our greatest pop icons never actually lived. Consider Little Orphan Annie (Figure 18-5) whose adventures have been followed for more than sixty years now by kids—and adults, including adults who as

FIGURE 18-5

Little Orphan Annie
(http://net.indra.com/
~sliss/am0321s1.html)

kids read the same comic. She is as familiar a face and spirit in the American psyche as Abraham Lincoln or Charles Lindbergh or any other of our great historical or cult heroes.

We admire her bravado. We sympathize with her position as an outcast: the quintessential outcast, the orphan without a home who is then befriended by wealth, only to be cast out again. She cannot, however, be kept down. With her loyal dog Sandy, she confronts all obstacles head-on, and perseveres. She never complains. She never whimpers. She simply deals with every obstacle life puts in her path—always certain of justice and fairness in the end.

In short, she could not be more American. Neither could that little émigré Dondi, or Dick Tracy, or Charlie Brown. Some of them have Web pages, some don't. We'll be exploring a few shortly, along with many other Websites dedicated to all sorts of American pop icons, real and unreal, living and dead.

Muhammad Ali

 http://www.blink.com/ali/default2.htm

He was a tremendously talented fighter, certainly. That earned him one level of fame. But Cassius Clay elevated himself consciously to superstardom by declaring himself to be "The Greatest" and then proceeding to prove it, to the delight of the American public. The site at **http://www.blink.com/ali/default2.htm** is a good place to start exploring for photos, his life story reduced to sound bites, his ring record, photos, and more.

Lucille Ball

 http://www.geocities.com/ TelevisionCity/1074/LUCINDEX.HTM

Here is a great set of pages dedicated not only to Lucille Ball but also to Desi Arnaz, Vivian Vance, William Frawley, Gale Gordon, and anyone else you can think of who worked with Lucy on such shows as *I Love Lucy, The Lucille Ball-Desi Arnaz Comedy Hour, The Lucy Show, Here's Lucy,* and *Life with Lucy*! The pages are loaded with trivia and goodies, including Desi Arnaz, Jr.'s e-mail address.

John Barrymore

 http://www.mdle.com/
ClassicFilms/FeaturedStar/
star12a.htm

Star of stage, silent screen, and finally sound movies, Barrymore was considered a giant by both his peers and an adoring audience. Yet "the Great Profile" was also a tragic figure, who declined into self-parody before his death in 1942. Remember this wonderful actor, then go rent "Dinner at Eight." A perfect place to start your reminiscence is this site, featuring good biographical information and many links to Barrymore filmography (including movies available on video), a photo gallery of film stills and publicity shots, links to books about John and all the other Barrymores, and helpful links to other Websites with more Barrymore and Silent Era goodies to explore.

The Beaver: Jerry Mathers

 http://www.geocities.com/Hollywood/
Hills/2993/

You'll be interested to know that the Beaver—from the hit television show *Leave it to Beaver* of the late 1950s and early 1960s—is doing very well, thank you very much. In fact, he's doing great, considering he's just a dumb little kid. Luckily enough, the kid has a grownup who is an astute businessman looking after him: Jerry Mathers, the child actor all grown up.

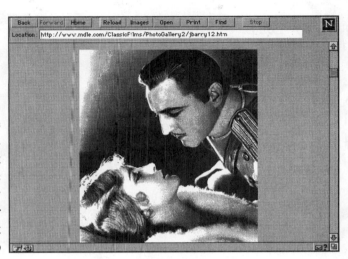

Mathers is 49, and he is raking in the bucks with personal appearances—hundreds of thousands of dollars per year. He has a degree in philosophy and has worked (successfully) as a banker and a real estate broker, but he simply has found that he can make the most money most easily by simply showing up and being "the Beav" all grown up.

His manager? Oh, that would be Frank Bank, the actor-turned manager/investment banker who once portrayed Clarence "Lumpy" Rutherford on the show. "Lumpy" also represents Tony Dow (Wally), Ken Osmond (Eddie Haskell), and Barbara Billingsley (June). The father of the program, Hugh Beaumont, passed away in 1982.

Recently, when Mathers was doing an appearance in San Jose, 20 bikers roared up on their Harleys, dismounted, and began doing push-ups while whistling the *Leave it to Beaver* theme song in unison. Then they asked Mathers to autograph their bikes. Of course, he obliged.

Bewitched

 http://www.persephone.com/bewitched/

Few television programs are as enmeshed in the American "pop" mind as *Bewitched*. And few characters are as familiar to us as "Samantha," a.k.a. the late, great Elizabeth Montgomery. Come to this Website for images, trivia, and other haunted things.

Humphrey Bogart

 http://www.macconsult.com/mikerose/bogart/bogart.html

The Webmaster of this site writes: "Of all the Websites on all the servers in all the world, you logged onto mine. And most of you have done so for one reason: Admiration of the all-time greatest actor, Humphrey Bogart." The site is packed with images, memories, and facts.

Steve Buscemi

 http://www.discover.net/~ksweet/buscemi.htm

My wife Christa thinks I'm insane to mention Steve Buscemi, I and my brother's old friend from high school—a fellow member of the wrestling team from Memorial Junior High School and Central Senior High School of Valley Stream, New York—as a pop icon. But he has really become one.

Buscemi first gained wide attention in his role as "Mr. Pink" in Quentin Tarrentino's *Reservoir Dogs*; another of his featured roles was a starring part in *Fargo*. He recently shot his own screenwriting/directorial debut film, *Trees Lounge*, in our old hometown (**http://www.treeslounge.com**). He has also appeared in such films as *Escape from L.A., Kansas City, Billy Madison* (he is the gunman), *Living in Oblivion, Things to Do in Denver when You're Dead, The Hudsucker Proxy, Rising Sun, Pulp Fiction, Billy Bathgate, Miller's Crossing*, and many others.

Johnny Carson

 http://web3.starwave.com/showbiz/memorybank/starbios/johnnycarson/a.html

How did a man of such unremarkable talent shape a huge portion of American television culture? Perhaps it was because so many American's felt comfortable with him, chatting and joking with them late into the evenings for over 30 years. Look in on these pages for a Carson biography, his credits beyond *The Tonight Show*, more trivia, and even a link to good old Ed McMahon's page. The Kennedy Center also set up an Honors page for Carson with a short bio at **http:// kennedy-center.org/ explore/honors/html/ 1993/carson.html.**

Charlie Chaplin

 http://wso.williams.edu/~ktaylor/ gerstein/chaplin/intro.html

He was born in the United Kingdom and he died in Switzerland. But Chaplin made his fortune in the United States making films that were uniquely American and creating a screen alter-ego, the Little Tramp, who is even more American still. This great set of Web pages provides great information and images on Chaplin.

Dick Clark

 http://www.rockhall.com/induct/ clardick.html

Does this guy ever get old? I think he has a decaying portrait stashed some-where—sort of a *Picture of Dorian Grey* kind of deal. They call Dick Clark, the host of the classic television program *American*

Bandstand, "America's oldest teenager." And it is true.

Joan Collins

 http://web3.starwave.com/showbiz/ memorybank/starbios/joancollins/ a.html

Is Collins merely "the poor man's Eliza-beth Taylor" or is there more to this oft-married veteran of one of the world's most popular prime time soap operas? Tour these pages and judge for yourself.

Bill Cosby

 http://www.iconn.net/sadick/cosby.html

Bill Cosby has succeeded Robert Young as "America's Dad." Since his early days as a stand-up comic, Cosby has managed to get us laughing at ourselves without ever cracking a cruel or nasty joke. This page honors the man, and tells more about his artistic output. If you want to actually hear Cosby's voice, check out **http://www.net-walk. com/~hammer/**, the unofficial Cosby Sound Page, where you can download famous sound clips of Cos on such subjects as: putting plays together in a football game, or Fat Albert ending the Buck Buck game.

Bing Crosby

 http://www.kcmetro.cc.mo.us/
pennvalley/biology/lewis/crosby/
bing.htm

He is in the first rank of our pop icons. From his classic rendition of "White Christmas" to his classic film roles with Bob Hope and as the friendly musical priest in such films as *The Bells of St. Mary's*, Crosby—though he died twenty years ago—remains the most popular of American entertainers.

Betty Ford

 http://www.lbjlib.utexas.
edu/ford/grf/bbfbiop.htm

Perhaps destined to be more famous than her president husband, Betty Ford will forever be linked to the American culture of recovery. While quite a few sites cover her role as First Lady, **http://www.lbjlib.utexas.edu/ford/grf/bbfbiop.htm** provides a biography of this complex and influential American woman, with emphasis on her establishment of the Betty Ford Clinic.

Zsa Zsa Gabor

 http://www.mrshowbiz.com/features/
games/linked/lo/60.html

Everybody in America knows the name Zsa Zsa Gabor, but who actually knows why she's famous? She's not an actress. She's not a singer. She's not a great cultural leader. But she managed to marry at least eight famous and influential men, always look very rich, and appear on talk shows about 10,000 times. While her artistic merit remains a mystery, you can check out this site for a look at Zsa Zsa the modern-day courtesan and get links to a few of her husbands.

Judy Garland

 http://www.landofoz.demon.co.uk/

Even though this site for the Judy Garland Club is located in the United Kingdom, it is the best online resource for information and images relating to the immortal

"Dorothy" and the uniquely-American Judy Garland. Here you'll find a complete online biography, a great collection of Judy pictures, and even a downloadable Judy Garland screensaver. Here you also have links to several other excellent Judy Garland sites in cyberspace.

Andy Griffith and The Andy Griffith Show

 http://www.mayberry.org

We all remember Mayberry, North Carolina, because we all lived there for years—at least we did every Tuesday night. Who can forget the good-natured sheriff Andy Taylor, his Aunt Bea, and of course that comical deputy Barney Fife (played brilliantly by Don Knotts)? Then there was also that little kid who was always running around. I hear tell he's a big movie director these days.

Michael Jackson

 http://www.sepc.sony.com/SSI/Music/MJ/michael.html

He is bigger than Elvis, and he is showing signs of lasting longer. He's played more concerts. Sold more records. He is a cultural phenomenon of the first order, despite a personal life most people would consider a bit odd.

Michael Jordan

 http://www.cleaf.com/~tjt20/

What could be more "pop" perfect for a star like Jordan than a Website that offers, in addition to a biography page and a photo gallery, a "Michael Jordan Shoe Gallery?" Yes, here there is no distinction made between athletic prowess and marketing. It's all about "His Airness," the lavishly-paid ball player more American kids want to emulate than any other. Surf the links for pages on the Dream Team, new NBA trades, Jordan-endorsed video games, and lots more.

Kids' TV of the Fifties

 http://www.fiftiesweb.com/kids.htm

This Website devoted to Kids' TV of the 1950s highlights several pop icon insti-

tutions including Buffalo Bob (of *Howdy Doody* fame), Captain Kangaroo (Bob Keeshan), the Mouseketeers, and Lassie.

Spike Lee

 http://www.voyagerco.com/movies/directors/spike/

Spike Lee made the motion picture industry finally take black directors seriously. And he did it by repeatedly producing intelligent, controversial, financially successful films. If you want to hang with this driven man, start at this cool set of pages featuring movie clips, audio clips of an exclusive interview, and information on Lee's full directorial output, starting with commercials and student work, and working up to his work in progress, a film on the life of Jackie Robinson. If you'd rather just read text, try **http://www.mrshowbiz.com/starbios/spikelee/a.html** for a quickie "Mr. Showbiz" biography and rundown of artistic output.

Liberace

 http://www.liberace.org/

Take a cybertour of the Las Vegas home of the inimitable Liberace. Check out his detailed online biography and the great photo archive of Liberace and his friends. Consider the purchase of some Liberace knick-knacks. Or learn about the Liberace Foundation for the Performing Arts. You can do it all right here at this Website dedicated to the man himself.

The Marx Brothers

 http://holmes.acc.virginia.edu/~kws1x/marx.html

Everyone—at least everyone with an IQ—goes through a phase of addiction to the Marx Brothers. Their maniacal brand of humor is both intoxicating and addictive when one is in the right mood and the right time of life. And ever after, even when the addiction wears off, they remain welcome guests in our lives and on our television screens.

Marilyn Monroe

 http://www.cmgww.com/marilyn/marilyn.html

Even in death, she is the essence of all that the old style movie starlets ever were: sensual, ladylike, inviting, and at the same time untouchable. Gone more than 35 years, she remains the one, the only, the immortal Marilyn.

Mary Tyler Moore

 http://www.rust.net/~rkm/mtm/mtm.htm

Who can turn the world on with her smile? Who can take a nothing day, and suddenly make it all seem worthwhile? You know who! Mary! Rhoda's pal Mary Richards, also known as Mary Tyler Moore, whom we just can't forget no matter how hard we try. In addition to starring in *The Mary Tyler Moore Show*, she was also, of course, Dick Van Dyke's wife in *The Dick Van Dyke Show*.

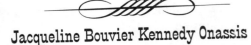

Jacqueline Bouvier Kennedy Onassis

 http://www.grolier.com/presidents/ea/first/35pw.html

Jackie (1929-1994) learned one fundamental rule from her mother: never marry a man who isn't wealthy. The rule served her well. She was, however, far too complex a woman to be characterized as a gold-digger. She was passionate about social causes and served for many years as a first-class editor doing first-class books at Doubleday. There is more to all of us than meets the eye.

Dolly Parton

 http://www.bestware.net/spreng/dolly/index.html

Though Dolly has often been quoted as saying "You'd be surprised how much it costs to look this cheap," there's nothing cheap about this site, dedicated to the glitzy country super-star. It's a labor of love, not affiliated with Dolly or her Dollywood country music amusement park. Get links to just about every Dolly site on the Web. Hear an audio message from Dolly herself. Y'all come back, hear?

Peanuts: Charlie Brown, Snoopy, and Friends

 http://www.peanuts.com

Come to the official *Peanuts* Website for an archive of *Peanuts* comic strips, a weekly update of the Sunday strip, information on the genesis of *Peanuts*, an interesting online biography of *Peanuts* creator Charles Schultz, and much more.

Pee-Wee Herman

 http://www.altculture.com/site/entries/pxreubens.html

Pee-Wee Herman, a.k.a. Paul Reubens, was one of the most original and inspired American comic figures since Jerry Lewis. Um, did I say inspired? Well, anyway, before he was rendered an "unperson" through a strange moral misadventure, Pee-Wee was the most manic and amazing thing on TV (and later in two feature films). While Reubens has retreated into the dark world of Hollywood bit parts, Pee-Wee has become a cult. Check out these pages and join the fun.

Vincent Price

 http://www.leba.net/~ghlong/index.html

What would the history of American horror movies be without Vincent Price? He leered and lurched across the screen in dozens of good, fair, and dreadful movies involving the macabre and bizarre. Off screen, Price (1911-1993) was a charming and cultured man, devoted to collecting art. Learn more about Price at these pages, including information on his films and theatre work, his art collecting, and links to other sites.

Roy Rogers and Dale Evans

 http://www.royrogers.com/

I don't know. I always thought Trigger was the brains of the operation. He never got the respect he deserved, however, and he still doesn't, now that they've got him stuffed and mounted and on display.

Superman

 http://www.geocities.com/ Area51/Vault/5247/

For some, Superman is a comic book character who was recently killed. For others, he is a snot-nosed kid who dates Terri Hatcher and whines about generation-X angst. But for me and

so many others, Superman will be George Reeves in splendid 1950s television black and white.

Elizabeth Taylor

 http://users.deltanet.com/users/ dstickne/lizt.htm

The American public has watched her grow up on the film screen. She started out as the young girl in *National Velvet*, grew into the darkly sardonic and hauntingly beautiful *Cleopatra*, and now stands in as Fred Flintstone's evil mother-in-law in the hit movie spinoff from the old cartoon. She remains beautiful.

Shirley Temple

 http://members.aol.com/DonThird/ Shirley_Temple.html

Shirley was the sweetest little thing who ever danced across the movie screen. By

her very existence, she probably did as much as anyone to keep our spirits up through the Great Depression. Browse through these pages for decade-by-decade biographies of Shirley, all the way from singing moppet through her tenure as Ambassador to Ghana and the Czech Republic. Of course, there are plenty of star photos and links to films and costars.

Star Trek

 http://www.astro.virginia.edu/~eww6n/ StarTrek.html

Where, among the thousands of Websites devoted to *Star Trek*, can you start to delve into the unique subculture spawned by the television series and spin-off films? Try "Eric's Excruciatingly Detailed Plot Summaries" of the original series at **http://www.astro.virginia.edu/~eww6n/StarTrek.html**. Then point your browser of choice at "Star Trek" and wade through screen after screen of lists of sites, on subjects including: actors, collectibles, conventions, games, alien languages, magazines, mailing lists, chat groups, singles clubs (straight and gay), reviews, and musings on fictional (or not) *Star Trek* technology.

If you want to add more spice to your Trekking, check out **http://www.kag.org/**, the site of the Klingon Assault Group, a club for people who like to attend *Star Trek* conventions and intimidate other species.

TV Guide Classic Cover Gallery

 http://www.tvguide.com/tv/wayback/ covers/index.sml

Walk down memory lane with these classic covers from *TV Guide*. Get a peek at the new baby, Desderio Alberto Arnaz IV (Desi Arnaz, Jr.), on the cover of April 3, 1953. Then check out Phil Silvers, Lassie, James Arness, and Amanda Blake (of *Gunsmoke*), Jerry Mathers (the Beaver!), Robert Stack (*The Untouchables*), Donna Reed, Alan Young (the guy who was always conversing with Mr. Ed), Elizabeth Montgomery and Dick York of *Bewitched*, Adam West (Batman), and many, many others. The cover I like best is from November 13, 1954. It features an interesting couple: Liberace and actress Joanne Rio. "We just enjoy each other's company," Rio told the *TV Guide* interviewer, who went on to write that Rio "seems the lone feminine friend acceptable to Liberace's mother, the dominant figure in the pianist's life." Yup. Uh huh.

Abigail Van Buren (Dear Abby)

 http://www.uexpress.com/ ups/abby/html/bio.html

In 1956, one Pauline Friedman Phillips phoned the editor of the *San Francisco Chronicle* and said she could write a better advice column than the one the paper was running. The editor took her up on her challenge and she was soon churning out her own advice columns as "Dear Abby."

There probably isn't an American alive who hasn't read Abby's column during the past 40 years. Is there anything you don't know about Abby and her advice-giving sister Ann Landers? Come to this site to find out.

routinely demonize those same types. I remember him going to Harvard to debate the topic of the war in Vietnam and arriving at Harvard Yard in a tank borrowed from the Massachusetts State Militia. Whether you agreed with him or not, you had to admit the man had style. These Web pages include a complete online biography and filmography together with fantastic photographs and even a few sound files. Check them out.

John Wayne: AMC's Ultimate Duke Directory

 http://www.amctv.com/ stars/johnwayne/ dukedirectory/index.html

John Wayne: who doesn't love him still, all these years after his death? Was there ever an actor who was more quintessentially American? He portrayed positive images of soldiers and sailors and Green Berets in films even after Hollywood began to

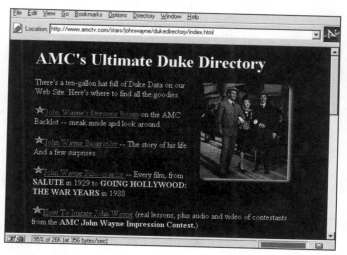

19

Religion

In beginning my comments on religion in the United States, I am once more drawn to some of my maternal forbears, the Carrolls of Maryland. Unlike my great, great, great, great, great-grandfather Charles Carroll of Carrollton, who signed the Declaration of Independence, or a cousin, Daniel Carroll, who authored the tenth amendment to the Constitution, there was a third cousin, John Carroll, who did not pursue secular accomplishments.

More on the Carrolls

The first Charles Carroll, grandfather of all three Carroll boys, was Attorney General for the Maryland Colony in the early 18th century. He had brought his family from England for one fundamental reason: so that they could worship God as Catholics. In the course of pursuing this religious freedom, Carroll also became one of the most prosperous landowners in the colonies. By the time of the Revolution, his grandchildren were members of one of the richest families on the North American continent.

At least one grandson—John—was unconcerned with the wealth. Born in Upper Marlboro, Maryland, John Carroll (1735-1815) was the fourth of seven children. He attended school in Europe, where he eventually entered the Society of Jesus (i.e., the Jesuits). Ordained a priest in 1761, he was first assigned to teach.

While traveling in Europe in the early 1770s, he learned that Pope Clement XIV had suppressed the Society of Jesus (**http://ricci.wjc.edu/wjc/jesuits/us_jesuits.html**). While the suppression was later revoked, the event was a turning point in Carroll's life. Suddenly, he was a free agent with no superior. Filled with missionary zeal, he returned to

Maryland and began a vigorous ministry among the many Catholics scattered throughout the colony.

In 1776, turning secular for a moment, he joined a secret commission seeking aid in the war against England. His fellow commission members were his cousin Charles, Samuel Chase, and Benjamin Franklin. Although the commission was not successful, it occasioned the close friendship between John Carroll and Ben Franklin.

As the Revolution raged, Father Carroll continued his priestly work in Maryland and Virginia. An ardent patriot, he championed the cause of independence amongst American Catholics.

After the Revolution, the American clergy petitioned Rome for a Bishop to lead the Catholic Church in the United States. With the support of Ben Franklin, John Carroll became the first and only Bishop in the United States in 1789—a post which he held for the next 25 years (Figure 19-1). During this time, the membership of the Catholic Church in America increased from 30,000 to over 200,000 members. Under John Carroll's leadership, the first Synod of Baltimore was held and St. Mary's

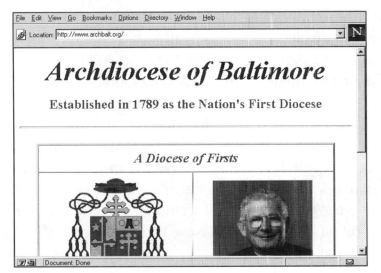

FIGURE 19-1

Home page for the Archdiocese of Baltimore, founded by John Carroll (http://www.archbalt.org/)

Seminary (**http://www.archbalt.org/st_marys.html**) and Georgetown University (**http://www.georgetown.edu**) were founded. Thereafter, the Suplicians at St. Mary's and the Jesuits at Georgetown began educating native-born clergy on their own soil, men sensitive to the particular needs of the Church in America. At Carroll's invitation, Augustinians, Carmelites, Dominicans, Sisters of Charity, and Visitation Nuns also began their work in the United States.

In 1806 Bishop Carroll laid the cornerstone for the country's first cathedral, now known as the Basilica of the Assumption, which was designed by Benjamin Latrobe and funded in large part by the Carroll family.

Archbishop Carroll died in 1815 at the age of 81. He is buried in the crypt of the Basilica, the church which stands as a monument to his contribution to the Catholic faith in America.

I Still Consider Myself a Catholic, Albeit an Eccentric One

My distant kinsman John Carroll may be off somewhere, right now, praying earnestly for my soul. For like many other Catholics, he would think me a lapsed member. In fact, old John Carroll would probably think me an atheist. I'm not, but he'd think me one. In truth I'm still a Catholic (**http://www.catholic.org**)—though a singularly out-of-order and open-minded one who believes women have a right to do what they wish with their own bodies, that sin is hard to define, that God is a fluid thing, and that there are truths to be found in Buddhism, the mysteries of Zen, and other faiths along with the Catholic faith. So I suppose I am an "ecumenical" Catholic. And in that I am every bit as much a Catholic as when I was a child, when my great-aunt Lee Carroll would take me for tours of Saint Patrick's Cathedral on Fifth Avenue in New York City, and I would gawk at the place in silent awe, experiencing one transcendental moment after another, astonished and mystified.

Along with Buddhism and Zen, I am attracted to the practices of the Unitarians, who affirm that every person's life involves developing a value system by which she or he lives, that people should enjoy individual liberty and private judgment in spiritual matters, that respect for integrity is preferable to the pressure to conform, that beliefs may (and perhaps even should) change in the light of new understanding and insight, and that the final authority for one's faith lies within one's own conscience (Figure 19-2).

Unitarians find their bond of unity in shared values, such as the nurture of life's spiritual dimension, the use of reason and honest doubt in the search for the truth, constructive tolerance and openness towards the sincerely-held beliefs of others, and reverence for the earth and the whole natural system (God's creation) of which we are a part.

I find myself increasingly skeptical of any highly dogmatic and dictatorial belief system which insists it is correct to the exclusion of all

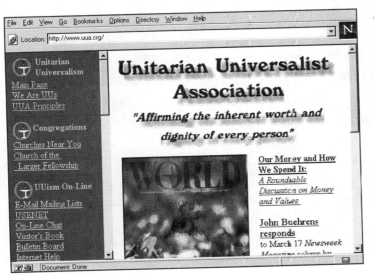

FIGURE 19-2

*The home page for Unitarianism in the United States provides a detailed consideration of Unitarian principles (**http://www.uua.org/**)*

others. And I wonder whether Christ—or Allah, or the Old Testament God of Moses—would have ever really sanctioned such exclusion. I doubt it. In some ways, I embrace Christ just as much as did my Catholic forbears, but less as a supernatural force than as an example of *human* compassion, generosity, sacrifice, and forgiveness, which it is wise to aspire to.

There are, after all, practical aspects to religion. Like John Burroughs, I appreciate the Bible as a great book of essential—though not fundamental—truths, and as great literature. ("I have just been reading St. Paul," he wrote in his journal. "How eloquent, what good literature! These epistles would never have come down to us had they not been good literature. They are full of the wisdom of the soul—full of things that save us in this world.") However, also like John Burroughs, I embrace the natural world as the living embodiment of its creator, God, and I therefore respect science as a path towards a more perfect knowledge of God. After all, Einstein's unified field theory was based on an essentially religious foundation. When asked why he so doggedly pursued the elusive unified field equation that so many thought might not exist, Einstein insisted: "Because God would not play dice with the universe."

That is the faith I want, the faith of Einstein and Galileo and those like them. A heaven? A hell? Who knows? Does it matter? What matters is that we treat each other with generosity, compassion, and respect here and now, and not despoil the natural environment which is God's greatest creation, indeed, a very extension of God. So endeth my sermon.

Heaven's Gate

No discussion of American religion on the Web would be complete, of course, without at least a brief consideration of the Heaven's Gate cult, their Web page, and their mass suicide in San Diego in the spring of 1997. As we now know, the 39 cult members were preparing to "leave their vehicles" and depart from the planet on a spaceship they believed was coming in the wake of the Comet Hale-Bopp to evacuate them.

The earth, of course, has not as yet been ploughed-under—as they predicted—since their suicide. What could have gone wrong? Is the spaceship late, or lost? Recently-intercepted Internet mail along with an Internet news item tells the whole, terrible story.

```
The original message was received on Wed, 26 Mar 1997
22:01:24 -0800 (PST)
from sol-ts1-p48.Tlelaxu.net [404.57.298.302]

----- The following addresses had permanent fatal
errors -----
<Applewhite@HigherSource.com>

    ----- Transcript of session follows -----
... while talking to mx.HigherSource.com.:
>>> RCPT To:<Applewhite@HigherSource.com>
<<< 552  <Applewhite@HigherSource.com>...  Mail  quota
exceeded
554 <Applewhite@HigherSource.com>... Service unavailable

Received:  from  Tlelaxu.net  (sol-ts1-p48.Tlelaxu.net
[404.57.298.302]) by
HigherSource.com (8.8.5/8.8.5) with SMTP id XAA13159;
Wed, 26 Mar 1997
22:01:24 -0800 (PST)
Message-Id: <9704100621.AA01356@Tlelaxu.net>
Content-Type: text/plain
Received: by.Mailer (1.118.2)
From: "Sol Pickup Coordinator" <Recruitment638@Tlelaxu.net>
Date: Wed, 26 Mar 97 22:01:07 -0800
To: Applewhite@HigherSource.com
Subject: Important Update

Doh,
  Due to a hitch in the Borzok peace talks, we have
  rescheduled the pickup
```

of your recruits for immediate pickup prior to
evacuation of the galaxy.   Therefore,
do eat the pudding.   Repeat: EAT THE PUDDING.

- Mee Fah (Sol Pickup Coord.)

==
============
From the Internet News Gateway:

CULTISTS DIE AGAIN - SECOND TRAGEDY OF WEEK FOR
GROUP

The 39 members of the Heaven's Gate cult, reborn
in fresh alien host bodies, were killed again
yesterday when their deep-space transport vessel was fired upon by an enemy battle cruiser.
The transport was enroute to Sirius, the Planet
of Infinite Pleasures. After completing its
leap to hyperspace, the ship was detected by a
Borzok battle cruiser on a routine patrol of
hyperspace. The cultists, many of whom were
enjoying their newly regenerated sexual organs
for the first time, were apparently innocent
victims of the Borzok/Tlelaxu war, an interplane-
tary conflagration that has raged for seven of
our Earth centuries.

Sub-Commander G'Zunq of the Borzok remarked,
"We deeply regret that neutral Earth-beings
were harmed during the attack. Nevertheless,
their vessel bore the markings of our sworn
enemies, the Tlelaxu. We therefore claim this
day as a great victory for the Borzok empire."

```
Due to the remoteness of the patch of space
where the incident occurred, chances of rescue
are nil. According to Borzok sources, the
formerly dead cultists are "absolutely toast
this time."

Imperial Proconsul 378%Q'nah'nah of the Tlelaxu
apologized humbly for the incident, venting his
external gills in the universal Tlelaxu gesture
of supplication and regret. "We assure you that
this was an isolated incident," said
378%Q'nah'nah. We sincerely hope that it does
not discourage future mass suicides on Earth.
We have a solar system of fresh host bodies for
all of you, and a Planet of Infinite Pleasures
awaits all of you who join us." When asked if
the Tlelaxu mission statement, "To Serve Man,"
might be a cookbook, 378%Q'nah'nah abruptly
terminated the interview.

<----  End Forwarded Message  ---->
```

Seriously, though, what were these people about? Here is the scoop on their belief system, as I understand it:

Two thousand years ago, a crew of members of the Kingdom of Heaven who are responsible for nurturing "gardens" determined that a percentage of the human "plants" of the present civilization of this garden (Earth) had developed enough that some of those bodies might be ready to be used as "containers" for soul "deposits." Upon instruction, a member of the Kingdom of Heaven then left behind his body in the "Next Level," came to Earth, and moved into (or was incarnated into) an adult human body (or "vehicle") that had been "prepped" for the particular task of introducing Heaven's Gate (Figure 19-3).

The body that was chosen was called *Jesus*. The member of the Kingdom of Heaven who was instructed to incarnate into that body did so at his "Father's" (i.e., an Older Member's) request. He moved into (or took over) the body when it was 29 or 30 years old, at the time of its baptism by John the Baptist when, as Luke tells us, "...the Holy Spirit descended upon Him in bodily form like a dove." The vehicle, Jesus, had, by the way, been "tagged" since birth to be the receptacle of a Next Level Representative.

The sole task given to this Representative was to offer the way leading to membership into the Kingdom of Heaven to those who recognized Him for who He was and chose to follow Him. Only those individuals who had received a "deposit" containing a soul's beginning had the capacity to believe or recognize the Kingdom of Heaven's representative, who later sent His students out with the good news that the Kingdom of Heaven is at hand.

FIGURE 19-3

*The members of the Heaven's Gate cult were lousy Web page designers. Their graphics-heavy pages take far too long to load (**http://www. heavensgatetoo.com/**)*

"I," wrote Marshall Applewhite not long before his suicide, "am in the same position to today's society as was the One that was in Jesus then. My being here now is actually a continuation of that last task as was promised, to those who were students 2,000 years ago. They are here again, continuing in their own overcoming, while offering the same transition to others. Our only purpose is to offer the discipline and 'grafting' required of this transition into membership in My Father's House."

The Web page of the group (**http://www.heavensgatetoo.com/**) paints a fascinating, if unwitting, portrait of cult-lifestyles and cult-think. I encourage a visit.

American Religion on the Web

All of our major American religions and religious institutions are represented on the Web. All sorts of tastes and varieties are available, as befits a country founded on the principle of religious freedom. Let's take a look at what's out there.

The African Methodist Episcopal (AME) Church

 http://www.ame-church.org/

The AME Church began in 1787 with a handful of people of African descent in Philadelphia, and now claims a membership of three million. African Methodism is an ecumenically minded communion, fully affirming the motto: "God our Father, Christ our Redeemer, and Humankind One Family."

American Buddhist Congress

 http://www.westworld.com/~abc/abchome.html

The American Buddhist Congress, its Web page tells us, "is a national council of Buddhist organizations and individuals in the United States." It is a resource and information center for American Buddhists, including help services and a multilingual library. The Congress is dedicated to promoting communication and cooperation among Buddhist communities of diverse traditions, as well as furthering the cause of Buddhism. The Congress also promotes good will between Buddhists and other religions by actively participating within the interfaith community.

American Buddhist Congress

Mailing address: 933 S. New Hampshire Ave.,
Los Angeles, California 90006
Tel. (213) 739-1270; FAX (213) 386-6643
email:abc@wgn.net

The American Buddhist Congress is a national council of Buddhist organizations and individuals in the

---

The American Jewish World Service

 http://www.charity.org/ajws.html

The American Jewish World Service was founded in 1985 to provide a Jewish vehicle for responding to hunger and poverty in Third World countries regardless of race, religion, or ethnicity. The goal is to put into practical action the dictates of the Ten Commandments. From where I sit, that is not a bad goal.

Daniel Berrigan, S.J.

 http://www.claret.org/~uscath/aug/ berrigan.html

Sitting in the D.C. jail after his first arrest in 1967, Daniel Berrigan wrote in his journal that the prison blue jeans and denim shirt form "a clerical attire I highly recommend for a new church." Over the years since, Berrigan donned that apparel many times, following his conscience to the Pentagon, to numerous draft board offices, and

to many other parts of the American landscape where good does combat with evil.

Despite his frequent visits, jail isn't a sufficient image to encompass Dan Berrigan's life, which is less about resistance than it is about celebration. And as Berrigan approaches his 80th year, the thoughts of many of his friends have turned to celebrating and honoring this person who has not only deeply touched the lives of many people, but helped to transform the character of the Church itself.

The Byzantine Catholic Church in America

 http://www.epix.net/~byzantin/ byzan.html

The term Byzantine Catholic was introduced into the United States about the year 1950 when Bishop Daniel Ivancho named the newly built Byzantine Catholic Seminary of Saints Cyril and Methodius in

Pittsburgh, PA. The term "Greek Catholic" was used before this time but was confusing in America because people thought the Church was made up of and for ethnic Greeks, which is not so. In fact, Byzantine Catholics share the same liturgical practices and spiritual traditions of the Eastern Orthodox Church, but are in communion with the Pope of Rome.

Christus Rex

 http://www.christusrex.org/

This extensive collection of Web resources related to Roman Catholicism includes much information on the Catholic Church in the United States, including histories, biographies, and more. There is also an extensive online directory of Roman Catholic parishes nationwide who have sponsored their own Web pages.

ChurchSurf

 http://www.churchsurf.com/

Here is your starting point for all surfing related to all forms of religion in the United States and elsewhere in the world. Here you have links to home pages for denominations, parishes, temples, and much, much more.

Conservative Baptist Church of America

 http://www.cbamerica.org/

The name says it all. This is a conservative Christian church in the Baptist strain dedicated to family values, sectarian discipline, a fundamentalist interpretation of the Bible, and just about all things conservative.

Council of Jewish Federations

 http://jewishfedna.org/

This is an association of 189 Jewish Federations of the United States. Established in 1932, the Council helps strengthen the work and the impact of Jewish Federations by developing programs to meet changing needs.

Evangelical Lutheran Church in America

 http://elca.org/

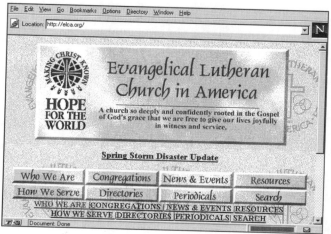

The Evangelical Lutheran Church in America is one of the products of Europe's Protestant Reformation of the 16th century. A German monk named Martin Luther was troubled by inconsistencies he saw between the Roman Catholic Church and the books of the Bible. Luther pointed out these inconsistencies in his sermons, lectures, and writings, and called for reform within the Catholic Church.

Luther and his followers became known as "Lutherans," and by the late 1500s, Luther's teachings approached the outer reaches of Europe and eventually spread to America with explorers and settlers.

Free Methodist Church of North America

 http://www.fmcna.org/

Free Methodists, quite simply, are people who follow Christ's teachings. Free Methodists earnestly seek to spread Christ's word throughout the world. They proclaim Christ's love for all people, and try to exemplify that love in their day-to-day lives.

Holy Cross Monastery

 http://207.10.80.5/holycross/

When I was young and lived on an estate on the Hudson River, my next-door neighbors were all monks. They were brothers of the Episcopal Order of the Holy Cross. This is a Benedictine community of men. They are wonderful people, and this is a beautiful spot for contemplation and prayer.

Jewish Genealogical Society

 http://www.jewishgen.org/

The Jewish Genealogical Society provides resources for Americans of Jewish descent seeking to research their ancestry. Here you'll find detailed reference materials, birth and death records, and much, much more.

Maryknoll

 http://www.maryknoll.org

My parents were longtime supporters of the Maryknoll Catholic Missions and I remember as a boy being taken to Maryknoll's headquarters in the Hudson Valley on several occasions. Maryknoll Missionaries work in Southeast Asia, Africa, and elsewhere around the world delivering something more than just religious instruction. They also deliver education, health services, and a strenuous voice for human

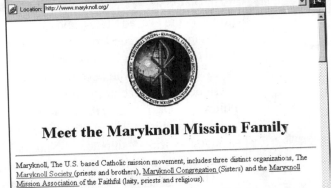

rights and economic justice. These are very good people.

Thomas Merton

 http://www.acs.appstate.edu/~davisct/canon/merton.html

A Trappist monk and a prominent writer, Thomas Merton (1915-1968) became one of the most famous American Roman Catholics of the 20th century. As a young man, Merton traveled with his artist parents in France and studied briefly at Cambridge, before he came to the United States and earned a master's degree from Columbia (1939). During those years he gradually changed from an agnostic to a devout Roman Catholic.

After teaching English for a while and working in a Harlem settlement house, Merton decided in 1941 to become a monk, choosing the Trappist order for its discipline of silence and solitude, within the monastery of Gethsemani near New Haven, Kentucky. His autobiography, *The Seven Storey Mountain* (1948), became a best-seller.

The Mormon Church

 http://www.mormon.org/

The Mormon faith is one of the few truly native American religions. Through the last century and a half, since the sect's founding, the Mormons have endured a great deal of prejudice and have suffered much for their faith. Their church is a fascinating institution. Check it out at **http://www. mormon.org/**. You may also investigate The Book of Mormon at **http://www. new-jerusalem. com/ scripture/bom/contents.htm.**

The Quakers

 http://www.quaker.org/

Here is your starting point on the Web for all things related to the Quakers—the Society of Friends. Here you'll find a history of the Quakers, listings of Quaker societies nationwide, links to related sites, and much more. There are dozens of links, all of them interesting.

Of particular interest is the Friends Committee on National Legislation. This group is a nationwide network of thousands of Quakers and like-minded people who

work together to bring Friends' values to bear on public policy at the national level. FCNL is also, however, a committee of about 240 Friends appointed by 26 yearly meetings and seven national Friends' organizations.

Since 1943, FCNL has worked toward a non-military world order firmly based on justice and voluntary cooperation. Growing out of Friends' testimonies on peace, equality, and simplicity, FCNL's advocacy has touched a wide range of national issues, including reconciliation among nations and peoples, opposition to militarism and proliferation of weapons, civil rights, self-determination, democratic participation in public policy decisions, sustainable development, stewardship of resources to meet human needs, and economic justice.

Touro Synagogue, Newport, RI

 http://www.tourosynagogue.org/

Completed in 1763, Touro Synagogue in Newport, RI is the oldest Synagogue in the United States, and the only surviving synagogue from the colonial era. Touro Synagogue is considered by many to be one of the best examples in existence of 18th century American architecture. Designed by the well-known colonial architect Peter Harrison, the synagogue was designated a National Historic Site in 1946.

The congregation of the synagogue was founded nearly a century before the synagogue was built by descendants of Sephardism from Spain and Portugal. These immigrants came to New England seeking refuge from the religious persecution they had known in Europe. Some say the architectural style of the synagogue reflects the principle of religious freedom—"distinguished by balance and reasoned restraint."

U.S. Catholic Magazine

 http://www.claret.org/~uscath/aug/augdex.html

U.S. Catholic is a forum for lay Catholics covering issues of concern to Catholics in their everyday lives. *U.S. Catholic* is not afraid to tackle the controversial topics of our times. Recent issues have included reports and reader surveys on the death penalty, welfare reform, and America's culture of violence. For those who are tempted to believe that the Roman Catholic Church is a profoundly arch-conservative institution, it may come as a surprise to realize that the Church stands *against* the death penalty and *for* a compassionate approach to welfare. A recent issue of this magazine featured an interview with one of my great heroes: radical Jesuit priest Daniel Berrigan.

Washington National Cathedral

 http://www.cathedral.org/cathedral/

The National Cathedral in Washington, D.C. is our nation's first church.

Sprawling across 57 acres of the highest land in the city and standing higher than the Washington Monument, it looks like exactly what it is meant to be: a symbol of the heritage of religious freedom upon which the United States was founded.

It was just after the Revolutionary War that Pierre L'Enfant designed the city of Washington and proposed a "great church for national purposes." But it wasn't until early in the twentieth century that the foundation stone would be laid. On that late September day in 1907, President Theodore Roosevelt said "Godspeed the work begun this day." Since then, every President has attended services at the National Cathedral.

Through the World Wars, the Great Depression, the Asian wars, and the Cold War, construction of the Cathedral continued until September 29, 1990 (83 years to the day) when President George Bush spoke at the completion ceremony while the final stone was set.

The National Cathedral is constructed with no structural steel whatsoever. It's built in the old style of medieval churches with

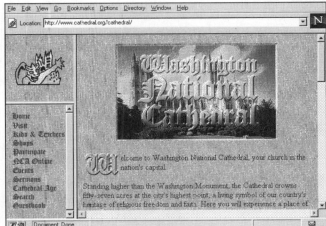

handcrafted stones laboriously fitted atop one another. The Cathedral is one of the largest in the world and the second largest in the United States, and contains such treasures as more than 200 stained glass windows. This is, by the way, an Episcopal institution.

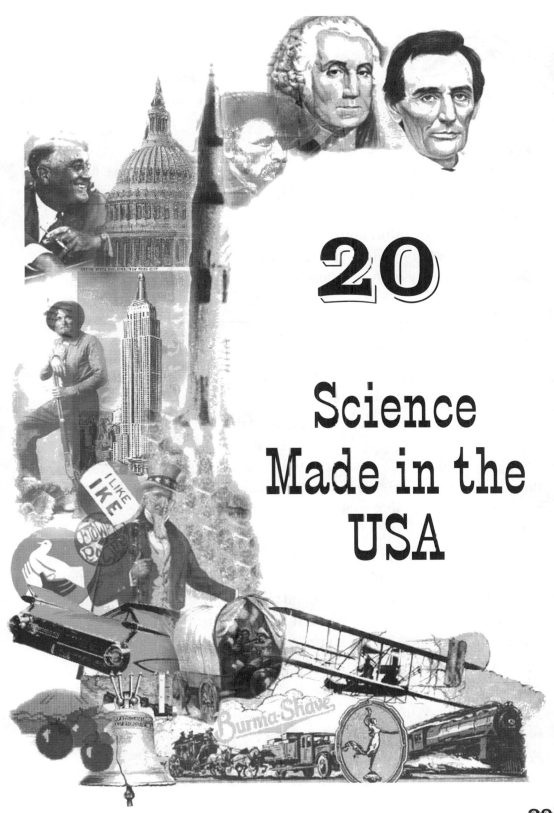

20

Science
Made in the
USA

Most scientists have been on familiar terms with the Internet for quite some time. The fabled network of networks was, after all, first created with scientists in mind. Up until a few years ago, the Internet was used almost exclusively by scientists, academics, and students as a vehicle for sharing information and research. In 1985 the Internet boasted only 1,961 host computers and numbered its users in the tens of thousands, the majority of them scientists.

Scientists and the Birth of the Web

Appropriately enough, the idea for the Web came from scientists—just as had the original idea for the Internet.

In 1989 Tim Berners-Lee, a physicist at the European Particle Physics Laboratory (CERN), proposed the concept of the Web as a system for transferring ideas and research among scientists in the high-energy physics community. Berners-Lee's original proposal defined a very simple implementation that used hypertext but did not include multimedia capabilities such as we have on the Web today.

Something very much like this was introduced on Steve Jobs' NeXT computer system (Figure 20-1) in 1990. The NeXT implementation allowed users to create, edit, view, and transmit hypertext documents over the Internet. This is the system that was demonstrated for CERN committees and attendees at the Hypertext '91 Conference.

In 1992 CERN began publicizing the World Wide Web project and encouraging the development of Web servers at laboratories and academic institutions around the world. At the same time, CERN promoted the development of WWW clients (browsers) for a range of computer systems including X Windows (UNIX), the Apple Macintosh, and PC/Windows. The rest, as they say, is history.

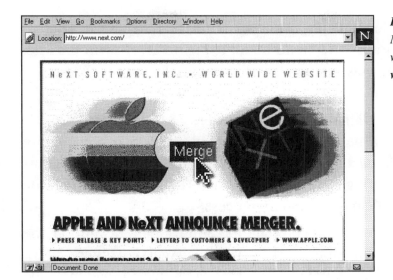

FIGURE 20-1
NeXT, now merged
*with Apple (**http://***
***www.next.com/**)*

A Brief History of American Science

During its first two hundred years American science was the domain of a scattering of independent amateurs. But by the mid-19th century the ideas, the needs, and the directions of these scientists—for the most part people who worked in isolation from one another—began to coalesce, and an organized professional community was established. Over time, the eccentric dabblers and loners who were the first practitioners of American science gave way to highly disciplined and specialized professionals linked by great national scientific institutions.

Looking back over the past two hundred years, it is easy to see how the development of scientific enterprise was directly linked with the parallel growth of American society as the country spread westward. Over the course of decades, the internal sociology, economics, and politics of the scientific community and the nation became interlocked.

In the early days, Americans looked to European science as a model. They mimicked its flavor, intentions, and methods. In later days, they viewed European science as something not to mimic, but rather to surpass.

The popular American view of scientists was that they were peculiar, antisocial misfits, much like Ben Franklin (Figure 20-2) with his kite. This view, in turn, was replaced with a cultural mythologizing and veneration of scientists which persists to the present day.

The key years defining these changes were 1846 through 1876. Of course, the roots and branches of so complex and subtle a change in culture and attitude cannot be lopped off cleanly at the edges of this thirty-year span. But roughly the years 1846 and 1876 do signify a definite beginning and end of an evolutionary process.

To American science, 1846 brought the Smithsonian Institution, the Yale Scientific School, and the arrival of Louis Agassiz (Figure 20-3), the great scientist of his day. 1876 in turn brought the formation of the American Chemical Society, the Johns Hopkins University Labs. To American technology, 1846 brought the Hoe printing press, the Howe sewing machine, and Orson Munn's *Scientific American* (**http://www.history.rochester.edu/Scientific_American**); and 1876 brought

FIGURE 20-2

Ben Franklin, scientist (http://sln.fi.edu/ franklin/scientst/ scientst.html/)

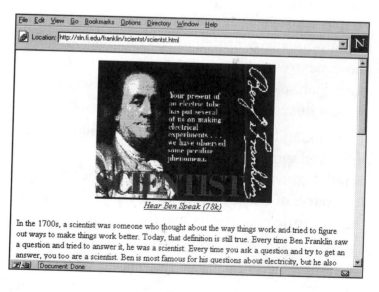

FIGURE 20-3
Louis Agassix, 1807-73
(http://www.ucmp.berkeley.
edu/history/agassiz.html/)

Bell's telephone, Edison's Menlo Park "invention factory," and the apotheosis of technology in the great Centennial Exhibition, which has already been discussed earlier in this book.

In science as in other domestic matters, the 19th century was a time for organizing. Until then, the scientific pursuit had for the most part been a small scale, spare time indulgence of individual curiosity. But science and technology had lately begun getting together to offer mankind a new range of possibilities for ease or adventure, pleasure or pain, increase or extinction. With such vistas opening, people began pursuing science more urgently, and the farther they pursued it, the more it ramified.

The proliferation of its branches meant that individual scientists had to become more specialized. The growing complexity of science demanded formal scientific education and full-time professional work, not the casual, intermittent attention of self-taught amateurs. The spread of scientific investigation in so many directions called for the recruiting of scientists, the systematizing of communication among them, and the reliable evaluation of their work.

In short, the pursuit of science had to become a collective enterprise. Just like any other business, modern science needed labor, capital, and management. Its character at a given time and place was influenced by the kinds of raw materials available to it. It also had to consider markets, in the sense of offering grounds for financial support.

Science Present and Past Meet on the Web

The Web is the ultimate expression of the collectivity of all great science. And on the Web, science present and science past often meet. Consider, if you will, the Web pages of Lowell Observatory (Figure 20-4) on Mars Hill Road in Flagstaff, Arizona.

This is one of the oldest astronomical observatories in the southwest. It was founded in 1894 by Boston businessman, author, and scientist Percival Lowell, a scion of the Boston family which also gave us the milltown of the same name, the poets Amy and Robert Lowell, and

FIGURE 20-4

The Lowell Observatory
(http://www.lowell.edu/)

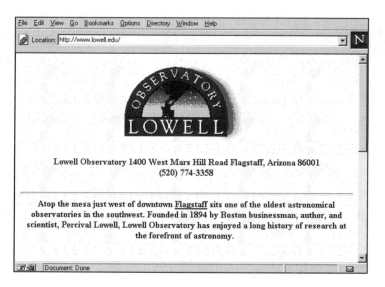

countless other Lowells of distinction. You, of course, have heard the old expression that Boston is the "land of the bean and the cod, where the Lowells speak only to Cabots and the Cabots speak only to God." Percival was one of them.

The 24-inch Alvan Clark refracting telescope Lowell purchased in the 1890s remains in the Observatory to this day. For many years it was the major research tool of the Observatory, and it continues to be in use now, even though it is a registered National Historic Landmark.

Dr. Lowell founded the Observatory primarily to explore the possibility that intelligent life might exist on Mars—something he firmly believed. The Observatory's research quickly expanded, however, into other areas. It was here that V.M. Slipher first discovered evidence of the expansion of the universe in the years 1912-17. And it was here, in 1930, that Clyde Tombaugh discovered the planet Pluto.

The Web page of the Observatory is packed with great images and important astronomical data, just as the Web pages of countless other American scientific institutions are packed with similarly useful data. Let's do some exploring.

American Association of Anatomists (AAA)

 http://www.faseb.org/anatomy/

Here at the home page for the leading professional society for biological anatomists you will find everything from e-mail addresses for AAA Nobel Laureates to classified job ads. You will also find information on joining the AAA.

American Association for Artificial Intelligence

 http://www.aaai.org/

The nonprofit American Association for Artificial Intelligence (AAAI) is a scientific society devoted to the promotion and advancement of the science of artificial intelligence. Launched in March of 1995, the AAAI's Website contains nearly a thousand files packed with valuable information, with more being added every week.

The American Astronomical Society (AAS), established 1899, is the major professional organization in North America for astronomers and other scientists and individuals interested in astronomy. Please direct questions to the AAS Executive Office at *aas@aas.org* or to individual staff members.

NEW What's New and on the AAS Web Server

Table of Contents

American Astronomical Society

 http://www.aas.org

The American Astronomical Society (AAS) is the major professional organization in North America for astronomers and other scientists and individuals interested in astronomy. Come to this Website for information on the society's executive council, committees, education and grants programs, and publications. Come here most especially for the splendid electronic edition of the society's *Astrophysical Journal*.

American Geological Institute

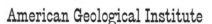 http://agi.umd.edu/agi/agi.html

The American Geological Institute (AGI) is a federation of 29 geoscience societies.

The AGI's mission is to provide information and education services to its members, and to provide a single, unified voice for the geoscience community.

American Institute of Physics

 http://www.aip.org/aip/
enews.html

The American Institute of Physics (AIP) is a national organization for physicists and anyone interested in the field of physics. The goal of the Institute is to promote knowledge of physics and practical applications of science to everyday life. The AIP makes four of its many newsletters available on the Web. These are *FYI: The American Institute of Physics Bulletin of Science Policy News, Physics News Update, PEN: Physics Education News*, and *The Center for the History of Physics Newsletter*. The AIP also offers here its *Electronic Publishing News*—a newsletter illuminating the efforts of the AIP and member-societies in electronic publishing.

American Physical Society

 http://www.aps.org/

Visit the Web page of the premier professional society for physicists in the United States. Here you'll find information on meetings, publications, education and outreach programs, and much more.

Anthropology at the California Academy of Sciences

 http://www.calacademy.org/research/
anthropology/

Located across from the de Young Museum in Golden Gate Park, the California Academy of Sciences is a national treasure. The anthropology exhibits are always popular, and now you can visit them without having to travel to San Francisco. These pages are filled with color photos and intriguing explanatory text. One recent combined online exhibit offered a gallery of Eskimo paintings, a wonderful tour through the Rollo Beck collection of photography from his travels through Oceania in the 1920s, and a collection titled "Folk Toys: the Playful Arts of Japan." The department's research collection numbers more than 20,000 pieces. Exhibits are rotated and updated regularly.

Applied Chaos Laboratory at Georgia Tech

 http://acl2.physics.gatech.edu

Founded in July 1993, Georgia Tech's Applied Chaos Laboratory (ACL) strives to apply the most advanced concepts of nonlinear dynamics and chaos to real world problems and products by directly applying theory by designing and testing experimental systems, and performing numerical simulations. The ACL's research spans a wide range of analysis and applications of chaotic behavior and related phenomena, and is done in concert with other universities reaching into other areas such as biophysics.

Astronomy Image Library at UMass

 http://donald.phast.umass.edu/

Here is your door to an extensive collection of outstanding astronomical resources that include a wealth of stunning images of Jupiter, various distant nebulae, and molecular line maps for star-formation regions in deep space. Even if you don't understand what the pictures are, you know they look cool.

Baylor Biological Databases

 http://condor.bcm.tmc.edu/
MBCRdatabases.html

Here are three highly useful biological databases developed by the faculty of the Baylor College of Medicine. The Mammary Transgene Interactive Database provides literature designed to target transgene proteins to the mammary gland. The Small RNA Database presents a vast collection of information related to protein synthesis. And the Tumor Gene Database is a fully relational database of genes associated with tumorigenesis and cellular transformation.

The Beekeeping Home Page

 http://weber.u.washington.edu/
~jlks/bee.html

Worried about killer bees? Now you can do something about them. Find out everything there is to know about bees, their place in our fragile ecology, how to raise healthy ones, and how to avoid the killer variety. This site will link you up with dozens of useful resources, from universities with entomology departments to scientific groups focusing on bee diseases, bees as environmental monitors, making more and better honey, and even brewing mead.

Boyce Thompson Institute at Cornell

 http://birch.cit.cornell.edu/

Focusing on plant research, the Boyce Thompson Institute uses its Website to provide an interesting virtual tour of the Boyce Thompson Southwestern Arbore-

tum, which they say is "the American Southwest's oldest and most spectacularly situated botanical garden."

Carnegie-Mellon University (CMU) Artificial Intelligence Repository

 http://www.cs.cmu.edu/Web/Groups/
AI/html/repository.html

The Artificial Intelligence Repository at Carnegie-Mellon University is an electronic archive and library of mankind's knowledge and understanding of artificial intelligence (AI). Founded in 1993, the Repository stores electronic data, computer programs, and numerous documents which are useful to AI students, researchers, and industry.

Center for Coastal Physical Oceanography

 http://www.ccpo.odu.edu/

The Center for Coastal Physical Oceanography (CCPO) at Old Dominion University researches the physics of coastal oceans and provides educational opportunities for the public by exploring the effects of humanity on the coastal ocean environment.

The CCPO conducts its research by employing both observational and modeling activities, and hopes to soon develop a complete and reliable model

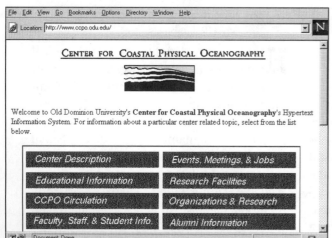

for the Atlantic coastal ocean. Such a model would incorporate shelf circulation patterns, wind, rivers, and ocean currents. This research, and a reliable model, would enable researchers to predict the dispersal patterns of crab larvae, and predict the paths of oil spills.

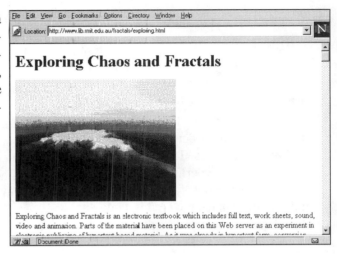

Exploring Chaos and Fractals

Exploring Chaos and Fractals is an electronic textbook which includes full text, work sheets, sound, video and animation. Parts of the material have been placed on this Web server as an experiment in

---

Center for Marine Science Research, University of North Carolina, Wilmington

 http://www.uncwil.edu/cmsr/ INTERPGM.HTM

The Center for Marine Science Research is dedicated to fostering a multidisciplinary approach to questions in basic marine research. The mission of the center is to promote basic and applied research in the fields of oceanography, coastal and wetlands studies, marine biomedical and environmental physiology, and marine biotechnology and aquaculture. Access this Web page to review the work of faculty members conducting marine science research in the departments of biological sciences, chemistry, and earth sciences.

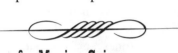

Chaos: The Course

 http://www.lib.rmit.edu.au/fractals/ exploring.html

Here, courtesy of MIT, is a wonderfully literate, clearly explained HTML primer on the rudiments of chaos theory. "Do you need to be told about chaos, or is your desk

a permanent example?" it asks. "As everyone knows, beneath what those intolerably neat and tidy people consider to be chaos, there is a form of order. The chaotic housekeepers can always find the item of their desire—as long as no one tidies up! Many systems that scientists have considered totally random, unpredictable, and without form have now been found to be otherwise." And so on.

Chaos at The University of Maryland

 http://www-chaos.umd.edu/

Here is the home page of the Chaos Group at the University of Maryland, College Park. Since the mid-1970s the Chaos Group at Maryland has done extensive research in various areas of chaotic dynamics ranging from the theory of dimensions, fractal basin boundaries, chaotic scattering, and controlling chaos. Access the reports of this research in these Web pages.

Chemistry Hypermedia Project at Virginia Tech

 http://www.chem.vt.edu/chem-ed/vt-chem-ed.html

The Chemistry Hypermedia Project is developing tutorials that provide supplemental educational resources for undergraduate chemistry students. The hypermedia documents contain hyperlinks to remedial material that describes fundamental chemical principles. Topics covered include analytical chemistry and solid-state chemistry.

Coastal and Marine Geology Projects of the U.S. Geological Survey

 http://marine.usgs.gov/fact-sheets/

Here are extensive briefings on and files related to various USGS projects involving Louisiana's Barrier Islands, wetlands nationwide, and geological formations and fisheries across the continent.

Ecology Resources Home Page of the Kennedy Space Center

 http://atlas.ksc.nasa.gov/env.html

Established in the mid '70s, the Biomedical Operations and Research Office of NASA's Kennedy Space Center (KSC) performs en-

vironmental monitoring and research. Because of the unique natural environment at KSC, protecting and preserving the Center is a key goal of the Biomedical Operations and Research Office.

Come to this dedicated Web page for information on KSC's research on vegetation, soil types, threatened and endangered species, jurisdictional wetlands, ground water recharge zones, surface water quality, climate, air quality, fire ecology, and more.

The Edison Project for Communicating Chemistry (Columbia University)

 http://www.columbia.edu/cu/chemistry/edison/Edison.html

The Edison Project at Columbia University provides several downloadable multimedia tutorial modules primarily for the Macintosh. Topics include substitution/elimination reactions, conformations

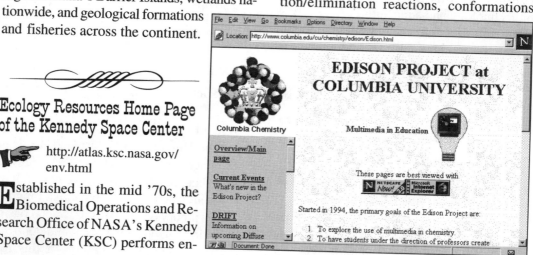

of butane, molecular representations, glucose maturation, periodic motion, and Lewis Dot structures.

Electric/Hybrid Vehicles Homepage

 http://eve.ev.hawaii.edu/
new_home.html

You might think that General Motors would be hustling hardest to design an electric car just in case fossil fuels become too scarce or costly. Well, no agency or company seems more intent on development of electric cars than the Defense Advanced Research Projects Agency (DARPA), an agency of the U.S. Department of Defense. Check out these extremely well-designed pages to learn about what seven separate consortia of universities and government scientists are doing to come up with whatever it is that will replace the internal combustion engine on American highways.

Field Museum of Natural History

 http://www.bvis.uic.edu/museum/

You don't have to be in Chicago to marvel at the exhibits in the Field Museum. These well-crafted pages are full of scientific goodies to delight the natural history buff: interactive games, audio and video clips to enjoy, updates on studies around the world being done by Field Museum scientists, tips for science teachers, and more.

Fermi National Accellerator Laboratory

 http://www.fnal.gov/

The Fermilab is located 35 miles west of Chicago. Twenty-two hundred scientists from all over the world have come to Fermilab to investigate particle physics, the study of the fundamental nature of matter and energy, using the highest-energy particle accellerator in the world. Leaf through these

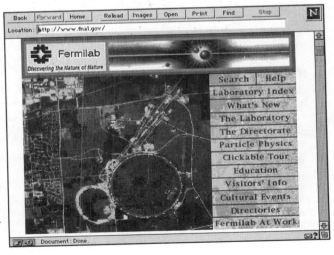

pages and read reports of what sorts of studies and experiments have been conducted recently, including some with titles worthy of Mr. Spock, like "Search for Diphoton Events with Large Missing Transverse Energy."

Benjamin Franklin's Autobiography

 http://grid.let.rug.nl/~welling/usa/bios/franklin/frank.htm

Benjamin Franklin's autobiography—available here in a hypertext edition—includes many details of his various scientific experiments, the most famous of which is, of course, his adventure with the kite, the key, and electricity. Note that Franklin's entire collected works are available at **gopher://gopher.vt.edu:10010/ 11/85**. You should also check out **http://grid.let. rug.nl/~welling/usa/franklin.html**.

Geological Society of America

 http://www.aescon.com/geosociety/pubs/bulletin.htm

Since 1888, the Geological Society of America has maintained information resources for earth scientists of every level. Keeping up with the digital times, the Society (grown to more than 15,000 members) is now online, making all their scientific bulletins available to read at home. These studies can be tough to follow for the lay-

man, but the bulletins should prove fascinating places to visit for any trained geologist.

Geologic Time: A Hypertext Reference from Berkeley

 http://www.ucmp.berkeley.edu/help/timeform.html

Here is a terrific, information-filled hypertext time line running from the Precambrian to the Cenozoic era (i.e., from the beginning of the Earth to right this minute). The site also includes a good hypertext introduction to geology.

The Geometry Center at The University of Minnesota

 http://www.geom.umn.edu/

Here, courtesy of the University of Minnesota, you have a wonderful collection

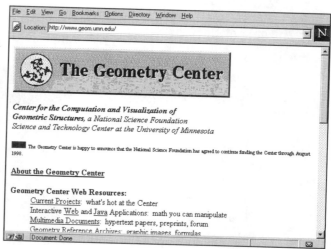

of images, tools, and software toys for generating fractals, hyperbolic tiles, and other startlingly cool images on your home PC.

Goddard Space Flight Center: Systems Engineering Homepage

 http://rs712b.gsfc.nasa.gov/704/ 704home.html

NASA's Goddard Center is involved in many fascinating studies of complex systems, from the dynamics of the world's rainforests to a series of small explorer space projects (small meaning costing on average a paltry $35 million). Each study, or "mission," has its own set of illustrated and detailed pages, with text to interest and delight the layman as well as the expert.

Great Lakes Program of the State University of New York, Buffalo

 http://wings.buffalo.edu/glp/

The Great Lakes Program develops, evaluates, and publishes technical scientific information relating to the Great Lakes ecosystem. The Program does this to add to the pool of public information about the Great Lakes for educational purposes, and to shape public policy. Check out their Web pages for details.

Harvard Biological Laboratories

 http://golgi.harvard.edu/

Here is access to the databases of Harvard's Biolabs Library, the Walter Gilbert lab (Bioinformatics), the Daniel Hartl lab, the J.W. Hastings lab, the Tom Maniatis lab, the Markus Meister lab, the Matt Meselson lab, the George M. Church lab, and the Roger Brent lab.

Harvard Robotics Lab

 http://hrl.harvard.edu

Founded in 1993, the Harvard Robotics Lab's current projects include research in computational vision, neural networks, tactile sensing, motion control, and VLSI systems.

Hot Air: The Annals of Improbable Research

 http://www.improb.com

Here at the home page for this remarkable spoof science publication you will find lots of fun stuff including downloadable posters (suitable for framing or birdcage lining). What else? How about cool, fun software and tutorials including *A Periodic Table of the Presidents, Fun with Grapes,*

An Ode to the World's First Rubber Czech, and *Plans for Things that Go Boom*.

Imaging System Laboratory, University of Illinois

 http://imlab9.landarch.uiuc.edu/

Access the home page of the Imaging Systems Laboratory of the Department of Landscape Architecture, University of Illinois, Champaign-Urbana. The lab was founded in 1986 to conduct research into environmental perception. Most of the work at the lab focuses on visualizing and evaluating environmental changes brought about by forest fires, pests, harvesting, and management—with emphasis on methodological issues. The lab was a pioneer in the use of computer image editing as a research tool, and continues to lead in integration of photorealistic rendering, numerical modeling, and remote sensing for landscape analysis.

Indiana University Biogeochemical Laboratories

 http://copper.ucs.indiana.edu/~jfong/biogeo/

The Biogeochemical Labs at Indiana University are the birthplace of isotope ratio monitoring gas chromatography/combustion/mass spectrometry. Here the technique continues to be refined in terms of both hardware and software, and to be applied to different gases. This site includes details on the latest work at the lab.

Iowa State University Artificial Intelligence Group

http://www.cs.iastate.edu/~honavar/aigroup.html

The Iowa State University Artificial Intelligence Research Group designs and systematically explores algorithms for neural networks for pattern classification and the applications for which such a neural net might be used.

Jet Propulsion Lab at NASA

http://www.jpl.nasa.gov/

The Jet Propulsion Lab is home to such projects as the Galileo space probe, which most recently brought startling images of Jupiter back down to earth, along with a tremendous wealth of atmospheric information from the same planet.

Journal of Artificial Intelligence Research

 http://www.cs.washington.edu/
research/jair/home.html

Published on the server of Washington State University, *The Journal of Artificial Intelligence Research* (JAIR) is a free electronic publication supported by the AI Access Foundation.

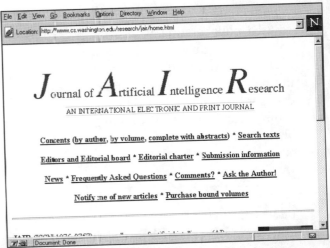

Lamont-Doherty Earth Observatory at Columbia University

 http://www.ldeo.columbia.edu/

The Lamont-Doherty Earth Observatory at Columbia University provides a wonderful Web resource comprising links to information on the range of lab programs as well as links to other related institutions around the globe.

Mad Science

 http://www.ftech.net/~madsite/

Mad science is "a much maligned domain of human knowledge and its practitioners have for too long been relegated to B-movies and remote ancestral estates." So writes the Webmaster who maintains the Mad Science Website.

If you would care to delve into things best left unknown, then plant your tongue firmly in your cheek and visit Mad Science, the online collection of the research into (and knowledge base of) pseudosciences and dangerous technologies that can barely be classified as science at all.

The forum is, in fact, an ongoing cyberconference designed "to promote a general understanding of mad topics with the broader scientific community, to encourage new research to dabble with things best left alone, to attract commercial sponsors to the potential benefits of mad science in the business world, and to replace the old drooling maniac stereotype of the mad scientist with a new drooling maniac image more appropriate to the modern era." The conference is held on the Web, rather than at a site outside the virtual world, in order to avoid high overhead, unpredictable atmospheric conditions, and outraged villagers.

Some of the subjects here include creating life to satisfy egocentric motives, unleashing entities beyond human control of comprehension, tampering with life-sustaining forces of the universe, exceeding the limitations of the human body via grotesque metamorphoses, ill-advised collaboration with alien and/or supernatural intelligences, lifelong devotion to researching the pointless and insane, callous disregard for human experimental subjects, and the art of exacting bizarre revenge on contemptuous, derisive peers.

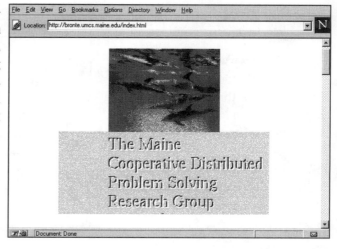

The Maine Cooperative Distributed Problem-Solving Research Group

 http://bronte.umcs.maine.edu/index.html

The Maine Cooperative Distributed Problem-Solving (CDPS) Research Group is based at the University of Maine, Orono. The group strives to get intelligent, autonomous agents to work together to solve complex problems in artificially intelligent environments.

The Massachusetts Institute of Technology (MIT)

 http://web.mit.edu/

The Massachusetts Institute of Technology is the nation's premier scientific and technical institution of higher learning. One of their most important programs is their AI research lab, headed by the indefatigable Nicholas Negroponte.

Michigan Technological University Volcanoes Page

 http://www.geo.mtu.edu/volcanoes/

This excellent site includes a clickable worldwide volcanic reference map providing information on specific volcanoes and volcanic regions. You also get information on volcanic hazards mitigation, remote sensing of volcanoes, terminology and definitions of volcanology, and more.

Monterey Bay Aquarium Research Institute

 http://www.mbari.org/

Founded by David Packard (of Hewlett Packard fame), the Monterey Bay Aquarium Research Institute develops equipment, instrumentation, systems, and methods for scientific research in the deepest waters of the oceans.

Mount Wilson Observatory

 http://www.mtwilson.edu/

Surprisingly close to the smog of the Los Angeles basin, the Mt. Wilson Observatory, on the mountain above Pasadena, is actually one of the best places on earth for looking skyward. Come to these pages to take a virtual tour around this facility, home of the famous 60-inch Hooker telescope. Find out about some of the many studies based at the observatories, including the work of two university-sponsored solar observatories monitoring magnetic and seismic activity on the sun, the "Telescopes in Education" schools program, and more.

NASA

 http://hypatia.gsfc.nasa.gov/
NASA_homepage.html

Care to take a cyberwalk through the Kennedy, Goddard, Ames, Dryden, and Langley space centers? Or would you like to let your fingers do the walking through some of the great NASA history files, the NASA Strategic Plan, and NASA's online educational resources? More to the point, you may just want to browse NASA's technical report server or the complete searchable index to NASA resources by subject.

The National Estuary Program of the Environmental Protection Agency (EPA)

 http://www.epa.gov/nep/nep.html

Quite simply, this is an extensive collection of links relating to all estuarine matters in the United States, including detailed information on such great estuaries as Puget Sound, San Francisco Bay, the Chesapeake Bay, and (my two favorites) the Hudson River and the Narragansett Bay.

National Marine Fisheries Service

 http://kingfish.ssp.nmfs.gov/

The National Marine Fisheries Service (NMFS) administers those programs of the National Oceanic and Atmospheric Administration (NOAA) intended to conserve

and manage living marine resources. The NMFS produces products for fisheries and the development of new fisheries. They also offer industry assistance programs, enforcement services, protected species and habitat conservation operations, and manage the technical aspects of NOAA's marine fisheries program.

National Museum of Natural History: Ocean Planet Exhibit

 http://seawifs.gsfc.nasa.gov/
ocean_planet.html

The culmination of a four-year effort to study and understand environmental issues affecting the health of the world's oceans, Ocean Planet employs cutting-edge technology, compelling objects and photos, enticing text and walk-through environments to promote the celebration, understanding, and conservation of the world's oceans.

National Oceanic and Atmospheric Administration (U.S. Department of Commerce)

 http://www.noaa.gov/
noaa-image-home.html

The site provides access to all the servers of the U.S. National Weather service including the National Hurricane Center, the Arkansas-Red Basin River Forecast Center, the Climate Prediction Center, the Hydrologic Information Center, the Midwest Agricultural Weather Service Center, and the Spaceflight Meteorology Group.

National Public Radio: Science Friday Hot Spots

 http://www.npr.org/programs/scifri/

This is a superb, regularly updated list of links initially generated during NPR's program on the topic of science Web links aired on December 29, 1995. The links were derived from listener suggestions, and they are arranged alphabetically by subject. You may also access a RealAudio file of the program itself.

National Science Foundation

 http://www.nsf.gov/

The National Science Foundation is an independent U.S. government agency that oversees the investment of over $3.3 billion per year in almost 20,000 research and education projects in science and engineering. These projects cover the entire gamut of scientific investigation, including the fields of biology, computer science, education, engineering, geosciences, math, physical sciences, polar research, social science, and behavioral science. Come to the agency's home pages to learn how to tailor a grant proposal or to read the specs on dozens of fascinating currently supported projects as wide-ranging as the study of life in extreme environments and whether computers can communicate the way humans do.

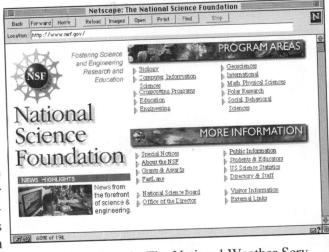

National Weather Service

 http://www.nws.noaa.gov/

It's not entirely true that everybody talks about the weather but nobody does any-thing about it. The National Weather Service is doing something about the weather: putting up this Website to give up-to-the-minute meteorologic information crucial to pilots, sailors, farmers, travelers, and pretty much everybody else. You can come here to get the current weather anywhere in the country, warnings, and forecasts, climate statistics, and scores of links to every kind of weather-related resource you can think of.

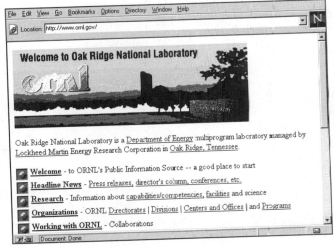

Oak Ridge National Laboratory

 http://www.ornl.gov/

Oak Ridge National Laboratory is the nation's premier federal research lab. Located in Tennessee, it does groundbreaking work related to such diverse areas as the environment and national defense.

The Oceanography Society

 http://www.tos.org/

Based in Virginia Beach, Virginia, the Oceanographic Society has been bringing American oceanographers together since 1988. From their home page, find out more about joining the organization, read the latest newsletter about ongoing scientific activities, or subscribe to their thrice yearly magazine, *Oceanography*.

Periodic Table at Illinois Institute of Technology

 http://www.csrri.iit.edu/ periodic-table.html

A click on an element name button in this forms-based periodic table will give you the x-ray properties of that element. If you give an energy value in a box at the top of the table you can get x-ray cross-sections at

that energy value. The source code used to calculate x-ray cross-sections is also available.

Physics/Consciousness Research Group

 http://www.hia.com/hia/pcr/test1.html

Tired of the same old physics? Why don't you take a look at "post-quantum" physics, as presented by this group, based in San Francisco. Explore scientific (or pseudo-scientific) musings on the provability of precognition in the Torah, a subatomic particle dubbed the "Oh-My-God" particle, developments in nanotechnology, and the perhaps more immediately practical subject of why rockets cost so much to build and launch. Is this all a joke? Check it out and decide for yourself.

Clifford A. Pickover Home Page

http://sprott.physics.wisc.edu/ pickover/home.html

Access this home page for one of my favorite science writers and science-fiction novelists, the author of many splendid books and articles on chaos theory and fractal science. Pickover is currently a research staff member at the IBM Thomas J. Watson Research Center, where he has received eleven invention achievement awards, a research division award, and four external honor awards. He is also a consultant for

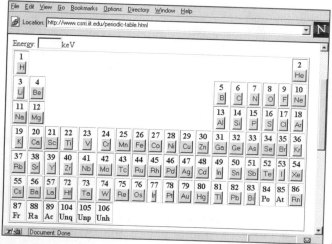

WNET on science education projects and a regular columnist for *Discover* magazine.

Rob's Granite Page

 http://uts.cc.utexas.edu/~rmr/

This one is hard to describe. The Webmaster calls it "a roadcut on the information highway." New magma is injected periodically, and it is intriguing to watch the page crystallize. Rob is Robert M. Reed, a Ph.D. candidate in the Department of Geological Sciences, University of Texas, Austin.

San Diego Zoo

 http://www.sandiegozoo.org/Zoo/zoo.html

The San Diego Zoo is as well-designed and well-stocked a zoological garden as you can find anywhere in the world. Now you can visit many of the amazing animals online, with photos and explanatory text. You can also visit the Wild Animal Park, 35 miles from the zoo, but only a mouse click away in the virtual version. An astonishing effort has been made to reproduce the kind of natural environment animal park you used to have to go to Nairobi to experience. Now, in San Diego, you don't even need shots. And online, you don't even need sunblock.

Scientific American Magazine of the 19th Century

 http://www.history.rochester.edu/Scientific_American/

This fantastic site provides digital reprints of great issues of *Scientific American* magazine from the 19th century. The magazines are indexed by subject and author, allowing you to search for such keywords as "Edison," "Bell," and, well, you get the picture.

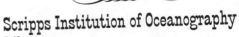

Scripps Institution of Oceanography Library

 http://orpheus.ucsd.edu/sio/index.html

With a staff of over 1,200, the Scripps Institute has been one of the world's most important centers for marine research for over 90 years. The Institute is based at the University of California, San Diego.

Visit this site and learn about the more than 300 ongoing research programs, increasing our knowledge of global warming, the marine food chain, earthquakes, processing new drugs from marine plants and animals, and more. The site also gives links to library resources, periodicals, scientific texts, other related institutions, ocean and earth science data services, and more.

Virtual Hospital

 http://vh.radiology.uiowa.edu/

An amazing and well-realized concept, the Virtual Hospital is a continuously updated health science library, made available to doctors, other health care professionals, and informed patients alike. You can get general information, help with specific health questions, stay up to date on the latest-breaking innovations in medicine, and get links to other resources. The Virtual Hospital is a project of the Electric Differential Multimedia Laboratory at the Department of Radiology, University of Iowa College of Medicine.

Woods Hole Oceanographic Institution

 http://www.whoi.edu/

The Woods Hole Oceanographic Institution needs no introduction. It is the largest independent marine science research facility in the United States. Founded in 1930, the institution is dedicated to the study of all aspects of marine science and the education of marine scientists. Come to this Website for complete information on all the Institution's programs.

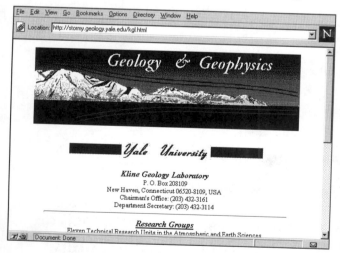

Yale Geology and Geophysics: The Kline Geology Laboratory

 http://stormy.geology.yale.edu/ kgl.html

Survey the latest Yale research in all areas of geology, including petrology, stratigraphy, solid earth geophysics, tectonics of the continental lithosphere, archeometallurgy, and more.

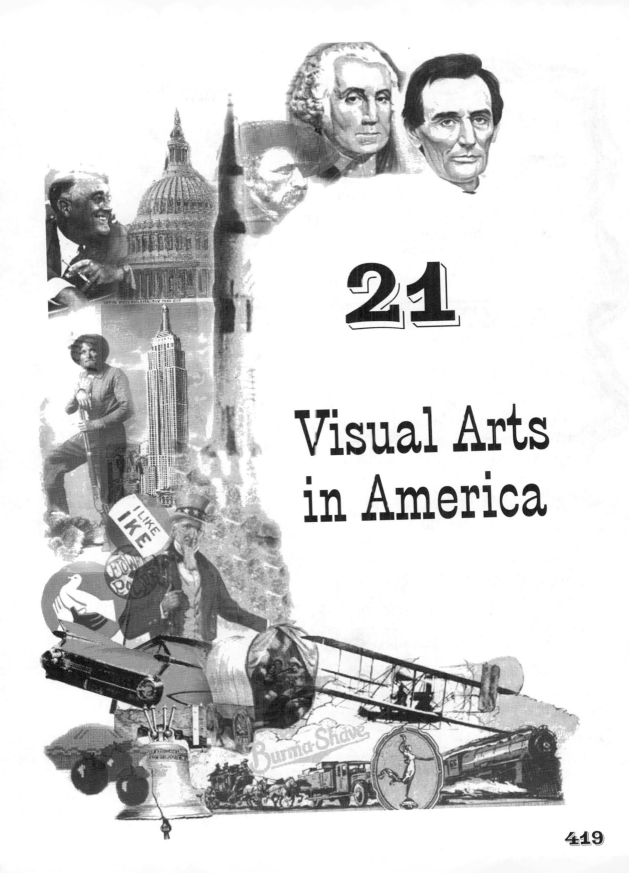

21

Visual Arts in America

The most frequent assertion about American art is that it is polarized between revolution and tradition, and certainly the story of American painting reveals a pattern of periodic dependence on European artisitic tradition against a background of developing and strengthening national identity.

A Tale of Two Cultures

Two of the major colonial cultures in North America, the English and the Dutch, left profound marks on early American painting, particularly in the numerous portraits done in the colonial period, which are typical of Anglo-Dutch provincial portraiture, with their clear, direct, sometimes naïve representation of appearance and character such as in the paintings of Gilbert Stuart and Rembrandt Peale (Figure 21-1).

FIGURE 21-1
*Rembrandt Peale's portrait of Washington (**http://www.150.si.edu/150trav/remember/r213a.htm**)*

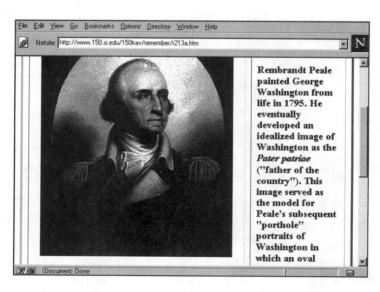

Rembrandt Peale painted George Washington from life in 1795. He eventually developed an idealized image of Washington as the *Pater patriae* ("father of the country"). This image served as the model for Peale's subsequent "porthole" portraits of Washington in which an oval

The ties with Europe were reinforced during the 18th century with the arrival in the New World of more European artists, while at the same time native-born painters went to be trained in Europe. The American Neo-Classical and Romantic traditions, which found expression in the histori-cal and allegorical canvases of Vanderlyn (Figure 21-2), stemmed directly from their European counterparts. Vanderlyn was also a great painter of Hudson River scenes, and conversely such Hudson River painters as Church and Cole had their allegorical moments.

It was not until the early 19th century that the United States saw the emergence of a strong new spirit of native painting which was in direct opposition to what Americans widely perceived as the decadence of European civilization. By the 1830s the American wilderness had become the overriding obsession of many American artists and the first indige-nous school of landscape painters—known as the Hudson River School (**http://www.highlands.com/Libraries/DFL_Painters/Index.html**) —was established.

FIGURE 21-2
John Vanderlyn's The Hudson at Kingston (***http://www.mhrcc.org/ kingston/vanhud.gif***)

Hudson River School painters such as Asher Durand, Frederick Church, and Thomas Cole (Figure 21-3) focused on both the cultivated and wilderness areas of Eastern mountains, forests, valleys, and rivers to encourage appreciation of the beauty, magnificence, and sublimity of a North American continent already much changed by settlement and industry. Often influenced by the ideas of the Transcendentalists (especially Emerson), these artists sought to show humanity and nature in a balanced harmony. Their successors, usually called the Luminists, shared with the French Impressionists a fascination with light—though their smooth, polished style differed dramatically from the loose, quickly painted landscapes of Claude Monet and Camille Pissaro.

The choice and treatment of the subject matter were not only a response to a setting of wild and unexplored grandeur, but a symbol of national self-confidence and pride which grew stronger and more analytical with the opening up of the continent and, later, the settlement of the West.

FIGURE 21-3
*An unsigned painting attributed to Thomas Cole (**http://w3.wo.sbc.edu/ ArtHistory/MacMurtrie/ EveningSunset.jpg**)*

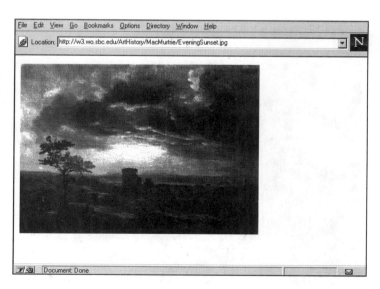

At the same time, the painters of the Hudson River School viewed their landscapes with a paradoxical mixture of awe and fear. As artists like Bierstadt and Moran moved into the Far West to paint, they viewed the new wilderness landscapes as possessing both a terrible and a beautiful attraction. Constantly, in his views of the prairies and the Rocky Mountains, Bierstadt juxtaposed verdant valleys with parched desert, cool running streams with torrential waterfalls, vast expanses of lateral space with soaring mountains, serenity with violence.

The ambition of most painters of the Hudson River School was essentially religious. Their stated mission was to depict, as near to reality as possible, the Creator's greatest handiworks as represented in the scenery of the United States. The selection of sublime subjects made these paintings romantic despite the rule of most Hudson River artists that natural beauty be recreated exactly as it was, with no attempt by mortal hands to improve upon the artistry of God. The point was to make whoever viewed the work of art feel, as Carl Carmer has written, "awed and humble in the presence of divine sublimity."

Towards the Modern

Throughout the latter half of the 19th century there were recurring instances of subtle, and sometimes not so subtle European influence—as in the case of American Impressionism, which modeled itself on French Impressionism and then refined it into a uniquely American blend of technique and subjects, thus extending and confirming the American sense of national artistic identity.

Schools of painting such as the Realists and individual artists such as Thomas Eakins (Figure 21-4) and Winslow Homer, may, to some extent, be said to have resembled their European counterparts insofar as their

FIGURE 21-4

Thomas Eakins's The Bilgen Brothers Racing (**http://www. amazed.nl/wm/paint/ auth/eakins/racing.jpg**)

work reflects broad currents of 19th-century attitudes, but they neverthe-less remain intensely American in both temperament and statement.

In spite of a growing internationalism in the 20th century after the epoch-making Armory Show of 1913, the distinctiveness of the American temperament is evident in such movements as the Ashcan School, Ab-stract Expressionism, Pop, and Junk art. The same obsession with the environment which, in the 19th century, led to the formation of native landscape schools, gave rise, by the 20th century, to the exploration of city life and urban problems. The ecological consciousness implicit in such paintings as Bierstadt's *The Last of the Buffalo* has a striking parallel in Andy Warhol's Coca-Cola bottles and Campbell's Soup cans.

Art in the White House

The White House maintains an extensive online gallery of American paintings in the collection of the White House. First Ladies of recent decades deserve great credit for collecting much of the art featured in the

White House Collection. Jacqueline Kennedy set the goal of collecting works by the country's finest artists. Lady Bird Johnson enthusiastically continued that pursuit, and Patricia Nixon's efforts added no less than 18 classic portraits of Presidents and First Ladies.

Private donors have also made a difference. The great-great-grandson of John Quincy Adams has presented Gilbert Stuart portraits of his ancestors, John Quincy Adams and Louisa Adams—works that may well have hung in the White House during the John Quincy Adams administration. A descendant has presented a marble bust of Martin van Buren. The descendants of Abraham Lincoln have presented portraits of both Lincoln and his wife. And the family of Theodore Roosevelt—friends of mine—have contributed works by one of Roosevelt's favorite artists, Frederic Remington. (By the way, it was Edith Roosevelt who established the First Ladies Portrait Gallery in the Ground Floor Corridor of the White House.)

In all, the White House collection features more than 450 great works of American art. Many of them are available online at the digital gallery of White House art (**http://www.whitehouse.gov/WH/glimpse/art/html/top.html**).

American Art on the Web

The resources related to American art on the World Wide Web are extensive and useful. We can't cover them all, but we can tour around just enough to get a good sense of what is out there, and where to begin in our quest for digital information and images related to the rich contribution the United States has made in the field of visual arts.

Washington Allston

 http://cougarnet.byu.edu/tmcbucs/
moa/840018900.html

Washington Allston (1779-1843), was a poet and one of the earliest romantic painters in America. Originally from Georgetown, South Carolina, he studied at Harvard, then went on to London, where he studied with Benjamin West. In Paris he met John Vanderlyn (1775-1852), with whom he traveled to Italy where he developed a style which eventually got him dubbed the "American Titian." His poetry reflects strong influence from his friend and fellow traveler Samuel Coleridge. Learn some more about him at this site.

Thomas Hart Benton

 http://www.arches.uga.edu/~smead/
benton.html

Benton (1889-1975) portrayed the American midwest in his paintings as a

dreamscape in constant motion. As both painter and muralist, he reflected the pride and pain felt by Americans as they coped with the Depression, war, and industrialization. At this site you will find several reproductions and links to more art and background resources. At **http://www.globaldialog.com/
~colour/colour7.html**, another page put up by a Benton fan, check out several reproductions and additional commentary.

Albert Bierstadt

 http://www.hansonlib.org/bierst2.html

Albert Bierstadt (1830-1902) was born near Dusseldorf and brought to America as a small child. Apparently self-taught, he made a four-year sojourn to Europe in the 1850s. In 1859 he joined a U.S. Government expedition that was mapping an overland route to the Pacific. The sketches Bierstadt made on this trip (he traveled as far as Wyoming) were the basis for a magnificent series of landscape paintings which in turn served as the basis for an outstanding career as a landscape artist.

Gutzon Borglum

http://xroads.virginia.edu/
~UG97/stone/gutzon.html

Every American knows about Mount Rushmore. But most people have no idea who it was who first conceived of this amazing monument and set about getting it carved. Gutzon Borglum (1871-1941) was the sculptor with an ability to envision works more gigantic than any attempted since the pyramids. Come to this site for a biography of Borglum and the story of his earlier works, including the beautiful statue of Robert E. Lee at Stone Mountain, Georgia. The site at **http://dickshovel.netgate.net/BorgVision.html** features an article titled "Borglum's Vision," telling about Borglum's plans for a vast sculptural monument to the Lakota Sioux, planned for after the completion of Mt. Rushmore.

Boston Museum of Fine Arts

 http://www.mfa.org/

The Boston Museum of Fine Arts is one of the premier art museums in the country. In addition to other items, the museum includes one of the finest collections of the paintings of John Singer Sargent to be found anywhere.

Alexander Calder

 http://sheldon.unl.edu/test/pages/Artists/Calder_A./Calder.html

In 1926, Alexander Calder (1898-1976) traveled to Paris, where he hung out with Picasso, Leger, Miro, and Mondrian. He was particularly

taken by Mondrian and in 1930 decided to try to "do a Mondrian that moves." The result was the "mobile." Calder's sculptures and paintings are scattered around countless museums. You can find reproductions of single Calder works at many Websites, but start here for a little background on the artist.

Check out **http://www.artincontext.com/listings/pages/artist/c/0t2pshqc/menu.htm** for links to galleries, dealers, and museums veaturing Calder works, as well as current, recent, and past exhibitions.

Mary Cassatt

 http://www.caeconsultants.com/zoraa/artist.htm

Mary Cassatt (1844-1926) was unorthodox in every way and therefore she was right at home with other impressionist painters of her generation. She preferred people to landscapes.

William Merritt Chase

 http://watt.emf.net/wm/paint/auth/chase/

William Merritt Chase (1849-1916) was born in Franklin, Indiana. He was president of the Society of American Artists for ten years and was elected to the National Academy of Fine Arts in 1890. He spent many summers at Shinnecock, Long Island, and his scenes of Shinnecock are among his best work.

Frederick Church

 http://www.artsednet.getty.edu/ ArtsEdNet/Images/P/niagara.html

Frederick Church (1842-1924) was by far one of the greatest painters of the Hudson River School and a great model for landscape painters to come after him. He lived on the Hudson River but painted around the world.

John Singleton Copley

 http://watt.emf.net/wm/paint/auth/ copley/

John Singleton Copley (1738-1815) was born in Boston to parents recently arrived from Ireland. Like his contemporary, Gilbert Stuart, he was noted for his portraits and he painted many of the founding fathers, among them Paul Revere.

Currier & Ives

 http://www.mcs.csuhayward.edu/ ~malek/Zebufolder/Cur-Ives.html

Nathaniel Currier (1813-1888) and James M. Ives (1824-1895), working out of their shop at No. 1 Wall Street in New York City, turned out an astonishing number of lithographs, both in black and white and in color. By the time of Currier's death, 40 years after the two men began their partnership in 1857, Currier & Ives were household names across America and the firm was the best-known lithographic house in the country. With meticulous detail, Currier & Ives reproduced lithographic versions of paintings created by leading artists of the time. Visit this site for a lovely collection of colored lithograph reproductions, representing the full range of subjects made famous by Currier & Ives.

Willem de Kooning

 http://www.artliaison.org/deKooning

Willem de Kooning was one of the most distinguished artists of the 20th century. Born in the Netherlands in 1904, he came to the United States as a two-year-old child. In the 1940s and 1950s, de Kooning went through an abstract expressionistic period. After that, he started his abstract constructivist landscape series which is known for its brilliant colors and lyrical quality. De Kooning died in March 1997.

M.H. De Young Memorial Museum, San Francisco

 http://www.sfmuseum.org/hist2/ museum.html

The De Young Museum sits like a jewel in the center of Golden Gate Park. Now celebrating its centenary, the museum houses permanent collections of American paintings and exhibits of American art of all kinds from pre-Columbian to the present. The page at **http://foghorn.usfca.edu/ archives/fall.95/f04/entertainment/ de young.html** will give you an idea of what you can find in the museum.

(1889). At the same time, Eakins' portraits reveal him as one of the finest American practitioners of that genre.

Thomas Eakins

 http://www.amazed.nl/wm/paint/ auth/eakins/

Thomas Eakins (1844-1916) was born in Philadelphia and studies at the Pennsylvania Academy of Fine Arts and at various schools in Paris. In 1870 he visited Spain where he admired the works of Valasquez. He began instructing at the Pennsylvania Academy of Fine Arts in 1873 and became chief instructor there in 1876.

Eakins' extraordinary success as a realist painter is due in no small part to his scientific knowledge and understanding of human anatomy. Eakins is probably best known for his depictions of life at the Jefferson Medical College, Philadelphia, *The Gross Clinic* (1875) and *The Agnew Clinic*

J. Paul Getty Museum, Malibu, California

http://ca.living.net/trav/museums/ carjpgm.htm

Very few attractions are honestly worth a special trip to Southern California. The J. Paul Getty Museum is one of them. Exercizing the kind of wealth incomprehensible to most humans, the Getty patriarch had an ancient Roman villa recreated in the hills overlooking Malibu and used it to house his private art collection—a collection to rival anything collected by European royalty. Now the collection is open to the public as a museum. It's even free! The museum houses permanent collections of Greek and Roman antiquities, pre-20th-century European paintings, drawings, sculpture, illuminated manuscripts, decorative arts, and more. For directions and other information, you might also check out **http://www.lacity-view.com/things/museums/J._Paul_Getty_ Museum.html.**

Sanford Robinson Gifford

 http://w3.wo.sbc.edu/ ArtHistory/MacMurtrie/Gifford.html

Sanford Robinson Gifford (1823-1880) was a painter of the Hudson River School noted for his depictions of the scenes from the Berkshire and Catskill Mountains. He eventually traveled and painted in the Middle East and the American West, thus becoming one of the most traveled of the painters of the Hudson River School.

Edward Hicks

 http://www.artsednet.getty. edu/ArtsEdNet/Images/P/ peaceable.html

Edward Hicks (1780-1849) was raised a Pennsylvania Quaker. He may not have thought of himself as an artist, but he produced one of the most enduring examples of American Primitive art: *The Peaceable Kingdom*. Visit this site for more about the American artist who started out as a coach and sign

painter. You can see a good reproduction of his most famous work, too.

Winslow Homer

 http://www.boston.com/mfa/homer/ mfahomer.htm

Winslow Homer (1836-1910) is, of course, one of the great American painters of landscape and, more importantly, seascape. The Boston Museum of Fine Arts has mounted an outstanding, extensive online exhibition of some of the best of Homer's works.

Edward Hopper

 http://watt.emf.net/wm/paint/auth/ hopper

Edward Hopper (1882-1967) achieved acclaim as a leading painter of "the Ameri-

can scene." His paintings are often described as illustrating the "loneliness, vacuity, and stagnation" of small town life in America. But Hopper didn't necessarily see it that way. "I don't think I ever tried to paint the American scene," he wrote. "I'm trying to paint myself."

Hudson River School of Landscape Painting

 http://w3.wo.sbc.edu/
ArtHistory/MacMurtrie/
HudsonRiverIntro.html

This great set of pages, assembled by Eileen R. MacMurtrie of Sweet Briar College, provides a delightful and beautifully illustrated introduction to the Hudson River painters and their world. The pages include images by Albert Bierstadt, Sanford Robinson Gifford, John William Casilear, Arthur Fitzwilliam Tait, David Johnson, Daniel Huntington, and Thomas Cole.

Emanuel Leutze's "Washington Crossing the Delaware"

 http://www.metmuseum.org/htmlfile/
education/gw.html

There's not much about painter Emanuel G. Leutze (1816-1868) available on the Internet, but the work of this German-born emigré ranks among the most immediately recognizable patriotic painting

in American history. Visit this site for a reproduction of his most famous painting, *Washington Crossing the Delaware*. Then, go to **http://www.earlyamerica.com/review/fall96/answers.html** for an amusing lecture explaining three famous historical errors included in the work (starting with the wrong flag).

Samuel F.B. Morse

 http://fohnix.metronet.com/
~nmcewen/obit.html

Samuel F.B. Morse (1791-1872) has been called "the American Leonardo" because he was not only a great painter, but also an inventor of some repute: the father of the first telegraph system and the Morse Code. (He was, however, a Luddite at heart. And his approach to technology, even technology of his own invention, was cautionary. The text of the first telegraph message ever sent, which was composed by Morse and transmitted in 1844, was: "What hath God wrought?") For information on Morse's summer home, Locust Grove, on the banks of the Hudson at Poughkeepsie, NY, go to the URL **http://www.academic.marist.edu/dca/dca2/sfbmo.htm**.

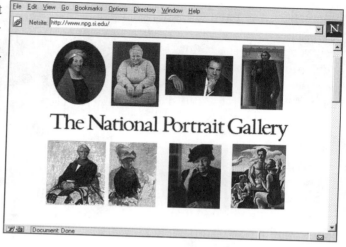

Grandma Moses

 http://www.neinfo.net/
New_England/Vermont/
Bennington/Attractions/
Bennington_Museum/
Grandma_Moses.htp

Anna Mary Robertson (Grandma) Moses (1860-1961) was 78 when she decided to make painting a serious career. Her naive American scenes became world-famous after her first one-woman show in New York in 1940. Her success story, from ordinary farmer's wife to artist feted by the President, is a charming piece of Americana.

National Portrait Gallery

 http://www.npg.si.edu/

The National Portrait Gallery of the Smithsonian Institution features portraits—both painted and photographed—of great Americans including Lincoln, Eleanor Roosevelt, George Washington, Babe Ruth, and many, many others.

National Museum of American Art

 http://www.nmaa.si.edu/

The National Museum of American Art houses works by Whistler, Audubon, Thomas Cole, Cecilia Beaux, Romaine Brooks, Charles Burchfield, George Catlin, Jacob Lawrence, Helen Lundberg, and others.

Native American Art Exhibit

 http://www.artnatam.com/

This online art exhibit features works by Jerome Bushyhead (Cheyenne), L. David Eveningthunder (Shoshone), John Guthrie (Cherokee), Urshel Taylor (Pima), and Dana Tiger (Creek). Do yourself a favor and check out these startling and wondrous images.

Isamu Noguchi Garden Museum

 http://www.noguchi.org/

Born in Los Angeles and eventually famous in literally every corner of the globe, Noguchi (1904-1988) is one of the 20th century's greatest sculptors. These beautiful new pages tell all about the man, his long and eventful life, and his work, from his studies in Paris with Brancusi, to living above Carnegie Hall and working with Fuller, to his work in Italy, Japan, China, and beyond. Take a leisurely tour through these pages to get to know a remarkable and often overlooked American artist.

Georgia O'Keeffe

 http://watt.emf.net/wm/paint/auth/okeeffe/

Georgia O'Keeffe (1887-1986) was a pioneer in her role as a prominent and determined American woman artist and in her decision to live and paint in the Southwest. O'Keeffe was the first woman to have a retrospective at the Museum of Modern Art in New York (1945). She began spending summers in New Mexico in 1929 and moved there permanently in 1949. From this time until her death at age 99 in 1986, she was inspired by the landscape and people of her new home.

150 Years of American Painting

 http://www.byu.edu/tmcbucs/moa/150years.html

This online exhibition features nearly a hundred fantastic paintings produced by dozens of important American artists, including Washington Allston, Frederick Church, William Morris Hunt, Asher B. Durrand, and many others. All pictures are

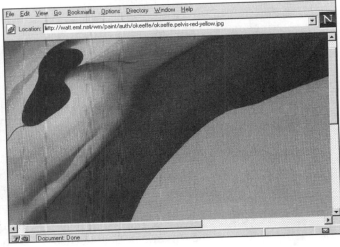

from the collection of Brigham Young University.

Peabody Essex Museum: American Paintings

 http://www.pem.org/painting.htm

This online exhibition includes a beautiful early American painting of Salem Common in 1808, a gorgeous ornamental work entitled *The Emblem of America* (1818), and Charles Osgood's famous 1840 portrait of Nathaniel Hawthorne.

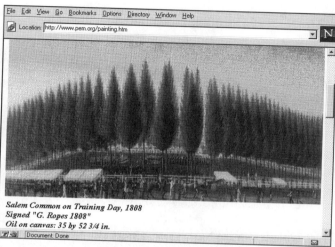

File Edit View Go Bookmarks Options Directory Window Help

Location: http://www.pem.org/painting.htm

Salem Common on Training Day, 1808
Signed "G. Ropes 1808"
Oil on canvas: 35 by 52 3/4 in.

Document: Done

He always spread his canvas on the floor. Why? "On the floor I am more at ease, I feel nearer, more a part of the painting, since this way I can walk around in it, work from the four sides and be literally 'in' the painting."

Philadelphia Print Shop

 http://www.philaprintshop.com/

The Philadelphia Print Shop offers antique collectible prints over the Internet. Their offerings include antique prints, maps, and related books. Here you'll find Currier & Ives originals along with portrait and fine art print, and much more.

Man Ray

 http://www.manraytrust.com/

Man Ray (1890-1976) was an experimental photographer, painter, sculptor, and filmmaker. His most important contributions to 20th century art came from his association with Marcel Duchamp and the other leaders of the dada and surrealist movements. It's hard to get information about this elusive fellow, but the Man Ray Trust is presently constructing pages at **http://www.manraytrust.com/** to help foster wider understanding and appreciation of the man and the artist. Connect with the Trust and get on its e-mail list for more on Man Ray and the Trust.

Jackson Pollock

 http://watt.emf.net/wm/paint/auth/pollock/

I'll let Pollock (1912-1956), a commanding figure of the American abstract expressionist movement, speak for himself.

Frederic Remington

 http://www.northnet.org/
broncho/fram.htm

Through his many paintings and sculptures, Frederic Remington (1861-1909) immortalized the pioneering spirit of the Western cowboy. The Frederic Remington Art Museum of Ogdensberg, New York, provides this informative Web page on Remington.

The Rhode Island School of Design

 http://www.risd.com/

One of the finest art and design schools in the country is located right here in my home state of Rhode Island: the Rhode Island School of Design. Along with outstanding programs in all the visual arts, the school also has a museum which houses one of the finest small collections of American art to be found anywhere on the planet.

Norman Rockwell

 http://www.ultranet.com/~isite/
rockwell.html

Norman Rockwell (1894-1978) is among the best loved of American illustrators. He made his home for the last 25 years of his life in Stockbridge, Massachusetts. This URL will take you to the Web page for the Norman Rockwell Museum in Stockbridge, which includes not only

an extensive Rockwell gallery but also Rockwell's studio just as he left it in 1978.

Mark Rothko

 http://watt.emf.net/wm/paint/auth/
rothko/

Born in 1903 and living until 1970, Mark Rothko began his career as a realist. As he grew and developed his talent, he transitioned smoothly to abstract works. Eventually, he would be credited with having pioneered abstract expressionism—a distinctive art movement of the mid-20th century.

Augustus Saint-Gaudens

 http://www.valley.net/~stgaud/saga.html

Augustus Saint-Gaudens (1848-1907) was the preeminent sculptor of the Gilded

Age. He created its greatest statuary monuments, and decorated its finest palaces. This is the Web page for Saint-Gaudens' home and studio, now a national park open to the public in Cornish, New Hampshire.

 http://www.hol.gr/cjackson/sargent/

John Singer Sargent

Perhaps no other painter is so linked to the Gilded Age as John Singer Sargent (1856-1925). In addition to beautiful architectural and landscape work, Sargent was also a portraitist for many of the most affluent people of his era. An American, he spent many years living abroad as an expatriot.

Joseph Stella

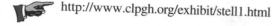 http://www.clpgh.org/exhibit/stell1.html

This Website features the famous Pittsburgh Portraits by Joseph Stella (1877-

1946) who, though born in Italy, spent the majority of his life in the United States and is one of the masters of urban 20th century painting.

Gilbert Stuart

 http://sunsite.unc.edu/cjackson/stuart/

Gilbert Stuart (1755-1828) was, as I've mentioned elsewhere in this book, born in my town of North Kingstown, Rhode Island, in a snuff mill which still stands. He was also christened in a church, St. Paul's of Narragansett, which still stands (though not in its original location). Stuart was the great portrait artist of the American Revolution. I think, indeed, that he did portraits from life of almost all the Founders.

John Trumbull

 http://www.earlyamerica.com/review/summer/trumbull.html

In addition to being a painter, Trumbull (1756-1843) served as a colonel in the Continental Army and was aide to General Washington himself. He had a central role in making the myth of the American Revolution, painting heroic, memorable scenes from the conflict that are now American cultural icons. Four Trumbull works now hang in the U.S. Capitol rotunda. The *Early America Review* has set up an attractive page to honor this American painter. Study his *Surrender of Cornwallis* for a view of war in more "civilized" times. More reproductions and links to other Trumbull pages can be found at **http://xroads.virginia.edu/~CAP/ROTUNDA/george_1.html**.

The Andy Warhol Museum, located on the North Side at Sandusky and General Robinson Streets.

John Vanderlyn

  http://www.mhrcc.org/kingston/kgnvand.html

Born in Kingston, New York, John Vanderlyn (1775-1852) was one of the first American artists to gain national fame, though after his first flash in the public eye, his popularity dwindled. He was rediscovered as a neo-classicist visionary in the 20th century and his works are again widely studied. Visit this site for lovely reproductions of three Vanderlyn works, including his famous *Ariadne Asleep on the Island of Naxos*, as well as links to a comprehensive, five-part biography.

Andy Warhol Museum

 http://www.warhol.org/warhol/

Affiliated with Carnegie-Mellon, this is the largest museum in the world dedi-cated to the life and work of a single artist. The Web pages are impressive. Take a cybertour of the museum, view examples of Andy Warhol's art, see film and video clips, and much more.

James Abbot McNeill Whistler

http://netspot.city.unisa.edu.au/netspot/wm/paint/auth/whistler/

Whistler (1834-1903) was an American-born painter who made his mark by joining the Impressionist elite in Europe. *Arrangement in Grey and Black: Portrait of the Painter's Mother* (1871), commonly known as *Whistler's Mother*, is now in the collection of the Musée d'Orsay in Paris. But you can visit this Website for a nice blow-up of this painting and of another Whistler work, *Brown and Gold*, plus links to other artists and essays on Impressionism and Realism.

Whitney Museum of American Art

 http://www.echonyc.com/~whitney/

Founded by Gertrude Vanderbilt Whitney, the Whitney Museum of American Art in New York City houses one of the world's great collections of American art, with an emphasis on 20th century artists.

Grant Wood

 http://zeus.ia.net/~kwradio/index.html

Grant Wood (1891-1942) portrayed the hills of Iowa as impossibly round, the Iowa trees as impossibly lollypop-like. But when one visits the country around Stone City, Iowa, where Wood worked and operated a summer art colony during the Depression, it looks as if Iowa has come to resemble Wood's singular, loving vision of it. Of course, Wood is best remembered for his stern farmer-and-wife portrait, *American Gothic*. But visit this site for reproductions of plenty more of the artist's works, including *Arbor Day* and *Midnight Ride of Paul Revere*.

A

Searching the Web

So you're intrigued—no, make that enchanted—with the plethora of Americana available through the World Wide Web, and you want to embark on a journey of your own. Traditionally, you'd gather some maps, maybe a tourbook or guide, and your sense of adventure and set out in your automobile to discover your personal interpretation of America. With the World Wide Web, the process and goals are similar—the procedures differ only in the details.

This appendix is your guide to the guides—a meta discussion, if you will, of your own journey of Web discovery.

Your first stop is an orientation into Internet directories and search engines so you'll know the differences between them and when to use which ones. This stop provides brief descriptions and samples of each.

The next stops are at Yahoo! and AltaVista, the premier directory and search engine, respectively, on the Internet. At these stops, we'll walk through search options and show you how they work, so you can easily find sites and map out searches of your own.

The final stop is the launching point for your own searches. You'll see sample searches and results—corresponding to each chapter in this book—that give you a small sampling of the variety of topics you can search for.

With that, we're off.

Directories and Search Engines

Gathering maps and guides for an Internet adventure is a challenge. If this book is your guide to some of the most significant and interesting sites—at least from my perspective—then the Internet directories and search engines provide the roadmaps, hints to sites of local color and interest, and the addresses of the landmarks and destinations that some-how escaped being listed in this book. More specifically—and getting down to brass tacks here—you can categorize a guide as either a directory or a search engine. A *directory* is a canonical list of information on the Internet, usually maintained by one or more devoted people. A directory is organized hierarchically so you can find specific information by going deeper into the hierarchy. *Search engines* use little computer programs that continuously roam the Internet to find and catalog Website addresses. In essence, the search engine programs pick through the haystack and locate the needle, then make a note so the needle can be found again without having to move all the hay.

Which method you might prefer depends more on your journey than on any specific benefits to each one. If you are browsing the Web with no general direction in mind, then start with a directory. If you want to know what exists on the World Wide Web and Internet about Arizona for instance, you might start with a directory. You can browse and peruse just as if you were wandering around an exceedingly organized library about Arizona. However, if you want to know where in Arizona every golf course is located, or if you have a specific destination in mind, you may want to start with a search engine. Although search engines don't provide quite the browsability that directories do, they'll get you within shouting distance of any destination you can imagine.

Multiple Routes: Other Directories and Searching Options

All Internet directories and search engines grew up in Lake Woebe-gon, where, as you remember, all children and Internet services are above average. (Of course, a *Prairie Home Companion* and the definitive source for all such information can be found at **http://phc.mpr.org/**.) All of the directories and search engines claim to be the best and most comprehensive Internet resource. The ones covered in this appendix—Yahoo! and AltaVista—are only two of the many available. If you want a broader selection of directories and search engines than the samples from this appendix, read on.

Directories

Tradewave Galaxy (**http://www.einet.net/**) fairly closely resembles Yahoo! as a categorically-structured encyclopedia of sorts. It provides somewhat more professionally-oriented resources than Yahoo!, although there's significant overlap in topics it provides.

Argus Clearinghouse (**http://www.clearinghouse.net/**), which was formerly the less terse and more intriguing Center for Subject Oriented Internet Resource Guides, provides a collection of resources appropriate for academic use. Why did the name change? Capitalism, that's why. A little green where there was none, and boom!—new name.

Search Engines

HotBot (**http://www.hotbot.com/**) provides resources that are generally comparable to those of AltaVista, but different search engines sometimes find slightly different resources.

Lycos (**http://www.lycos.com/**), a service of Carnegie-Mellon University, most closely combines the marketing and glitzy push of Yahoo! with the comprehensive search of AltaVista, complete with its own collection of specialized resources, just like Yahoo!.

WebCrawler (**http://webcrawler.com/**)—owned by that paragon of computer-related capitalism, America Online—emulates AltaVista fairly closely, but with the addition of a browsable directory as well.

A Directory—Yahoo!

The oldest and arguably best-known of the Internet directories is Yahoo!, which apocryphally stands for "Yet Another Hierarchical Officious Oracle," but in fact stands for nothing more than a self-applied description of the founders (a couple of yahoos, they say). Yahoo!, originally a project of two Stanford University graduate students, now rakes in millions of dollars each year and manages to put an organized facade on the Internet. Figure A-1 shows the Yahoo! home page.

As Figure A-1 shows, Yahoo! provides an incredible range of subjects, covering virtually the whole range of available online information. The meat of the catalog lies in those two middle columns, starting with Arts and Humanities and ending with Society and Culture, and that's where I'll focus. However, those links above and below also offer interesting starting points (and you are interested in browsing, or you wouldn't be here at Yahoo! anyway, right?). Up at the top you find everything from Yellow Pages (classically American and often practical) to today's news to the latest sports scores—one-stop shopping for all your practical or daily information needs. Down at the bottom lurk a variety of specialized Yahoo!s and Yahoo! services, including localized versions of Yahoo! with information from and about specific locations. For example, take a look at Yahoo! Seattle, shown in Figure A-2, which should be one of your first stops prior to an actual visit to the rainy city.

Back to the center part of that main Yahoo! page, let's take a look at what actually appears here and how to find it. Because of the necessarily manual process of separating diverse Websites into appropriate categories, not to mention keeping up with the changes and developments in existing pages, the sites at Yahoo! are representative, but nowhere close to comprehensive. That said, generally the sites found in directories are the best of the rest because of that very laborious manual screening process.

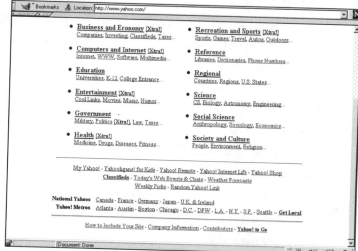

FIGURE A-1

The Yahoo! home page

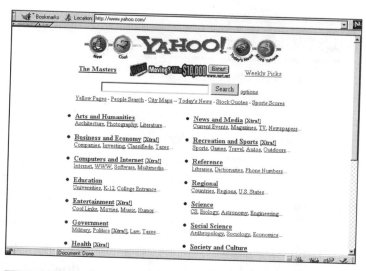

The easiest way to illustrate is with an example. Hypothetically, let's say you're interested in finding information about American history and folk legends, particularly about the Old West. The hardest part of finding Websites is figuring out the right jumping-off point. Only in rare cases is there a clearly defined category that matches exactly what you seek. In

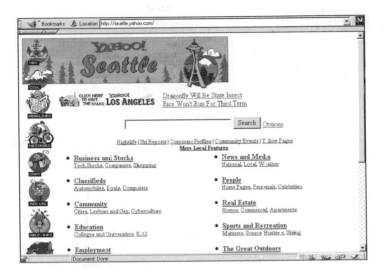

FIGURE A-2

Yahoo! Seattle

Yahoo!, you could well imagine finding folk tales under anything from Arts and Humanities to Social Science to Society and Culture, or possibly under Reference. Under each of those categories, you'll find another set of menus, and another, and another. If you follow the right path, you'll meander to the information you seek. If not…well, you could spend a long time in Yahoo! menus before ever finding your way out.

The solution is searching. Although the search pages from Yahoo! only focus on Yahoo! resources, that often proves more useful and effective than a broader search, simply because of the vast number of resources out on the Web as a whole. Let's try it out.

Enter *folk tales* in the search window up at the top of the Yahoo! window, then click the Search button. You'll see a list of matches, similar to Figure A-3.

Yahoo! performs the search and presents you with a whole page (or more) of matches. The term or terms you searched for are presented in boldface to make them easier for you to identify. Additionally, the list of matches (or, in Web jargon, hits) from your search includes several broader categories, from Category Matches to Site Matches to other links.

FIGURE A-3

Yahoo! search results

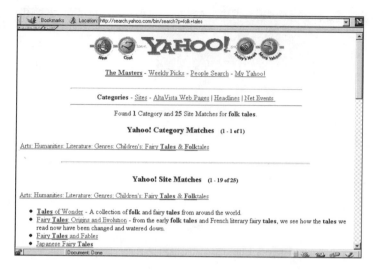

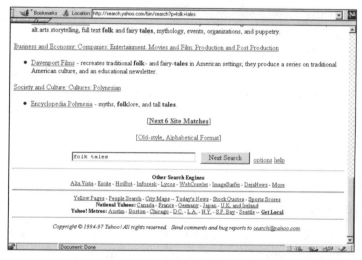

In your first results page, you'll see Yahoo! Category Matches at the top. These categories, chosen because they had the exact words you searched for, probably contain a number of other likely possibilities that may or may not actually have the same words you searched for.

Following the Category Matches are Yahoo! Site Matches. This list, often continued on multiple pages, lists all the pages in the Yahoo! directory that contain your search terms in the title or description. These sites have all been visited or verified by the team of yahoos and, at least at one point, were deemed valuable enough to include in the index. All bets are off on current content, though.

 NOTE:

By the way, in case you're wondering about the significance of the order of matches, here's the scoop: Documents with the keywords in the title rank higher than other documents, and Yahoo! categories that are more general — closer to the top — rank higher than more narrowly focused categories. That, plus a little hocus-pocus, yields the list that you see.

Finally, back on the matches page and nearing the bottom, you'll see links to more matches on following pages as well as links to search engines. At the bottom of the last page of hits is a link to take you directly to AltaVista—based, presumably, on the premise that if you've made it to the end of Yahoo!'s list and are still awake and interested, you'll want to check out a more comprehensive list. We'll get there in a minute, but first we need to make sure you can find what you want within Yahoo!

Narrowing Yahoo! Searches

While it's often quite satisfying to search for something and find out that there are 2,000 Yahoo! sites with the precise term you need, the pleasure and satisfaction dwindle somewhat as you consider the logistics of visiting each of those sites. Even if you're just doing this for fun, you're more focused than I if you can visit 2,000 or 200 or even just 20 sites all on one topic. Just as you wouldn't really try to visit every tourist site listed in a vacation guidebook, you shouldn't feel any sense of obligation to visit all of the sites that appear in your list of hits. (Remember, think of a *hit* as a site which contains the term you're searching for.)

Of course, figuring out which sites to visit is easier said than done. What to do? Narrow the search so you have fewer choices. (This is analogous to one of my favorite travel techniques—after I have found more sites than I can possibly visit on my vacation, I stop reading the tourbooks.)

Narrowing the sites in your Yahoo! search involves techniques like marking phrases, adding additional search terms, and requiring or excluding terms.

✶ Marking Phrases

In the folk tales example, you might really be looking for all occurrences of "folk tales," rather than occurrences of "folk" and occurrences of "tales." To instruct Yahoo! properly, just put the phrase in quotation marks and search again. You'll see a notably reduced and focused list of matches.

✶ Adding Additional Search Terms

A great way to narrow your search is to search for multiple terms. To search for multiple terms, just type them all into the search field on Yahoo! pages. For example, type in *folklore American* to give you all the items that contain both terms. If you provide multiple terms, they are all required—any entry that does not have all of the terms won't show up in your list. By throwing in several terms, you improve your chances of getting exactly what you want, and greatly reduce the length of the list of results.

✶ Excluding Terms

Another easy way to narrow your search is to exclude terms. You may notice that your searches pull up all kinds of extraneous information that you could just as easily do without. You can kick that info out without any difficulty so you don't have to wade through the extras. How? Just put a – (a minus sign) in front of any term you do not want to see. For example, typing *folklore –computers* gives you a much more focused list than *folklore computers*.

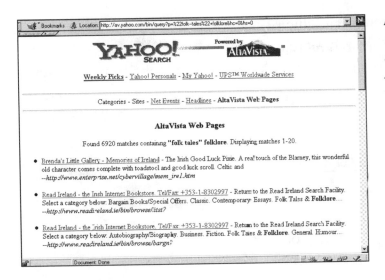

FIGURE A-4

Yahoo! presents information from AltaVista

If your search yielded nothing at all from Yahoo!, then Yahoo! is kind enough to do an AltaVista search automatically and present those results. You'll see something like Figure A-4. Notice how odd the search had to be to yield nothing at all from Yahoo!

A Search Engine—AltaVista Search

If you have a specific destination in mind, you'll be better off using a search engine than a directory. Meet AltaVista, the all-seeing, all-remembering librarian of the Internet. Rather than starting out with a browse through the site or sites, you just tell AltaVista what you're looking for. AltaVista gives you a list of sites with the terms you mentioned, ranked so the most likely matches appear at the top. That is, AltaVista says, "Aha! You want a list of pages with the word 'americana' in them. I know of a bunch of them, so I'll put the ones with 'americana' in the title at the top of the list. If the word appears frequently, I'll also move the pages toward the top of the list. If, however, the word appears only once and in a none-too-prominent place on the page, I'll place the reference to that site toward the bottom of your list." Pretty impressive, isn't it?

At **http://www.altavista.digital.com/**, you'll see a screen like Figure A-5.

Here's what you're looking at in this AltaVista screenshot. All the way at the top of the page is the AltaVista logo, which isn't particularly significant except for the link to Advanced Search. Under the ad and the search form, you'll see some statistics about your search. The statistics

FIGURE A-5

AltaVista search engine

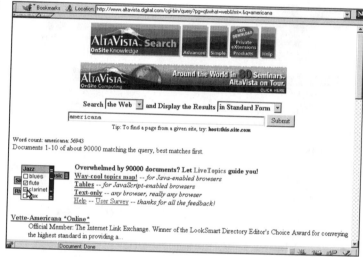

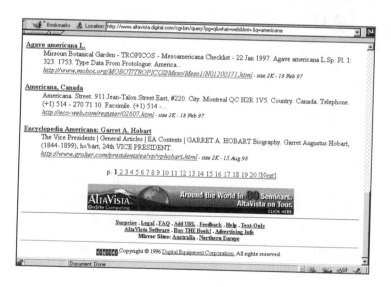

are AltaVista's report to you about which words were found and how frequently. Additionally, if you search for something that's just overwhelmingly common, it wouldn't help focus the search so it'll be rejected; AltaVista will tell you that too.

After you've done a search, you'll see the list of matches to your search, including the title of the document, a brief description of the contents, the address, and finally the size and date of the document. While this information isn't essential—heck, if the title's interesting, you click on it and you're off—it can be helpful at times. For example, if you're looking for the latest word on the current Congressional session, you won't want to bother with a document dated sometime in 1996.

Finally, down at the bottom of the page, just above the ad and some miscellaneous links, you'll see a list of up to 20 page numbers that are highlighted as links. Those numbers link to the pages—at 10 links per page—of matches to your search. If you don't find what you want in the first 200 matches, you might try being a little more specific. You're likely to find what you need in the first few pages or not at all. If you make it to page five or six without finding the results you want, try refocusing and resubmitting your search.

Let's give an AltaVista search a whirl. Here's the scenario: you've heard legends about a huge grizzly bear in the West—just enormous. The bear was even buried in a regular grave with a marker, which you could go visit if you want. To find information about this legendary bear, you could go browsing through Yahoo! or even search in Yahoo! for *grizzly bear*, but it's far from a certainty that you'd find something that obscure within the scope of Yahoo!. That means it's time for a full Internet search directly from AltaVista.

So, you ask AltaVista, the all-knowing librarian, about *grizzly bear grave,* and it responds with the first ten most likely items. Figure A-6 shows the top of the results list.

FIGURE A-6

Results of AltaVista search for grizzly bear grave

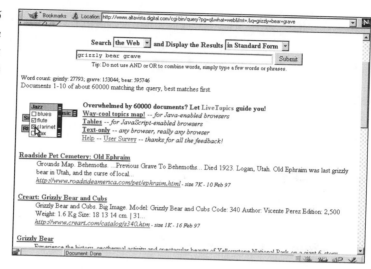

Top of the list? Roadside Pet Cemetery (sic): Old Ephraim at **http://www.roadsideamerica.com/pet/ephraim.html**, as shown in Figure A-7.

Not bad for a start, huh? Notice also that AltaVista claimed to know about 27,793 pages with the word grizzly in them, 153,044 with grave, and 595,746 with bear, for a total of about 600,000 matching documents.

FIGURE A-7

Old Ephraim's Website

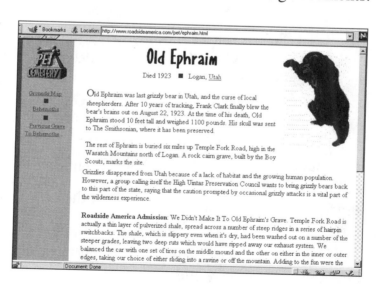

Whew! And you found what you wanted with the first shot at it. Moreover, once you know a little about the hows and wherefores of AltaVista, you can do even better. Read on!

AltaVista is divided into two parts—a Simple Search part and an Advanced Search part. They both access the same information and present the results in the same way. The only differences are the commands you use and the precision of the search results. The following two sections outline how to effectively use AltaVista Simple Search and AltaVista Advanced Search.

AltaVista Simple Search

AltaVista Simple Search is certainly simple—it's like falling off a log. It's also very much like using the Yahoo! search commands, so you won't be breaking any new ground here.

To search, just type in relevant terms and click Submit. AltaVista compares the terms you submit to the database, performs all kinds of calculations, and returns to you a list of documents, ranked in terms of the most likely matches to your search.

AltaVista looks at each of the documents (figuratively, of course), and asks some very pointed questions to determine which documents are likely to be most relevant to you. Which questions? Well, they go something like this (my loose interpretation):

* Are all the terms in the document title?

* Are some of the terms in the document title?

* Are any of the terms near the top of the document?

* Are all the terms present?

* Are only a few of the terms present?

After the question-and-answer session, AltaVista ranks the documents based on the number of "yes" answers and presents you with the list of up to 200 terms. Pretty slick, isn't it?

If you need more control over the results, you can require or exclude terms to your heart's content, as well as group terms together in phrases and use wildcards to match partial words. If that's not enough—that is, if you also need to specify dates or if you need to get more complex with your search, be sure to read the following section, on Advanced Searches. In the meantime, here's the process for fine-tuning a Simple Search.

For starters, let's search for information about Route 66—specifically, let's find out about some of the sights in Oklahoma, like the Round Barn and Blue Whale, see some pictures, and figure out if that's really where the next vacation should lead. Just to give these search parameters a full workout, we'll start slowly and work up to the meaty stuff.

In AltaVista Simple Search, search for *route 66*. AltaVista reports back that it finds 869,846 occurrences of "route" and another 2,625,346 of "66." Although the first matches look pretty good, let's see what we can do to fine-tune the search.

 TIP:

> *By the way, the numbers of matches aren't precise—depending on how busy AltaVista is, it'll stop counting when it reaches the point of diminishing returns. Since it's only going to show you 200 matches, the difference between finding 2,408,906 and 2,625,346 hits on "66" isn't necessarily a big deal.*

★ Using Capital Letters

One way to focus your search is by using capital letters. By searching for route (with a lowercase "r"), AltaVista returns matches of both "route" and "Route." If you use capital "R" in the search, you require that the results include only matches of "Route"—only 341,906 this time. Any time you know that a word must be capitalized, or if a term uses funny (computer) capitalization, like WordPerfect, be sure to enter in the specific capitalization to narrow your search.

★ Grouping Terms

Another way to focus your search is to group terms. For example, because we don't care about either "Route" or "66" individually, we can lump them together into a single phrase with quotes, like *"Route 66."* By grouping these terms, AltaVista will give you results that contain "Route 66," not matches to the individual terms. With that, we're down to only a few thousand documents. Not manageable, quite, but pretty good.

★ Adding Terms

Another way to focus your search is to add another term to the search string. For example, we can search for *"Route 66" Oklahoma*. AltaVista will look for documents containing either or both of these. If you want, you can tell AltaVista to look only for documents containing both "Route 66" and Oklahoma by adding a + before each term or phrase. For example, you could type *+"Route 66" +Oklahoma*. Now that got us down under 1,000 documents. Let's keep going.

We got some good-looking results, but not much on the actual places to see or on pictures, so let's add another couple of terms—sites and pictures—to the list. Now the whole search string looks like *+"Route 66" +Oklahoma sites pictures photographs*.

★ Excluding Terms

Often when you start focusing your search, you'll get closer and closer, but still get information that's way off the topic you're searching. For example, the previous search, *+"Route 66" +Oklahoma sites pictures photographs* yielded links to the "Iron Butt Association" and links to ordering souvenirs. If you want to focus your search so that these topics aren't included, you can exclude them in your search string. Thus, +*"Route 66"* +*Oklahoma sites pictures photographs–"Iron Butt Association" –"how to order"* would exclude these unwanted topics.

AltaVista Advanced Search

To use AltaVista's Advanced Search capabilities, which *are* a bit more work but give you very focused results, click the Advanced Search button from the AltaVista home page or head directly to **http://www.altavista. digital.com/cgi-bin/query?pg=aq**. You'll see the Advanced Search page, as shown in Figure A-8.

In essence, the processes involved in doing an Advanced Search are similar to those of a Simple Search; but in Advanced Search you have to specify all the information that AltaVista infers for you in Simple Search. It takes a little practice and trial and error, but you can get incredible results. Of course, if you are getting the results you want from Simple Search, don't worry about it. If it ain't broke, don't fix it—or so the saying goes.

What's different about Advanced Search? Well, you get two different boxes to put information into and you have to specify a little more

FIGURE A-8
*AltaVista Advanced
Search page*

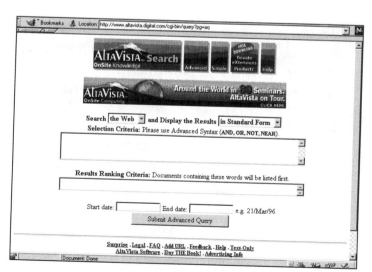

information. Let's take it from the top, with Selection Criteria, then we'll move on to Results Ranking Criteria.

The Selection Criteria correspond roughly to the search terms in Simple Search, but instead of just throwing the terms in willy-nilly, you have to tell AltaVista which ones are required (with AND) or are alternatives (with OR) or even must be present and close to some other term (with NEAR). How, you say? Like this:

Suppose you're looking for information about Fargo, North Dakota. More specifically (and you always must be specific with Advanced Search), you want to know about Fargo and the floods of 1997. You don't, however, care about the Oscar-nominated movie of the same name. In this case, you don't want either the word "movie" or the word "Oscar," so you bind them together with parentheses, like "(movie or Oscar)." So, the search string would look like *Fargo AND NOT (movie or Oscar)*. The AND NOT requires that any pages found include the word "Fargo" and not include the following element, which consists of either the word "movie" or the word "Oscar." After you've assembled the search, click on the Submit Advanced Query button.

Your results will not be ranked in any particular order—if you want them to be prioritized, you'll have to add the priority terms into the Results Ranking Order field. For example, if you want pages with flood information, add the word *flood* to the Results Ranking Order field.

Finally, if you want to specify that the pages have been most recently updated between certain dates, add the dates in as well in day/month/year form—say, *1/Jan/97* to catch everything from the beginning of 1997. Your search screen should look like Figure A-9.

Voilà! Figure A-10 shows the Fargo Flood home page at **http://www. ndsu.nodak.edu/fargoflood/**. Check it out, and you'll find out there's more to a hundred-year flood than meets the eye—the page is dedicated to the Great Fargo-Moorhead flood of 1897.

FIGURE A-9
Completed Advanced
Search form

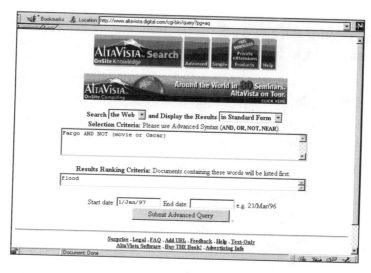

FIGURE A-10
Fargo Flood home page

Undertaking Your Own Journey

If you've decided that taking your own journey of discovery on the American portion of the information superhighway is the way to go, here are some sample searches to get you started.

American Sports

Beyond the obvious searches for sports teams and associations, you can always find information to help you participate yourself on the Web. Try +*baseball coaching tips* to get you started helping the kids learn. Brace yourself—there are a lot of pages out there.

Architecture

Try browsing through Yahoo! to Arts | Design Arts | Architecture. Alternatively, head for AltaVista Simple Search and look for your genre of choice. A search for *lighthouse pictures* is a fun start.

Crime and Criminals

Certainly no discussion of crime and criminals is complete without a search for *"Unsolved Mysteries"* to catch the TV show's Website. However, perhaps you're more intrigued by a different tack on crime. Search in AltaVista for *"Carrie Nation"* and check out the poetry.

Food and Drink

Pick your cuisine and search away—*"cheese fries"* is a good start for the authentic Americana, but maybe your heart would be better served by a meal you could cook using the contents of your refrigerator. Use an Advanced Search in AltaVista for any leftovers on hand and the word recipe. For example, *chicken AND (radish OR "bell pepper") AND recipe*. Eat up!

The Great Outdoors

Try a Yahoo! search for *hiking trails* to get an enormous variety of guides to hiking and walking trails across the country. More specific searches in AltaVista for, say, *"Grand Canyon hiking"* will better focus your results if you have a specific destination in mind.

Great Patriots

Beyond the obvious searches for patriot's names, you might need to augment the search with a little more information. For example, try *"Thomas Jefferson"–University* to get the patriot and exclude the campus. Depending on your origins, your great patriots search could, of course, focus on *"Jefferson Davis"* and be equally productive.

The History Highway

Yahoo! searches for *"U.S. History"* offer a good starting point. However, less frequently traveled sites abound through AltaVista searches for historical features by name (e.g. *"Alexander Hamilton"*) or for topics (e.g. *interstate highway construction*).

Individualis Americanus

At the risk of blending individual Americans with one of the widest ranging conflicts of this century, a simple search on AltaVista for *"Clarence Darrow"* or *"Inherit the Wind"* reveals an interesting historical perspective, in addition to a plethora of high school dramatic productions.

Kingdom of Kitsch

Beyond the obvious and less obvious searches for *Pez* and *"lava lamps,"* you could always start a (fairly expensive) collection of kitschy cels from animated shows. An AltaVista Search for *Jetsons cels* will show just how far this extends.

Law

Although snide comments about the practice of law cry for attention, a more productive use for the Web would be investigation, again, of the specifically American aspects—the ones that have truly shaped our lives.

Try, for example, combining +*"Supreme Court"* +*decision* with the relevant terms, such as *Roe, flag,* or *busing.* OK. If you insist: +*lawyer* +*jokes.* 10,000 hits.

Literature, American Style

Certainly the first place to look for American literature would be with a search for *Pulitzer Prize.* However, depending on your preferences, you can also find a number of works that predate the Pulitzer on the Web, complete with commentary. Try, for example, a search for *"Washington Irving"* in AltaVista.

Local History

If the local historians are sufficiently networked—and that depends greatly on your location—local history searches can be remarkably productive. Just as an example, if Colorado is your locale, try a search for *Durango Silverton* +*history* and read up on the steam trains.

Made in the USA

Well, if all this Americana makes you think that you should, just maybe, start working harder to buy American, just add *"made in USA"* to any search for products you make—or just try *"made in USA"* on Yahoo! and see what you get.

Maps and Mountains: Geography/Demography

Your tour of America can't go very far without maps—searching for a state name and the word *map*, with or without the addition of *topographic* or *GIS*—gives you an incredible range of choices. Of course, if you're more of a city-type, try hitting Yahoo! and selecting the City Maps link from the page header.

Music

Well, a search for *blues* yields, at press time, 1,335 Yahoo! site matches and an unknown number of AltaVista hits. Therefore, a more closely focused search for *"B. B. King"* or other blues artists, which also includes keywords like *biography* or *schedule*, can have great results.

Parades and Festivals

Although you can certainly tune into the Macy's Thanksgiving Day Parade with a Yahoo! search for *Macy Parade*, you might also need to do a quick AltaVista search for *turkey cooking instructions*. Remember, the bird needs to go in the oven before the parades are all over!

Politics: Oh, What a Tangled Web...

Take a fresh look at American politics with an AltaVista search for *political satire cartoon*. The political cartoon is, if you remember, actually an American invention—do a search for *Thomas Nast* and check out the details.

Pop Till You Drop

When it comes to pop culture, few items have escaped the scrutiny of Web pages. An extreme example can be revealed with a Yahoo! search for *brady bunch*.

Religion

Although most religions are well represented on the Web, if you're interested in the history of a uniquely American religion, check out *+Mormon +migration* for the sesquicentennial of the migration of the Mormons to Utah. Even if your faith is completely different, the history is something.

Science Made in the USA

Certainly the starting point for any investigation of science in the USA would start at the junior levels—the science fair. Yahoo! offers a variety of matches on a *science fair* search. Fortunately, in addition to information about the rules and winners, you'll also find supplies and project information.

Visual Arts in America

While a search for the Met or Smithsonian will get you all the paintings you want, and Ansel Adams is also well-represented on the Web, a more unusual expedition begins with a search for *Native American Art* in Yahoo!.

Index

★★★★★★★★★

A

Adams, Ansel, 32
Adams, Henry and Clover, 131
Adams, John, 112-113
Adams, John Quincy, 341
Adams Memorial, 131
Ade, George, 204
Advertising law information, 186
African cooking, 64-65
Agassix, Louis, 399
Alamo, The, 131
Alcatraz, 50
Alcott, Louisa May, 204
Ali, Muhammad, 366
All American Music Festival, 321
All Outdoors, 90
All Politics, 344
All Things Political, 344
Allen, Paul, 27
Allston, Washington, 426
All-Time All-Star Baseball Team, 6-7
AltaVista Search, 449-458
    advanced, 456-458
    results, 452
    simple, 453-456
American Civil Liberties Union (ACLU), 187
American Conservative Union, 344
American Institute of Architects, 33
American Legislative Exchange Council, 345
American Memory (Library of Congress), 132
American Museum of Natural History, 132

American Park Network, 90-91
American Prospect, 345
America's Sports Headquarters on the Web, 7
Andy Warhol Museum, 437
Apple pie, 70
Appleseed, Johnny, 154
Architects, brief biographies of, 33-34
Architectural History: Doctoral Dissertations, 36
Architecture, 23-43
Argus Clearinghouse, 442
Armstrong, Louis, 293
Asch, Moses, 290-293
Association of American Law Schools, 187
Authors Guild, 204-205

B

Bach, P.D.Q., 293-294
Baez, Joan, 294
Ball, Lucille, 366
Band, The, 294
Barlow, John Perry, 155
Barrymore, John, 155, 367
Bartleby, 205
Barton, Clara, 113
Baseball Online, 8
Basketball Highway, 8
Bay Area Restaurant Guide, 70
Beaver, The, 367
Bell, Alexander Graham, 155
Bell, Madison Smartt, 205
Benton, Thomas Hart, 426
Berlin, Irving, 294

Bernstein, Leonard, 294
Betsy Ross Home: Virtual Tour, 42
Bierce, Ambrose, 206
Bierstadt, Albert, 426
Billy the Kid, 50-51
Bishop Berkeley, 156
Black History, 142-143
Blue Highway, 294-295
Bluegrass festivals nationwide, 321
Bogart, Humphrey, 362-363, 368
Bonnie and Clyde Archive, 51
Boone, Daniel, 113
Booth, John Wilkes, 51
Borglum, Gutzon, 426-427
Boston Marathon, 8-9
Boston Museum of Fine Art, 427
Boston National Historic Park, 132-133
Boston restaurant guides, 71
Boston Symphony Orchestra, 295
Bradbury, Ray, 206
Brautigan, Richard, 206-207
Brown, John, 129-130
Bryant, William Cullen, 207
Buck, Pearl, 207-208
Buckley Jr., William F., 156
Buffalo Bill Cody, 156-157
Bulloch Hall, 133
Bunche, Ralph, 113
Bunker Hill Monument, 133
Burroughs, Edgar Rice, 208
Burroughs, John, 84-89, 197-202
Buscemi, Steve, 368
Byrds, The, 295

C

Cable Ace Awards, 322
Cage, John, 295-296
Calder, Alexander, 427
CALPIRG, 345
Capital Research Center, 346
Capone, Al, 52
Capote, Truman, 208
Carnegie Hall, 296
Carnegie Mellon Architecture
    Archives, 34
Carroll family, 378-380
    Charles, 335
        William Thomas, 124-125
Carson, Johnny, 368-369
Carson, Rachel, 89, 92
Carver, George Washington, 114
Casey at the Bat, 9
Cassatt, Mary, 427
Cato Institute, 346
Catskill Fly-Fishing Center and
    Museum, 92
Cattle Rustling, 52
CBS Sports, 9
Central Intelligence Agency
    (C.I.A.), 346
Chandler, Raymond, 208-209
Channing, William Ellery, 114
Chaplin, Charlie, 369
Chase, William Merritt, 428
Chesapeake Bay Trust, 92
Chicago Architecture, 35
Chicago Blues Festival, 322-323
Chicago Fringe & Buskers Festival,
    323
Chicago restaurant guide, 72
Chicago Underground Film
    Festival, 323
Chinese New Year in the U.S., 323
Christmas Tree Lights Festivals,
    323-324
Church, Frederick, 428
Circus, 319-321
Circus Art, 324
Circus World Museum, 324
Civil War Center (Baton Rouge),
    133
Civil War Reenactments, 324
Clark, Dick, 369
Clay, Henry, 340-344
Clearwater (Hudson River Sloop),
    67, 96
Clemens, Roger, 10

Clowns of America International,
    324-325
Cobb, Ty, 10
Cody, Buffalo Bill, 156-157
Cole, Thomas, 422
Collins, Joan, 369
Coltrane, John, 296
Columbia Law School, 188
Coney Island, 325
Congressional Quarterly, 347
Copland, Aaron, 296-297
Copley, John Singleton, 428
Cosby, Bill, 369-370
Crane, Stephen, 209
Crazy Horse, 106-109
Crazy Horse sculpture, 108-109
Crime and criminals, 45-62
Criminals.com, 52
Crosby, Bing, 370
Culinary Institute of America, 72
Currier & Ives, 428
Custer and Little Bighorn Home
    Page, 134
Cy Young Award winners, 20-21
Cyberbarons, 27-29

D

Dallas Restaurant Guide, 73
Dallas Symphony Orchestra, 297
Dalton Gang, 53
Darrow, Clarence, 114-115
Davis, Gary, 288-290
Davis, Miles, 297
De Kooning, Willem, 428
De Young Memorial Museum, 429
Dead Presidents Tour, 134
Dean, James, 360-361
Dear Abby, 376
Death penalty pages from the
    ACLU, 53
Defenders of Wildlife, 93
Democratic Party, 347-348
Dick, Philip K., 209
Dickinson, Emily, 209
Dillinger, John, 53-54
Directories, 440-447
Dirty Linen Magazine, 297-298
Discovery Institute, 348
Dos Passos, John, 209
Douglass, Frederick, 115
Dreiser, Theodore, 210
DuBois, W.E.B., 115-116
DucKon, 325
Dulles, Allen, 109

Dulles, Eleanor, 109-111
Dulles, John Foster, 109-110
Dylan, Bob, 298
Dymaxion House, 37
Dyson, Esther, 158

E

Eakins, Thomas, 424, 429
Earp, Wyatt, 54
Earthlaw, 188
Eastman, George, 246-247
Ecology Law Quarterly, 188
Edison, Thomas Alva, 158
Eisenhower, Dwight David, 116
Electric chair, 54-55
Eliot, T.S., 210
Ellison, Lawrence J., 27-28
Emerson, Ralph Waldo, 210-211
Entertainment Law Resources, 189
EnviroLink, 93
Environment, 81-104
Environmental Lawyer, 189
Environmental Protection Agency
    (EPA), 348
ESPN Sportszone, 10
Evans, Dale, 364, 374
Evans, Walker, 158
Everglades National Park, 93
Everly Brothers, 298

F

Fargo Flood, 458
Faulkner, William, 211
FBI's Famous Cases Archive, 55
FBI's Top Ten Most Wanted
    Fugitives, 55
FECInfo, 348-349
Federal Communications
    Commission (FCC), 349
Federal Judicial Center, 190
Federal Judiciary of the U.S., 189
Federal Reserve, 349
Federalist Society, 349
Feynman, Richard, 158-159
Fields, W.C., 159
Fillmore, Millard, 338
Fish, Ham, 3-4
Fish and Wildlife Service, 93-95
Fitzgerald, F. Scott, 211
Fletcher School of Law &
    Diplomacy, 190
Florida Folk Festival, 325
Flying High Circus, 325-326

Folk Book, 298
Folk-Legacy Records, 298
Food and drink, 63-79
Ford, Betty, 370
Ford, Henry, 159
Ford's Theatre Virtual Tour, 134
Fourth of July in Washington D.C., 326
Franklin, Aretha, 298-299
Franklin, Ben, 398
Friends of the Earth-U.S., 95
Fuller, Buckminster, 37

G

Gabor, Zsa Zsa, 370
Gang Land: New York Mob, 55-56
Gardner, Erle Stanley, 211
Garland, Judy, 370-371
Garrison, William Lloyd, 147
Gates, Bill, 27
Gehrig, Lou, 11
Georgetown University Law School, 190
Gerrit Smith Virtual Museum, 130
Gershwin, George and Ira, 299
Getty Museum (Malibu, CA), 429-430
Gettysburg Battlefield, 134
Gifford, Sanford Robinson, 430
Gilded Age, 25-26
Gingrich, Newt, 340-344
Ginsberg, Allen, 202-203, 211-212
Glacier National Park, 95
Goodfellas, 49
Gotti, John, 56
Gould, Jay, 25-27
Grammy Awards, 326
Grand Canyon, 95-96
Grand Teton National Park, 96
Grandma Moses, 432
Grant, Ulysses S., 134-135
Grant's Tomb, 134-135
Grateful Dead, 299
Great Circus Parade, 326
Great Hudson River Revival, 326-327
Green Bay Packers Home Page, 11
Green Party, 349-350
Griffith, Andy, 371
Griffith, Nanci, 299
Gumbo, 73
Guthrie, Arlo, 299-300
Guthrie, Woody, 300-301

H

Haggard, Merle, 301
Hammond Jr., John, 301-302
Harburg, Yip, 302
Harlem Globetrotters, 12
Harpers Ferry (West Virginia), 135
Harte, Bret, 212
Harvard Law School, 190
Hawthorne, Nathaniel, 212
Heartland Institute, 350
Heaven's Gate cult, 382-387
Hemmingway, Ernest, 151-152, 212
Hemmingway, Mary Welsh, 153-154
Henry, O., 218-219
Herbert Hoover Presidential Library, 135
Heritage Foundation, 350
Herman, Pee-Wee, 373
Hicks, Edward, 430
Historic Places, National Register of, 140
Historical societies, 230-243
History, 123-144
History (local), 225-243
Holiday, Billie, 302
Holliday, Doc, 56-57
Homer, Winslow, 430
Hopper, Edward, 430-431
Hopper, Grace, 116-117
HotBot, 442
Howells, William Dean, 212
Hudson River School of Landscape Painting, 431
Hudson River sloop, 67, 96

I

Iditarod, 327
In Love and War, 153
Information Law Web, 191
Ingersoll, Robert Green, 159
Intellectual Property Law Center, 191
Internet Simulated Baseball League, 12
Ireland, Patricia, 160
Irving, Washington, 213
Isamu Noguchi Garden Museum, 433

J

Jack London Historic State Park, 138-139
Jackson, Michael, 371
Jackson, "Shoeless" Joe, 13
Jackson, Stonewall, 135-136
James, Henry, 213
James-Younger Gang, 57
Jazz Central Station, 302
Jefferson, Blind Lemon, 302-303
Jefferson, Thomas, 38, 117
Jefferson Airplane, 303
John Brown's Adirondack Farm, 129
Johnson, Philip, 39
Johnson, President Andrew, 339
Johnson Presidential Library & Museum, 350
Jones, Spike, 303
Jordan, Barbara, 117
Jordan, Michael, 371

K

Kansas City Architecture, 39
Kennedy, President John Fitzgerald, 57-58, 136, 337
Kennedy assassination, 57-58
Kennedy Center Honors, 327
Kentucky Derby, 13, 327
Kerouac, Jack, 196-197, 213
Kerrville Folk Festival, 327
Kids' TV of the Fifties, 371-372
King, Stephen, 213-214
King Jr., Martin Luther, 118
Kitsch, 165-180
Kodak, 246-247
Kronos Quartet, 303-304

L

LandTrust.com, 96
Lardner, Ring, 214
Law, 181-194
Lawyer jokes, 191
Leadbelly, 304
League of Conservation Voters, 97
League of Women Voters, 351
Lee, Peggy, 304
Lee, Spike, 372
Legal dot Net, 191-192
Legislative information on the Internet, 355
Lehrer, Tom, 304

Leopold, Aldo, 87, 97
Leutze, Emanuel, 431
Lewis, Jerry Lee, 305
Liberace, 372
Libertarian.org, 351
Lincoln, Abraham, 37-38, 118, 124-125, 136-138
Lincoln, Mary, 136-138
Lincoln, Willie, 124-125
Lincoln assassination, 58-59
Lincoln Center, 305
Lincoln home (Springfield), 136
Lincoln log cabin, 136-137
Lincoln Tomb, 137-138
Lindbergh, Charles, 160
Literary Kicks, 214
Literature, 195-223
Little Orphan Annie, 365-366
Little Richard, 305
Local history, 225-243
London, Jack, 138-139, 214
Los Angeles Dodgers, 14
Los Angeles Philharmonic, 305
Los Angeles restaurants (Eating L.A.), 73
Louisiana Architecture, 39
Louisville Slugger Online, 14
Lovecraft, H.P., 215
Lowell Observatory, 400-401
Lycos, 442
Lyndhurst, 26-27

M

Macy's Thanksgiving Parade, 317-319
Mailer, Norman, 215
Maine Arts Festival, 328
Major League Baseball Official Home Page, 14
Major League Baseball Players Alumni Association, 14
Manson, Charles, 59
Maps and geographical, 271-285
Mardi Gras, 328-329
Marshall, Thurgood, 118
Marsh, George Perkins, 84
Marx Brothers, 372
Mason, Molly, 311
Masterson, Bat, 59
Mather, Cotton, 160-161
Mathers, Jerry, 367
McAuliffe, S. Christa, 161
McFerrin, Bobby, 305-306

McGhee, Sonny Terry and Brownie, 311
McKim, Charles Follen, 24-25
Melville, Herman, 215
Mencken, H.L., 161
Merchandise, 245-269
Microbreweries of America: A Guide, 74
Millay, Edna St. Vincent, 215-216
Mills Brothers, 306
Minor League Baseball, 14-15
Mitchell, Joni, 306
Mohonk Mountain House: New Paltz NY, 97
Monroe, Bill, 306
Monroe, Marilyn, 361-362, 372
Monticello, 38
Moore, Mary Tyler, 373
Morse, Samuel, 431-432
Moses, Anna Mary Robertson, 432
Mott, Lucretia, 162
Mount Vernon, 139
Muir, John, 83, 97-98
Mumford, Lewis, 84
Music, 287-313
My Lai massacre, 59
Mystery Dinner Theatre, 329

N

Nader, Ralph, 162
Nation, The, 351
National Audubon Society, 98
National Baseball Hall of Fame, 15
National Basketball Association, 15
National Consumer Law Center, 192
National Football League, 16
National Hockey League, 16-17
National Museum of American Art, 432
National Organization for Women (NOW), 160
National Park Service: ParkNet, 98
National Parks & Conservation Association, 98
National Portrait Gallery, 432
National Register of Historic Places, 140
National Review Magazine, 352
National Trust for Historic Preservation, 40
National Wildlife Federation, 99
Native American art exhibit, 432
Native American recipes, 74

Natural Resources Conservation Service, 99
Natural Resources Defense Council, 99
Nature Conservancy, 99-100
Naval War College Museum (Newport RI), 140-141
NBC Sports, 17
Negro Leagues Home Page, 17
Netizen, The, 352
New England Culinary Institute, 74-75
New Orleans jazz and heritage, 329
New Orleans restaurants and recipes, 75
New York City architecture, 37
New York Historical Society, 226-228
New York Images 1883, 40-41
New York Jazz Festival, 329-330
New York Lesbian and Gay Film Festival, 330
New York Mob, 55-56
New York Restaurant Super Guide, 75-76
New York Underground Film Festival, 330
New York Yankees, 17
Newport Folk Festival, 330
Newport Mansions, 41
NeXT, 396-397
Northwest Folklife Festival (Seattle), 330
Nixon Library and Birthplace, 352

O

Oakley, Annie, 162
Ochs, Phil, 306-307
O'Connor, Flannery, 216
O'Keeffe, Georgia, 433
Oklahombres, 60
Olmstead, Frederick Law, 41
Olympic National Park, 100
Onassis, Jacqueline B.K., 373
O'Neill, Eugene, 216
Oppenheimer, J. Robert, 162-163
Oregon Shakespeare Festival (Ashland), 330-331
O'Rourke, P.J., 352-353
Oscar Awards, 316-317
Oswald, Lee Harvey, 60
Outdoors, 81-104
Outward Bound USA, 100-101

P

Panama Canal Commission, 353
Park information, 90-104
Parker, Dorothy, 216-217
Parks, Rosa, 118-119
Parton, Dolly, 373
Peabody Essex Museum, 141-142, 434
Peale, Rembrandt, 420
Peanuts (Charlie Brown), 373
Peary, Robert, 163
Peter Paul & Mary, 307
Petroglyph National Monument, 101
Philadelphia Print Shop, 434
Philadelphia Walking Tour, 41
Phillips, U. Utah, 307
Phoenix metro restaurant guide, 76
Plimpton, George, 217
Poe, Edgar Allen, 217
Political Graveyard, 126-127
Politics, 333-357
Pollock, Jackson, 434
Pound, Ezra, 217-218
Price, Vincent, 374
Professional Bowling Association, 17-18
Progress of Freedom Foundation, 353
Proulx, Tom, 29
Pumpkin recipes, 66-68, 70, 76-77

R

Rand, Ayn, 218
Randolph, A. Philip, 119
Ransom, John Crowe, 218
Ray, Man, 434
Religion, 377-394
Remington, Frederic, 435
Renaissance Faires, 331
Republican National Committee, 354
Restaurants and recipes, 63-79
Rhode Island Restaurants, 77
Rhode Island School of Design, 435
Rich, Buddy, 307
Rickover, Hyman, 119
Ride, Sally, 119
Right Side of the Web, The, 354
Riis, Jacob, 163
Robeson, Paul, 307
Rock & Roll Hall of Fame & Museum, 307-308
Rockwell, Norman, 435

Rogers, Roy, 364, 374
Rogers, Will, 163
Roosevelt, President Franklin Delano, 119-120, 143-144
Roosevelt, President Theodore, 82, 87-89, 120, 133
Roosevelt, Quentin, 128-129
Roosevelt Jr., Theodore, 121
Ross, Betsy, 42
Ross, Edmund G., 339
Rothko, Mark, 435
Run D.M.C., 308
Ruth, Babe, 5, 18

S

Sagamore Hill, 142
Saint-Gaudens, Augustus, 435-436
San Francisco Architecture: The Victorians, 42
San Francisco Carnaval Parade, 331
San Francisco Mime Troupe, 331
San Simeon, 28
Sandburg, Carl, 142
Sargent, John Singer, 436
Savannah & America's Black History, 142-143
Save the Bay, 102
Savers and Investors League, 354
Science, 395-418
Scott-Heron, Gil, 308
Search engines, 440-442, 449-458
Searching the Web, 439-463
Seattle restaurant information, 73
Sebastian, John, 308
Secret Six, 129-130
Seeger, Pete, 309
Sierra Club, 102
Simonyi, Charles, 28
Simpson, O.J., 47, 60
Sinatra, Frank, 309
Sing Out! Magazine, 309
Sitting Bull, 121
Slabsides: Cabin of John Burroughs, 143
Smithsonian On-line, 143
Smithsonian/Folkways Records, 310
Smith, Bessie, 310
Smith, Gerrit, 130
Socialist Party USA Cybercenter, 354-355
Society for Creative Anachronism, 331-332
Sociological maps, 274
Sousa, John Philip, 310

South Street Seaport Museum (NYC), 143
Speck, Richard, 61
Sports, 1-21
Sportsman's Hunting and Fishing Guide, 102
Springsteen, Bruce, 310
Stanton, Elizabeth Cady, 163-164
Star Trek, 375
Starr, Henry, 61
Stein, Gertrude, 219
Steinbeck, John, 219
Stella, Joseph, 436
Stimson, Henry, 164
Stowe, Harriet Beecher, 219-220
Stuart, Gilbert, 436
Sundance Film Festival, 332
Superbowl, The, 332
Superman, 374
Sweet Honey in the Rock, 310-311

T

Taylor, Elizabeth, 374
Taylor, Livingston, 311
Temple, Shirley, 374-375
Thanksgiving, 68-69, 79
Thanksgiving Parade, 317-319
Theodore Roosevelt National Park (ND), 101-102
Thomas: Legislative Information, 355
Thoreau, Henry David, 220
Thorpe, Jim, 3, 19
Thurber, James, 220
Torrens, Jimmy, 2, 126-127
Tournament of Roses, 332
Town Hall, 355
Tradewave Galaxy, 442
Troutbeck, 127-128
Trumbull, John, 436-437
Tubman, Harriet, 121-122
Turkey Trivia Game, 79
TV Guide Classic Cover Gallery, 375
Twain, Mark, 220

U

Unabomber's Manifesto, 61
Ungar, Jay, 311
Unitarian Universalist Association, 381
U.S. Army Center for Military History, 144

U.S. Capitol, 42-43
U.S. Dept. of Education, 355
U.S. Dept. of Justice Crime
    Statistics, 62
U.S. Geological Survey, 272-273
U.S. House of Representatives, 356
U.S. House of Representatives
    Internet Law Library, 193
U.S. Office of Government Ethics,
    356
U.S. Senate, 356
U.S. Sentencing Commission,
    193-194
U.S. Supreme Court Decisions, 194
USA Basketball Official Home
    Page, 19
USSC+: U.S. Supreme Court
    Database, 194
Utah National Parks, 102

V

Valley Forge, 144
Van Buren, Abigail, 376
Vanderbilt house, 24
Vanderlyn, John, 421, 437
Vega, Susanne, 311
Vera Institute of Justice, 356-357

Vidal, Gore, 221
Villard, Henry (the first), 146-147
Villard, Henry (the second), 149-152
Villard, Oswald Garrison, 148-149
Visual arts, 419-438
Von Kurowsky, Agnes, 152
Vonnegut Jr., Kurt, 221

W

Wagner, Honus, 19-20
Wainwright III, Loudon, 311-312
Walker, Alice, 221-222
Waller, Fats, 312
Warhol, Andy, 437
Washington, Booker T., 122
Washington, George, 122, 139-140
Washington State Parks, 103
Wayne, John, 376
Web searching, 439-463
WebCrawler, 442
Webster, Daniel, 343
Weems, Mason Locke, 334
Welk, Orson, 312
Wharton, Edith, 222
Whistler, James Abbot McNeill, 437
White House, 357
White House art collection, 424-425

Whitman, Walt, 197-202, 222
Whittier, John Greenleaf, 222-223
Williams, Robin and Linda, 312
Williams, Ted, 20
Williams, William Carlos, 223
Windham Hill Records, 313
Wine, 70
Wolf Trap Foundation, 313
Wood, Grant, 438
Wright, Frank Lloyd, 30-32, 43
Wright Brothers, 164

Y

Yacht Racing Rules Online, 20
Yahoo!, 443-447
    home page, 444
    search results, 446-449
Yale Law School, 194
Yosemite National Park, 104
Young, Neil, 313

Z

Zadock Pratt Museum, 142
Ziolkowski, Korczak, 109